THE
HERBALL
OR GENERALL
Historie of
Plantes.

Gathered by Iohn Gerarde
of London Master in
CHIRVRGERIE

Very much
Enlarged and Amended by
Thomas Iohnson
Citizen and Apothecarye
of
LONDON

Gerard's Herball

The Essence thereof distilled by

MARCUS WOODWARD

from the Edition of TH. JOHNSON, 1636

SPRING BOOKS · LONDON

ORIGINALLY PUBLISHED 1927
THIS EDITION PUBLISHED 1964 BY
SPRING BOOKS · WESTBOOK HOUSE · FULHAM BROADWAY · LONDON

PRINTED IN ENGLAND BY RICHARD CLAY AND COMPANY LTD, BUNGAY, SUFFOLK

Table of Contents.

INTRODUCTION.

I.

Eulogy of Gerard.

JOHN GERARD'S name, his *Historie of Plants*, its glorious Elizabethan prose, the folk-lore steeping its pages, and all its quaint conceits about the "Vertues" of herbs, are known by reputation the world over. This is partly because no book on flowers or trees can be written without quotations from his glowing pages, but mainly because the work has won an unchallenged place of honour as the most delightful, fragrant, and refreshing of all old-time herbals: as it is by far the most amusing. Among many testimonies which might be gathered (if need be) as to the delight which discerning and sensitive minds have ever found in the "Herball", there comes first to remembrance a passage in the beautiful prose of W. H. Hudson; and it is a pleasure to transcribe this (from *Nature in Downland*), with its echo of Gerard's own flowing periods:

"Next to the delight of flowers themselves is to me that of listening to the old herbalist discoursing of the same; and this would I say of no other work on plant lore, for these are mostly a weariness to read. The old author is simple, not concerning himself over much about the reason of things, or as he would say he loveth not to dance in quagmires. . . . The colour of his style is never overworn, and he is for ever fresh and full of variety and agreeable surprises, like Nature herself, who maketh her plants not for meat and medicine only, but some to be esteemed for beauty alone, and as garlands and crowns for pleasure. Indeed, there is not seldom a lustre in his words that serves to remind one of the red whortle he greatly admired, which is full of juice of so orient and beautiful a colour to limn withal that Indian lacca cannot be compared thereunto. Nor let it be forgot that it was he who invented the name of Traveller's Joy; and by increasing the pleasure which all have in that green and silver adorner of our country ways and hedges, may even be said to have added something to Nature."

Our most diligent searcher of old Herbals, Miss Eleanour Sinclair Rohde, in *The Old English Herbals*, thus dwells on Gerard's charm:

"His Herbal gripped the imagination of the English garden-loving world, and now, after the lapse of three hundred years, it still retains its hold on us. There are English-speaking people the world over who may know nothing of any other, but at least by name they know Gerard's Herbal. . . . One reads his critics with the respect due to their superior learning, and then returns to Gerard's Herbal with the comfortable sensation of slipping away from a boring sermon into the pleasant spaciousness of an old-fashioned fairy-tale. For the majority of us are not scientific, nor do we care very much about being instructed. What we like is to read about daffodils and violets and gilliflowers and rosemary and thyme and all the other delicious old-fashioned English flowers. And when we can read about them in the matchless Elizabethan English we ask nothing more."

When reading Gerard we are wandering in the peace of an Elizabethan garden, with a companion who has a story for every flower and is full of wise philosophies. We are admiring his Violets: "It would be an unseemly thing", says he, "for him that doth look upon and handle fair and beautiful things, and who frequenteth and is conversant in fair and beautiful places, to have his mind not faire, but filthy and deformed." He inspires us with his own simple faith in the healing virtues of herbs. We must agree that Sweet Marjoram is for those who are given to over-much sighing; that the smell of Basil is good for the heart, takes away sorrowfulness and makes a man merry and glad. We shall lament the passing of the cunning cook who would serve the old salad-dishes; we do not doubt that Chervil roots are excellent in a salad, "if they be boiled and after dressed as the cunning cook knoweth how better than my selfe; which is very good for old people that are dull and without courage; it rejoiceth and comforteth the heart, and increases their lust and strength". Courage!—we may need it ourselves though not dull nor old, and where more easily could we find it than in a tankard flavoured with Borage?—

I Borage
Bring alwaies Courage.

Many things a cunning cook might make for us of Borage, for the driving away of sorrow and increasing the joy of the mind. In these times none strews Water-mint or the flowers of Meadow-Sweet in chambers to make hearts merry and delight the senses. Apothecaries no longer give us seeds of the Pæony in wine or mead to cure the Night Mare, or distil an oil of Cow Parsnip to assuage the Forgetful Evil, make us a garland of Penny-royal if we swim in the head, or a charm of Trefoil whereby no harm can come to us from the biting of any venomous beast. No more does the cunning housewife store that root of Solomon's Seal which takes away in one night or two at the most any bruise gotten by women's wilfulness in stumbling upon their hasty husbands' fists and such like.

With special delight we listen to our companion as he greets his flowers by their old English names: Live-for-ever, Herb Impious, Birds eyne, Jackanapes-on-horseback, Go-to-bed-at-noon, or the Childing Daisy. He tells us where he gathered his treasures, many in London: Bugloss in "Piccadilla", Clary in fields of Holborn, Mullein about Highgate, Lilies of the Vale on Hampstead Heath, Sagittaria in the Tower ditch, Mallow hard by the place of execution, Tyburn, or the Pimpernel Rose in a pasture near the village called Knightsbridge. Passing into the kitchen garden, we are reminded that our host was one of the first to grow Potatoes, and the first to print a picture of what he named the Virginian Potato. In fine, his "Herball", like Parkinson's "Paradisus", is truly a "Speaking Garden", one filled with a tranquil loveliness, with brave colours and the fragrance of damask roses.

II.

Life of Gerard.

JOHN GERARD was born at Nantwich, 1545. He was descended from some younger branch of the Gerards of Ince, in Lancashire, as was learnt from his Coat of Arms, printed in his Herbal; but there are no records at the College of Arms of his parentage. The spelling of his name with a final "e" was no doubt due to an engraver's error in the title-page. He was a pupil at Willaston near Nantwich, and probably there received all his scholastic education. At an early age he was drawn to the study of medicine, and travelled, possibly as a ship's surgeon, on board some merchant vessel, since he speaks of having been from "Narva unto Moscovia, . . . the Sownde, beyonde Denmarke", and again, "Denmarke, Swenia, Poland, Livonia, or Russia, or in any of those colde countries, where I have travelled"; possibly he visited the Mediterranean.

The Herbal throws one or two side-lights on his boyhood; he recalls the raspberry-picking days of his youth, and he boldly affirms that it is altogether untrue about the Yew-tree, that if any sleep under the shadow it causes sickness and sometimes death, and that birds many times die if they eat the fruit: "For when I was yong and went to schoole, divers of my schoole-fellowes and likewise my selfe did eat our fils of the berries of this tree, and have not only slept under the shadow thereof, but among the branches also, without any hurt at all, and that not one time, but many times". Johnson, the author's first editor, had his doubts: and certainly the experiments of eating yew-berries and sleeping in the yew-tree's branches were risky. Johnson remarks of the Yew: "Divers affirme, that in Province in France, and in most hot countries, it hath such a maligne qualitie, that it is not safe to sleepe or long to rest under the shadow thereof".

Gerard must have settled in London before 1577, since he speaks of having superintended the gardens belonging to Lord Burleigh, in the Strand, and at Theobalds in Hertfordshire, for twenty years, which occupation took up the greatest part of his time. His employer expended £10 weekly, to keep the poor employed in his gardens; "For my servants, I keep none to whom I pay not wages, and give liveries, which I know many do not". L'Obel mentions Lord Burleigh's garden in London, but as he is silent in his earlier works about Gerard, it seems he had not then made his mark as a successful gardener.

Hentzner, in his *Itinerarium*, describes at length the gardens at Theobalds, as they were under Gerard's superintendence. In our author's own garden in London he grew above a thousand different herbs, a garden of rarities raised by his skill which Anne of Denmark admired, with white thyme, with double-flowered peach, and all manner of flowers, strangers in England: "Yet I have them in my garden," he relates, time and again, in words ringing with triumph.

That he made friends in his profession is clear from the testimony printed in the Herbal by George Baker, "onc of the chife chirurgions in ordinarie" to Queen Elizabeth, who held a high opinion of Gerard's attainments, saying: "If I may speake without partialitie of the Author of this book, his great paines, no less expences in travelling far and neere for the attaining of his skill have bin extra-ordinarie. For he was never content with the knowledge of those simples which grow in those parts, but upon his proper cost and charges hath had out of all parts of the world all the rare simples which by any means he could attaine unto, not onely to have them brought, but hath procured by his excellent knowledge to have them growing in his garden, which as the time of the yeare doth serve may be seene: for there shall you see all manner of strange trees, herbes, roots, plants, floures, and other such rare things, that it would make a man wonder, how one of his degree, not having the purse of a number, could ever accomplish the same. I protest upon my conscience, I do not think for the knowledge of Plants, that he is inferiour to any: for I did once see him tried with one of the best strangers that ever came into England, and was accounted in Paris the onely man, being recommended unto me by that famous man Master Amb. Pareus; and he being here was desirous to goe abroad with some of our Herbarists, for the which I was the meane to bring them together, and one whole day we spent therein, searching the rarest Simples: but when it came to the triall, my French man did not know one to his foure. What doth this man deserve that hath taken so much paines for his countrey, in setting out a booke, that to this day never any in what language soever did the like?"

The Frenchman referred to could have been none other than Jean Robin who, in 1597, was appointed keeper of the King's garden in Paris. Gerard acknowledged in the Herbal the receipt of numbers of plants from his friend.

In the year 1595 Gerard was elected a member of the Court of Assistants of the Barber-Surgeons' Company; at that time no one could carry on the trade of "barbarie or chirurgerie" in the City without being at least a Freeman of that Company. In the next year he was commissioned to seek a better place for a "fruit-ground" than that in "East Smithfielde or ffetterlane". At this time he had a house in Holborn, then the most aristocratic portion of London, and his garden may have been the plot above mentioned. It is unlikely that it was on the northern side of Holborn, since during the last few years of Elizabeth's reign the future site of Ely Place and Hatton Garden was the famous garden of forty acres belonging to the Bishopric of Ely.

About this time Gerard drew up a sort of petition, intended to be signed by his patron Burleigh, to the University of Cambridge, urging the planting of gardens and the employment of himself as Herbarist. After "most hartie commendacions, &c.", and an involved preamble, it runs: "I thought yt good to moove you herin & to commend this bearer *Ihon Gerard* a servant of mine unto you: who by reason of his travaile into farre countries, his great practise & long experience is throughly acquainted with the generall & speciale differences, names, properties & privie markes of thousands of plants & trees. So yt if you intend a worke of such emolument to yrselves and all young students I shall be glad to have nominated and furnished you with so expert an *Herbarist*: & your selves I trust will think well of the motion and the man."

In this year, 1596, our Author made his first appearance in print, and issued a list of plants he had cultivated in his own garden for some years; this little work of twenty-four pages seems to have been the first professedly complete catalogue of any one garden ever published. The one copy, in duodecimo, known to exist of the first edition is a treasure of the British Museum.

The year following he was attacked by a "most greevous ague and of long continuance". He was appointed Junior Warden of the Barber-Surgeons. In December 1597, his immortal Herbal saw the light, whether published at his own risk or not is uncertain: Johnson says it was printed at Norton's charge. In January 1598 he was appointed one of the examiners of candidates for admission to the freedom of the Barber-Surgeons' Company. The next note of his affairs is dated November 1602, when a committee of the Company was called together to consider a question of a garden for " Mr. Gerrard ". No subsequent minute refers to this, but it is not unlikely that the action of the committee resulted in a lease being granted to Gerard by the Consort of James I., as under:

"Anna R.
"Anne by the grace of God Queene of England, Scotland ffraunce and Ireland. To ALL, & whome these pᵗnts shall come

greeting. KNOW YEE that for and in consideracon of the some of ffive shillings of lawfull money of England in the name of a ffyne to us before hand payd by John Gerrard of London Surgeon and *Herbarist* to the Kings ma^tie (whereof and wherew^th we acknowledge our self satisfied) as also for divers and sundry other causes and consideracons but especially of his singular and approved art skill and industrie in planting nursing and preserving plants hearbes flowers and fruits of all kindes We are pleased to graunt unto the said John Gerrard one garden plot or piece of ground belonginge and adjoning on the east part to o^r mansion house called Somersett howse. . . . YEELDING also and annswearing yearlie to and for our owne use onely at the due and proper seasons of the yeare a convenient proportion and quantitie of herbes flowers or fruite renewing or growing w^h in the said Garden plott or piece of grounde by the arte and industrie of the said John Gerrard if they be lawfully required and demanded Given under o^r seale at Whitehall the ffourteenth daie of *August* in the yeere of the Kings Matie of England ffraunce and Ireland the second and of Scotland the eight and thirtie."

Gerard did not long enjoy the use of this garden, parting in 1605 with all interest in the lease to Robert Earl of Salisbury, second son of Lord Burleigh, then Lord Treasurer of England and Secretary of State jointly with Sir Francis Walsingham. Possibly Gerard occupied a similar position in the household of the son as in that of the father.

In 1608 he was elected Master of the Barber-Surgeons' Company, and here, as the books of the Company are missing for the period, a curtain is dropped on his affairs. There is a note that in the year 1639 the Company paid 25s. 6d. for a copy of the Herbal. He died in February 1611–12, and was buried in St. Andrew's Church, Holborn. Of his family affairs little is known, except that he was married, and that his wife assisted him professionally.

Scattered through the Herbal are the names of many acquaintances, numbering more than fifty. Plants were sent to him from all the then accessible parts of the globe, and from men of almost every rank. Exotic plants came from Jean Robin, of the royal gardens in Paris, whose address is carefully recorded in the chapter "Of Barrenwoort", of which he was donor to Gerard: "It is called *Epimedium*;

I have thought to call it Barren woort in English". Other exotics came from Camerarius of Nuremberg, from Lord Zouch who sent him choice seeds from Crete, Spain and Italy, and Nicholas Lete, a London citizen: he was a merchant, wrote Gerard, greatly in love with rare and fair flowers, for which he sent to Syria, having a servant there and in many other countries. It was Lete who sent Gerard an orange tawny Gillyflower from Poland. British plants came from a Lancashire friend, Thomas Hesketh, and a physician, Stephen Bredwell, a learned and diligent searcher of Simples in the West of England. Another contributor, James Garret, was also an apothecary, a tulip grower who every season brought new plants of sundry colours not before seen, all of which to describe particularly were to roll Sisyphus's stone or number the sands. Gerard dispatched one of his assistants as a ship's surgeon to the Mediterranean that he might bring home new plants. It may be that Sir Walter Raleigh, a botanical collector, contributed to his garden.

Gerard himself travelled over a large part of England in search of Simples, but the statement in Salmon's Herbal (1710) that he lived in Lincolnshire refers to his editor, Johnson. Miss Rohde in her *Old English Herbals* suggests that Shakespeare may have seen Gerard's garden, for he lived for a time nearby: "In those days two such prominent men could scarcely have failed to know one another". Shakespeare, when writing some of his finest plays, 1598–1604, lived in the house of a Huguenot refugee, at the corner of Mugwell (Monkswell) Street, and almost opposite the Barber-Surgeons' Hall. And it is perhaps not insignificant that Shakespeare's plays are full of the old English herb-lore in which Gerard delighted.

No will of our Author has been found at Somerset House, but it seems improbable that he acquired wealth, and the printer of the Herbal may have been more successful than the compiler.[1]

For a glimpse of the man himself, we have but to turn to his half-length portrait engraved by William Rogers, facing page one

[1] Our authority for the life of Gerard is Dr. Benjamin Daydon Jackson, who in 1876 privately printed Gerard's catalogue of his garden plants, with a memoir of Gerard, notes on the plants, references to the Herbal, and the addition of modern names; to which source the present Editor is indebted for many of these notes, as for those in the Appendix. He gratefully acknowledges also as a source of information and inspiration Miss Eleanour Sinclair Rohde's books, especially *The Old English Herbals* (1922), with valuable Bibliographies, treating of many manuscript herbals from the tenth-century *Leech Book of Bald*, and the chief English printed herbals from the fifteenth century.

of his Herbal, of which a photogravure reproduction adorns our own title-page; we shall observe that he holds a branch of the potato plant. Beneath are his own arms, those of the City of London and of the Company of which he was Master. A variant of this portrait, engraved by Io. Payne, appears on the title-page of the Johnson editions of 1633 and 1636.

III.

Sources of the Herball.

GERARD has been harshly judged for failing to acknowledge the source of his Herbal's inspiration; but the day of his work is so far distant, and the circumstances of its production are so little known, that we may choose to ignore what critics have said, in our thankfulness for his own share of the work. Plagiarism was rife in those days, and we do not find Shakespeare making acknowledgement of the originals of his plays. The Herbal owes its charm to our Author; for throughout are his own undoubted observations, allusions to persons and places, and a deal of the contemporary folklore he collected, the whole richly seasoned by his sense of humour, whether patent or lurking slyly between the lines.

The history of the "Historie" runs thus: John Norton, Queen's printer, had commissioned a Dr. Priest, a member of the College of Physicians, to translate Dodoens's *Pemptades* (1583) from the Latin into English, but the translator dying before the completion of his task, the unfinished work came by some means into Gerard's hands. He altered the arrangement of the herbs into that of l'Obel in his *Adversaria*, referring but casually to Priest's labours with the remark that his work had perished with him.

No fewer than eighteen hundred illustrations adorned the Herbal. The wood blocks used by Tabernæmontanus (Bergzabern) in his *Eicones* (1590) with some others were procured from Frankfort by Norton; a few were supplied by Gerard, among which was the first published cut of the "Virginian" potato. Gerard misapplied many of the figures, and caused so much confusion in the early chapters of the Herbal, that James Garret, a London Apothecary, directed the printer's attention to the point, and l'Obel was invited to correct the work, and by his own account did so in a thousand places, until stopped by Gerard, who declared that the work was sufficiently accurate, and that his censor had forgotten the English language.

The original edition of 1597 is seldom quoted, for the enlarged and amended edition, by Thomas Johnson, of 1633, of which a second edition was printed three years later, is superior in every respect, and it was due to Johnson that the Herbal continued for a long time to be the standard work for English students.

Gerard in his preface was becomingly modest about his work, and stated that it was principally intended for gentlewomen. Yet there can be no doubt that he had as good practical knowledge of plants as any of his countrymen then living, and owing to his patronage by the most powerful statesman of the Elizabethan Court he had good opportunities of enriching the gardens under his care with new plants. His accuracy was not unimpeachable, and he recorded as natives of this country many plants which he could not have found here. Johnson and Parkinson, who came into notice a generation later, were decidedly his superiors in this respect. But his work gave an impetus to the study of botany such as no previous writer had accomplished.

Thomas Johnson's additions to the original text are marked through his edition, and this present one, by the signs † and ‡; the first indicating that he had amended the wording; the second, that he had written a clause anew, or had added an observation of his own. Johnson did a great work no doubt in making order of Gerard's vagaries, but proved an extremely unsympathetic editor, at times losing all patience with our Author, and handling him very severely. Time has brought its revenge, and we shall read many of his harshest strictures with a smile.

In a long preface, Johnson writes at large on the history of herbals, and gives notes about the ancient herbalists, beginning with Solomon and passing to others frequently mentioned by Gerard, notably Dioscorides, who in the days of Nero gave the world a Materia Medica. Gerard followed his method in giving the "descriptions" of herbs, "the names", "the place", and "the vertues". Among the translators of Dioscorides was Ruellius, a French physician who, according to Johnson, flourished in 1480. In the middle of the next century flourished the German physician and herbalist, the famous Fuchs (to whom we owe a debt or a grudge for the name of the Fuchsia), and at about this time another German, Gesner, and the Italian, Matthiolus. Then comes "Rembertus Dodonæus", a physician of Brabant, who set forth a history of plants in Dutch, which was turned into French by Clusius, and translated out of French into English by Master Henry Lite (or Lyte). A later edition of the works of Dodoens was the foundation of Gerard's work. In 1570 Peter Pena and Matthias de l'Obel published a herbal, and soon afterwards came Tabernamont's history of plants in German, with above two thousand figures (those used by Gerard).

Coming to contemporary herbalists, Johnson finds the first name worthy of mention to be that of Dr. William Turner, who in the year 1551 set forth his Herbal, adorned for the most part with the figures of Fuchs. In 1629 Mr. John Parkinson, an apothecary of London, published his *Paradisi in Sole Paradisus Terrestris*, his "Garden of all sorts of pleasant flowers which our English ayre will permitt to be noursed up", with a kitchen garden and an orchard.

Turning at last to Gerard, Johnson remarks that out of good will to the public advancement our Author endeavoured to perform more than he could well accomplish, which was partly through want of sufficient learning. (An example is given: he translated *Aster Atticus, Caules pedales terni aut quaterni*, "A stalk foure or five foot long"). Other quibbles follow, with a lukewarm word of praise in the end: Let none blame him for these defects, seeing he was neither wanting in pains nor good will; and there are none so simple but know that heavy burthens are with most pains undergone by the weakest men. "Although there were many faults in the worke, yet judge well of the Author."

IV.

The Present Edition.

SINCE 1636 lovers of the literature of flowers, seeking out Gerard's thoughts, have had to make content with such quotations as they could find in other books, should they not possess one of the scarce copies of his Herbal, or have the chance of studying one in a library. It is a formidable task merely to turn the pages, numbering sixteen hundred and thirty, of the huge, heavy folio, laden with something like half a million words.

While other Herbals have been re-issued, such as Nicholas Culpeper's *English Physician*, 1652, and John Parkinson's *Paradisi in Sole Paradisus Terrestris*, 1629, Gerard's, in its original form, is hardly suitable for present-day publication. Four-fifths of it would be regarded as tedious, such as the long descriptions of many forgotten varieties of plants, or laborious arguments and quotations about the names and identities.

There remains the fragrant essence, that which has given the work its fame, mostly Gerard's own observations as distinct from the original translation of Dodoens's Latin herbal. Of this pure essence, an endeavour has been made in this edition to preserve all that is most precious. No word has been altered, though all that is tedious or gross has been omitted. While most chapters have been short-ened, several remain exactly as originally printed. Notes given in an Appendix aim at identifying some of the plants described when there are difficulties.

Johnson was scornful of Gerard's classical knowledge, but failed in his editions to verify all the numerous quotations, or to put right all Gerard's or his printer's mistakes when using the language of "the Antients". After careful consideration it was decided to simplify the often heavily burdened paragraphs discussing "The Names" by omitting what would interest few, names given in Greek, Hebrew, High Dutch, Low Dutch, etc., and to omit Latin verses or other quotations of the sort to which translations in English were supplied.

The Herbal is an amazingly fine production, a notable example of the printing of its time. A well-preserved copy, in rich con-temporary binding, is well worth the high price for which a dealer would ask—perhaps £80 for an edition of 1636. Ink and paper remain wonderfully fresh after the lapse of centuries. Experts in book production marvel at the quality of the work, and it would be difficult, if not impossible, at the present day to equal the delicacy and clearness of the blocks, even with all the resources of the modern processes of engraving. The illustrations, some of them excellent botanical studies, are admired for their quality of design.

The primary aim of the editor and publishers has been to preserve as much as possible of the spirit of the original, both in its literary and typographical aspects. In this they arc greatly indebted to the printers, who have succeeded in retaining by the arts of good printing much of the beauty of the glorious old folio.

In selecting the best and most characteristic passages, it has been thought well to retain the original division into Books and Chapters and sectional headings which, arbitrary and misleading as they may sometimes be, are yet inseparable from the style and method of Gerard. Any other plan would have involved taking unwarrantable liberties and have resulted in a mere anthology, instead of the worthy miniature of the great Gerard which this edition sets out to be.

For the same reasons, the old haphazard spelling has been retained, only the "s", "u", "v" and "j" being printed in accordance with modern usage. The original punctuation, and the use of capitals, have been faithfully followed. The chapters have been renumbered in sequence, but the chapter numbers of the 1636 edition are shown in brackets. The first page of the Herbal is reproduced in facsimile.

The illustrations have been chosen from Johnson's edition of 1636. By reduction for the present quarto to about five-eighths of the size in which they appear in the folio, the proportion of block to printed page has been preserved, and the reproductions are, on the whole, clearer than the somewhat faded cuts in the surviving copies of the old editions.

Lastly, I wish to express my gratitude to Dr. Daydon Jackson, F.L.S., the distinguished botanist who has devoted his life to the work of the Linnean Society, of which he is ex-general secretary, and for fourteen years laboured at the stupendous task of perfecting the *Index Kewensis*, for his unsparing kindness in reading the proofs of this book, and checking my identifications of the plants.

I would also acknowledge the kindness of the Director of the Royal Botanic Gardens, Kew, for assistance in solving several problems.

MARCUS WOODWARD.

Hurstpierpoint, *July* 1927.

TO THE RIGHT HONORABLE
HIS SINGULAR GOOD LORD AND
MASTER, SIR William Cecil KNIGHT, BARON OF
Burghley, Master of the Court of Wards and Liveries, Chancellor of
the Universitie of Cambridge, Knight of the most noble Order of
the Garter, one of the Lords of her Majesties most honorable
Privy Councell, and Lord high Treasurer of *England*.

Mong the manifold creatures of God (right Honorable, and my singular good Lord) that have all in all ages diversly entertained many excellent wits, and drawn them to the contemplation of the divine wisdome, none have provoked mens studies more, or satisfied their desires so much as plants have done, and that upon just and worthy causes: for if delight may provoke mens labor, what greater delight is there than to behold the earth apparelled with plants, as with a robe of embroidered worke, set with Orient pearles and garnished with great diversitie of rare and costly jewels? If this varietie and perfection of colours may affect the eie, it is such in herbs and floures, that no *Apelles*, no *Zeuxis* ever could by any art express the like: if odours or if taste may worke satisfaction, they are both so soveraigne in plants, and so comfortable that no confection of the Apothecaries can equall their excellent vertue. But these delights are in the outward senses: the principal delight is in the mind, singularly enriched with the knowledge of these visible things, setting forth to us the invisible wisdome and admirable workmanship of Almighty God. The delight is great, but the use greater, and joyned often with necessitie. In the first ages of the world they were the ordinary meate of men, and have continued ever since of necessary use both for meates to maintaine life, and for medicine to recover

health. The hidden vertue of them is such, that (as *Pliny* noteth) the very bruit beasts have found it out: and (which is another use that he observes) from thence the Dyars tooke the beginning of their Art.

Furthermore, the necessary use of those fruits of the earth doth plainly appeare by the great charge and care of almost all men in planting & maintaining of gardens, not as ornaments onely, but as a necessarie provision also to their houses. And here beside the fruit, to speake againe in a word of delight, gardens, especialy such as your Honor hath, furnished with many rare Simples, do singularly delight, when in them a man doth behold a flourishing shew of Summer beauties in the midst of Winters force, and a goodly spring of flours, when abroad a leafe is not to be seene. Besides these and other causes, there are many examples of those that have honoured this science: for to passe by a multitude of the Philosophers, it may please your Honor to call to remembrance that which you know of some noble Princes, that have joyned this study with their most important matters of state: *Mithridates* the great was famous for his knowledge herein, as *Plutarch* noteth. *Euax* also King of Arabia, the happy garden of the world for principall Simples, wrot of this argument, as *Pliny* sheweth. *Dioclesian* likewise, might have had his praise, had he not drowned all his honour in the bloud of his persecution. To conclude this point, the example of *Solomon* is before the rest, and greater, whose wisdome and knowledge was such, that hee was able to set out the nature of all plants from the highest Cedar to the lowest Mosse. But my very good Lord, that which sometime was the study of great Phylosophers and mightie Princes, is now neglected, except it be of some few, whose spirit and wisdome hath carried them among other parts of wisdome and counsell, to a care and studie of speciall herbes, both for the furnishing of their gardens, and furtherance of their knowledge: among whom I may justly affirme and publish your Honor to be one, being my selfe one of your servants, and a long time witnesse thereof: for under your Lordship I have served, and that way emploied my principall study and almost all my time, now by the space of twenty yeares. To the large and singular furniture of this noble Island I have added from forreine places all the varietie of herbes and floures that I might any way obtaine, I have laboured with the soile to make it fit for plants, and with the plants, that they might delight in the soile, that so they might live and prosper under our clymat, as in their native and proper countrey: what my successe hath beene, and what my furniture is, I leave to the report of they that have seene your Lordships gardens, and the little plot of myne owne especiall care and husbandry. But because gardens are privat, and many times finding an ignorant or a negligent successor, come soone to ruine, there be that have sollicited me, first by my pen, and after by the Presse to make my labors common, and to free them from the danger whereunto a garden is subject: wherein when I was overcome, and had brought this History or report of the nature of Plants to a just volume, and had made it (as the Reader may by comparison see) richer than former Herbals, I found it no question unto whom I might dedicate my labors; for considering your good Lordship, I found none of whose favour and goodnes I might sooner presume, seeing I have found you ever my very good Lord and Master. Againe, considering my duty and your Honors merits, to whom may I better recommend my Labors, than to him unto whom I owe my selfe, and all that I am able in your service or devotion to performe? Therefore under hope of your Honorable and accustomed favor I present this Herball to your Lordships protection; and not as an exquisite Worke (for I know my meannesse) but as the greatest gift and chiefest argument of duty that my labour and service can affoord: wherof if there be no other fruit, yet this is of some use, that I have ministred Matter for Men of riper wits and deeper judgements to polish, and to adde to my large additions where any thing is defective, that in time the Worke may be perfect. Thus I humbly take my leave, beseeching God to grant you yet many daies to live to his glory, to the support of this State under her Majestie our dread Soveraigne, and that with great increase of honor in this world, and all fulnesse of glory in the world to come.

Your Lordships most humble

and obedient Servant,

IOHN GERARD.

To the courteous and well willing Readers.

Lthough my paines hav not beene spent (courteous Reader) in the gracious discoverie of golden Mines, nor in the tracing after silver veines, whereby my native country might be inriched with such merchandise as it hath most in request and admiration; yet hath my labour (I trust) been otherwise profitably imploied, in descrying of such a harmelesse treasure of herbes, trees, and plants, as the earth frankely without violence offereth unto our most necessary uses. Harmelesse I call them, because they were such delights as man in the perfectest state of his innocencie did erst injoy: and treasure I may well terme them seeing both Kings and Princes have esteemed them as Jewels; sith wise men have made their whole life as a pilgrimage to attaine to the knowledge of them: by the which they have gained the hearts of all, and opened the mouthes of many, in commendation of those rare vertues which are contained in these terrestriall creatures. I confesse blind Pluto is now adaies more sought after than quicke sighted Phœbus: and yet this dusty mettall, or excrement of the earth (which was first deeply buried least it should be an eie-sore to grieve the corrupt heart of man) by forcible entry made into the bowels of the earth, is rather snatched at of man to his owne destruction, than directly sent of God to the comfort of this life. And yet behold in the compassing of this worldly drosse, what care, what cost, what adventures, what mysticall proofes, and chymicall trials are set abroach; when as notwithstanding the chiefest end is but uncertaine wealth. Contrariwise, in the expert knowledge of herbes, what pleasure still renewed with variety? what small expence? what security? and yet what an apt and ordinary meanes to conduct man to that most desired benefit of health? which as I devoutly wish unto my native countrey, and to the carfull nursing mother of the same; so having bent my labours to the benefit of such as are studiously practised in the conservation thereof, I thought it a chiefe point of my dutie, thus out of my poore store to offer up these my far fetched experiments, together with mine owne countries unknowne treasure, combined in this compendious Herball (not unprofitable though unpolished) unto your wise constructions and courteous considerations. The drift whereof is a ready introduction to that excellent art of Simpling, which is neither so base nor contemptible as perhaps the English name may seeme to intimate: but such it is, as altogether hath beene a study for the wisest, an exercise for the noblest, a pastime for the best. From whence there spring floures not onely to adorne the garlands of the Muses, to decke the bosomes of the beautifull, to paint the gardens of the curious, to garnish the glorious crownes of Kings; but also such fruit as learned Dioscorides long travelled for; and princely Mithridates reserved as precious in his owne closet: Mithridates I meane, better knowne by his soveraigne Mithridate, than by his sometime speaking two and twenty languages. But what this famous Prince did by tradition, Euax king of the Arabians did deliver in a discourse written of the vertues of herbes, and dedicated it unto the Emperor Nero. Every greene Herbarist can make mention of the herbe Lysimachia, whose vertues were found out by King Lysimachus, and his vertues no lesse eternised in the selfe same plant, than the name of Phydias, queintly beaten into the shields of Pallas, or the first letters of Ajax or Hyacinthus (whether you please) registred in that beloved floure of Apollo. As for Artemisia, first called Παρθενις, whether the title thereof sprang from Ἄρτεμις, Diana, her selfe, or from the renowned Queene of Caria, which disclosed the use thereof unto *posterity, it surviveth as a monument to revive the memories of them both for ever. What should we speake of* Gentiana, *bearing still the cognisance of* Gentius? *or of divers other herbes taking their denominations of their princely inventors? What should I say of those royall personages,* Iuba, Attalus, Climenus, Achilles, Cyrus, Masynissa, Semyramis, Dioclesian? *but onely thus, to speake their Princely loves to Herbarisme, and their everlasting honors (which neither old* Plinius *dead, nor yong* Lipsius *living will permit to die?)* Crescent herbæ, crescetis amores: crescent herbæ, crescetis honores. *But had this wonted faculty wanted the authorisement of such a royall company, King* Solomon, *excelling all the rest for wisdome, of greater royalty than they all (though the Lillies of the field out-braved him) he onely (I say) might yeeld hereunto sufficient countenance and commendation, in that his lofty wisdome thought no scorne to stoupe unto the lowly plants. I list not seek the common colours of antiquitie, when notwithstanding the world can brag of no more antient Monument than Paradise and the garden of* Eden ; *and the Fruits of the earth may contend for seniority, seeing their Mother was the first Creature that conceived, and they themselves the first fruit she brought forth. Talke of perfect happinesse or pleasure, and what place was so fit for that as the garden place wherein* Adam *was set to be the Herbarist? Whither did the Poets hunt for their sincere delights, but into the gardens of* Alcinous, *of* Adonis, *and the Orchards of the* Hesperides? *Where did they dreame that heaven should be, but in the pleasant garden of* Elysium? *Whither doe all men walke for their honest recreation, but thither where the earth hath most beneficially painted her face with flourishing colours? And what season of the yeare more longed for than the Spring, whose gentle breath inticeth forth the kindly sweets, and makes them yeeld their fragrant smells? Who would therefore looke dangerously up at Planets, that might safely looke downe at Plants? And if true bee the proverb,* Quæ supra nos, nihil ad nos; *I suppose this new saying cannot be false,* Quæ infra nos, ea maximè ad nos. *Easie therefore is this treasure to be gained, and yet pretious. The science is nobly supported by wise and kingly Favorits: the subject thereof so necessarie and delectable, that nothing can be confected, either dèlicate for the taste, dainty for smell, pleasant for sight, wholsome for body, conservative or restorative for health, but it borroweth the rellish of an herb, the savor of a flour, the colour of a leafe, the juice of a plant, or the decoction of a root. And such is the treasure that this my Treatise is furnished withall; wherein though myne art be not able to countervaile Nature in her lively portraitures, yet have I counterfeited likenesse for life, shapes and shadowes for substance, being ready with the bad Painter to explaine the imperfections of my pensill with my pen, chusing rather to score upon my pictures such rude marks as may describe my meaning, than to let the beholder to guesse at random and misse. I have here therefore set downe not only the names of sundry Plants, but also their natures, their proportions and properties, their affects and effects, their increase and decrease, their flourishing and fading, their distinct varieties and severall qualities, as well of those which our owne country yeeldeth, as of others which I have fetched further, or drawn out by perusing divers Herbals set forth in other languages: wherein none of my countrymen have to my knowledge taken any paines, since that excellent Worke of Master Doctor* Turner. *After which time Master* Lyte *a worshipfull Gentleman translated* Dodonæus *out of French into English; and since that, Doctor* Priest *one of our London Colledge hath (as I heard) translated the last edition of* Dodonæus, *and meant to publish the same; but being prevented by death, his translation likewise perished. Lastly my selfe, one of the least among many, have presumed to set forth unto the view of the World, the first fruits of these myne owne Labours, which if they be such as may content the Reader, I shall thinke my selfe well rewarded; otherwise there is no man to be blamed but my selfe, being a Worke I confesse for greater Clerks to undertake: yet may my blunt attempt serve as a whetstone to set an edge upon sharper wits, by whom I wish this my course Discourse might be both fined and refined. Faults I confesse have escaped, some by the Printers oversight, some through defects in my selfe to perform so great a work, and some by means of the greatnesse of the Labour, and that I was constrained to seeke after my living, being void of friends to beare some part of the burthen. The rather therefore accept this at my hands (loving Country-men) as a token of my goodwill, and I trust that the best and well minded will not rashly condemne me, although something have passed worthy reprehension. But as for the slanderer or Envious I passe not for them, but return upon themselves anything they shall without cause either murmure in corners, or jangle in secret. Farewell.*

From my House in Holborn, within the Suburbs
   of London, this first of December, 1597.

Thy sincere and unfeigned Friend,

IOHN GERARD.

THE FIRST BOOKE OF
THE HISTORY OF PLANTS.

*Containing Graſſes, Ruſhes, Reeds, Corne, Flags, and Bulbous
or Onion-rooted Plants.*

IN this Hiſtorie of Plants it would be tedious, to vſe by way of introduction any curious diſcourſe vpon the generall diuiſion of Plants, contained in Latine vnder *Arbor, Frutex, Suffrutex, Herba :* or to ſpeake of the differing names of their ſeuerall parts, more in Latine than our vulgar tongue can well expreſſe. Or to go about to teach thee, or rather to be-guile thee by the ſmell or taſte, to gheſſe at the temperature of Plants : when as all and euery of theſe in their place ſhall haue their true face and note, whereby thou mayſt both know and vſe them.

In three bookes therefore, as in three gardens, all our Plants are beſtowed ; ſorted as neere as might be in kindred and neigh-bourhood.

The firſt booke hath Graſſes, Ruſhes, Corne, Reeds, Flags, Bulbous or Onion-rooted Plants.

The ſecond, moſt ſorts of Herbs vſed for meat, medicine, or ſweet ſmell.

The third hath Trees, Shrubs, Buſhes, Fruit-bearing Plants, Roſins, Gummes, Roſes, Heaths, Moſſes, Muſhroms, Corall, and ther ſeuerall kindes.

Each booke hath Chapters, as for each Herb a bed : and euery Plant preſents thee with the La-tine and Engliſh name in the title, placed ouer the picture of the Plant.

Then followeth the Kinds, Deſcription, Place, Time, Names, Natures, and Vertues, agreeing with the beſt receiued Opinions.

Laſt of all thou haſt a generall Index, as well in Latine as Engliſh, with a carefull ſupply like-wiſe of an *Index Bilinguis*, of Barbarous Names.

And thus hauing giuen thee a generall view of this Garden, now with our friendly Labors wee will accompanie thee and leade thee through a Graſſe-plot, little or nothing of many Herbariſts heretofore touched ; and begin with the moſt common or beſt knowne Graſſe, which is called in Latine *Gramen Pratenſe* ; and then by little and little conduct thee through moſt pleaſant gardens and other delightfull places, where any Herbe or Plant may be found fit for Meat or Medicine.

CHAP. I. *Of Medow-Grasse.*

THere be sundry and infinite kindes of Grasses not mentioned by the Antients, either as unnecessarie to be set downe, or unknowne to them: only they make mention of some few, whose wants we meane to supply, in such as have come to our knowledge, referring the rest to the curious searcher of Simples.

¶ *The Description.*

1   COmmon Medow Grasse hath very small tufts or roots, with thicke hairy threds depending upon the highest turfe, matting and creeping on the ground with a most thicke and apparant shew of wheaten leaves, lifting up long thinne jointed and light stalks, a foot or a cubit high, growing small and sharpe at the top, with a loose ear hanging downward, like the tuft or top of the common Reed.

2   Small Medow Grasse differeth from the former in the varietie of the soile; for as the first kinde groweth in medowes, so doth this small Grasse clothe the hilly and more dry grounds un-tilled, and barren by nature; a Grasse more fit for sheepe than for greater cattell. And because the kindes of Grasse do differ apparantly in root, tuft, stalke, leafe, sheath, eare, or crest, we may assure our selves that they are endowed with severall Vertues, formed by the Creator for the use of man, although they have been by a common negligence hidden and unknowne. And therefore in this our Labor we have placed each of them in their severall bed, where the diligent searcher of Nature may, if so he please, place his learned observations.

¶ *The Place.*

Common Medow-Grasse groweth of it selfe unset or unsowne, every where; but the small Medow-Grasse for the most part groweth upon dry and barren grounds, as partly we have touched in the Description.

¶ *The Time.*

Concerning the time when Grasse springeth and seedeth, I suppose there is none so simple but knoweth it, and that it con-tinueth all the whole yeare, seeding in June and July. Neither needeth it any propagation or replanting by seed or otherwise; no not so much as the watery Grasses, but that they recover themselves againe, although they have beene drowned in water all the Winter long, as may appeare in the wilde fennes in Lincolnshire, and such like places.

¶ *The Names.*

Gramen pratenſe.
Medow-Graſſe.

Grasse is called in Latine, *Gramen*; as it is thought, *à gradiendo, quod geniculatis internodiis serpat, crebroque novas spargat radices.* For it groweth, goeth, or spreadeth it selfe unset or unsowne naturally over all fields or grounds, cloathing them with a faire and perfect green. It is yearely mowed, in some places twice, and in some rare places thrice. Then is it dried and withered by the heate of the Sun, with often turning it; and then is it called in English, Hay: in French, *Le herbe du praiz.*

¶ *The Vertues.*

The roots of Grasse, according to *Galen*, doe glew and consolidate together new and bleeding wounds.

Hay sodden in water till it be tender, and applied hot to the chaps of beasts that be chap-fallen through long standing in pound or stable without meat, is a present remedie.

---

(17)   Chap. 2. *Of Couch-Grasse or Dogs-Grasse.*

¶ *The Description.*

† 1 THe common or best known dogs grasse or Couch-grasse hath long leaves of a whitish greene colour: the stalke is a cubit and a halfe high, with joints or knees like wheaten strawes, but these joints are covered with a little short downe or woollinesse. The plume or tuft is like the reed, but smaller and more chaffie, and of a grayish colour: it creepeth

in the ground hither and thither with long white roots, joynted at certaine distances, having a pleasant sweet tast: they are platted or wrapped one within another very intricately, insomuch as where it hapneth in gardens amongst pot-herbes, great labour must be taken before it can be destroyed, each piece being apt to grow, and every way to dilate it selfe.

¶ *The Place.*

This grows in gardens and arable lands, as an infirmitie or plague of the fields, nothing pleasing to husbandmen; for after the field is plowed, they are constrained to gather the roots together with harrowes and rakes, and being so gathered and laid upon heaps, they set them on fire lest they should grow againe.

¶ *The Time.*

These Grasses seldome come to shew their eare before July.

¶ *The Nature.*

Although that Couch-grasse be an unwelcome guest to fields and gardens, yet his physicke vertues do recompense those hurts.

¶ *The Vertues.*

Couch-grasse healeth green wounds.

(23)

CHAP. 3. *Of Cotton-Grasse.*

¶ *The Description.*

1   THis strange Cotton-Grasse doth rather resemble grasse than rushes, and may indifferently be taken for either, for that it doth participate of both. The stalke is small and rushy, garnished with many grassie leaves alongst the same, bearing at the top a bush or tuft of most pleasant downe or cotton like unto the most fine white silke.

2   This Water Gladiole, or grassy rush, of all others is the fairest and most pleasant to behold, and serveth very well for the decking and trimming up of houses, because of the beautie and braverie

thereof: consisting of sundry small leaves, of a white colour mixed with carnation, growing at the top of a bare and naked stalke, five or six foot long, and sometime more. The leaves are long and flaggie, not much unlike the common reed.

¶ *The Place and Time.*

1 Cotton grasse groweth upon bogy and such like moorish places, and it is to be seene upon the bogs in Hampsted heath. It groweth likewise in Highgate parke neere London.

2 Water Gladiole groweth in standing pooles, motes, and water ditches. I found it in great plenty at a Village fifteene miles from London called Bushey.

(30)   CHAP. 4. *Of Reeds.*

¶ *The Kindes.*

OF Reeds the Ancients have set downe many sorts.

¶ *The Description.*

1 THe common Reed hath long strawie stalkes, full of knotty joints or knees like unto corne, whereupon doe grow very long rough flaggy leaves. The tuft or spokie eare doth grow at the top of the stalkes, browne of colour, barren and without seed, and doth resemble a bush of feathers, which turneth into fine downe or cotton which is caried away with the winde. The root is thicke, long, and full of strings, dispersing themselves farre abroad, whereby it doth greatly increase.

2 This great sort of Reeds or Canes hath no particular description to answer your expectation, for that as yet there is not any man which hath written thereof, especially of the manner of growing of them, either of his owne knowledge or report from others, so that it shall suffice that ye know that that great cane is used especially in Constantinople and thereabout, of aged and wealthy Citisens, and also Noblemen and such great personages, to make them walking staves of, carving them at the top with sundry Scutchions, and

pretty toyes of imagerie for the beautifying of them; and so they of the better sort doe garnish them both with silver and gold.

3   In like manner the smaller sort hath not as yet beene seene growing of any that have beene curious in herbarisme, whereby they might set downe any certainty thereof; onely it hath beene used in Constantinople and thereabout, even to this day to make writing pens withall, for the which it doth very fitly serve, as also to make pipes, and such like things of pleasure.

¶ *The Place.*

The common Reed groweth in standing waters and in the edges and borders of rivers almost everywhere; and the other being the angling Cane for fishers groweth in Spaine and those hot Regions.

¶ *The Time.*

They flourish and floure from Aprill to the end of September, at which time they are cut downe for the use of man, as all do know.

¶ *The Vertues.*

The roots of reed stamped small draw forth thorns and splinters fixed in any part of mans body.

The same stamped with vinegre ease all luxations and members out of joynt.

And likewise stamped they heale hot and sharpe inflammations. The ashes of them mixed with vinegre helpe the scales and scurfe of the head, and the falling of the haire.

The great Reed or Cane is not used in physicke, but is esteemed to make slears for Weavers, sundry sorts of pipes, as also to light candles that stand before Images, and to make hedges and pales, as we do of lats and such like; and also to make certaine divisions in ships to divide the sweet oranges from the sowre, the Pomecitron and lemmons likewise in sunder, and many other purposes.

(31)   ### CHAP. 5. *Of Sugar-Cane.*

¶ *The Description.*

1   SUgar Cane is a pleasant and profitable Reed, having long stalkes seven or eight foot high, joynted or kneed like unto the great Cane; the leaves come forth of every joynt on every side of the stalke one, like unto wings, long, narrow, and sharpe pointed. The Cane it selfe, or stalke is not hollow as the other Canes or Reeds are, but full, and stuffed with a spongeous substance in taste exceeding sweet. The root is great and long, creeping along within the upper crust of the earth, which is likewise sweet and pleasant, but less hard or woody than other Canes or Reeds; from the which there doth shoot forth many young siens, which are cut away from the maine or mother plant, because they should not draw away the nourishment from the old stocke, and so get unto themselves a little moisture, or else some substance not much worth, and cause the stocke to be barren, and themselves little the better; which shoots do serve for plants to set abroad for encrease.

Arundo Saccharina.
Sugar Cane.

¶ *The Place.*

The Sugar Cane groweth in many parts of Europe at this day, as in Spaine, Portugal, Olbia, and in Provence. It groweth also in Barbarie, generally almost every where in the Canarie Islands, and in those of Madera, in the East and West Indies, and many other places. My selfe did plant some shoots thereof in my garden, and some in Flanders did the like: but the coldnesse of our clymat made an end of mine, and I think the Flemmings will have the like profit of their labour.

¶ *The Time.*

This Cane is planted at any time of the yeare in those hot

countries where it doth naturally grow, by reason they feare no frosts to hurt the young shoots at their first planting.

¶ *The Names.*

The Latines have called this plant *Arundo Saccharina*, with this additament, *Indica*, because it was first knowne or brought from India. Of some it is called, *Calamus Saccharatus*: in English, Sugar Cane.

¶ *The Use.*

Of the juyce of this Reed is made the most pleasant and profitable sweet, called Sugar, whereof is made infinite confections, confectures, Syrups and such like, as also preserving and conserving of sundry fruits, herbes, and floures, as Roses, Violets, Rosemary floures, and such like, which still retaine with them the name of Sugar, as Sugar Roset, Sugar Violet, &c. The which to write of would require a peculiar volume, and not pertinent unto this historie, for that it is not my purpose to make of my booke a Confectionary, a Sugar Bakers furnace, a Gentlewomans preserving pan, nor yet an Apothecaries shop or Dispensatorie; but onely to touch the chiefest matter that I purposed to handle in the beginning, that is, the nature, properties, and descriptions of plants. Notwithstanding I thinke it not amisse to shew unto you the ordering of these reeds when they be new gathered, as I received it from the mouth of an Indian my servant: he saith, They cut them in small pieces, and put them into a trough made of one whole tree, wherein they put a great stone in manner of a mill-stone, whereunto they tie a horse, buffle, or some other beast which draweth it round: in which trough they put those pieces of Canes, and so crush and grind them as we doe the barkes of trees for Tanners, or apples for Cyder. But in some places they use a great wheele wherein slaves doe tread and walke as dogs do in turning the spit: and some others doe feed as it were the bottome of the said wheele, wherein are some sharpe or hard things which doe cut and crush the Canes into powder. And some likewise have found the invention to turne the wheele with water works, as we doe our Iron mills. The Canes being thus brought into dust or powder, they put them into great cauldrons with a little water, where they boile untill there be no more sweet-nesse left in the crushed reeds. Then doe they straine them through mats or such like things, and put the liquor to boile againe unto the consistence of hony, which being cold is like unto sand both in shew and handling, but somewhat softer; and so afterwards it is carried into all parts of Europe, where it is by the Sugar Bakers artificially purged and refined to that whitenesse as we see.

CHAP. 6. *Of Paper Reed.*

PAper Reed hath many large flaggie leaves somewhat triangular and smooth, not much unlike those of Cats-taile, rising immediately from a tuft of roots compact of many strings, amongst the which it shooteth up two or three naked stalkes, square, and rising some six or seven cubits high above the water: at the top wherof there stands a tuft or bundle of chaffie threds set in comely order, resembling a tuft of floures, but barren and void of seed.

Papyrus Niloitca.
Paper Reed.

¶ *The Place.*

This kinde of Reed growes in the Rivers about Babylon, and neere the city Alcaire, in the river Nilus, and such other places of those countries.

¶ *The Time.*

The time of springing and flourishing answereth that of the common Reed.

¶ *The Names.*

This kinde of Reed, which I have Englished Paper Reed, or Paper plant, is the same (as I doe reade) that Paper was made of in Ægypt, before the invention of paper made of linnen clouts was found out. It is thought by men of great learning and understanding in the Scriptures, and set downe by them for truth, that this plant is the same Reed mentioned in the second chapter of *Exodus*; whereof was made that basket or cradle, which was dawbed within and without with slime of that countrey, called *Bitumen Judaicum*, wherein *Moses* was put being committed to the water, when *Pharaoh* gave commandement that all the male children of the Hebrewes should be drowned.

¶ *The Nature, Vertues, and Use.*

The roots of Paper Reed doe nourish, as may appeare by the people of Ægypt, which doe use to chew them in their mouthes, and swallow downe the juice, finding therein great delight and comfort.

(36)   CHAP. 7. *Of Burre-Reed.*

¶ *The Description.*

1   THe first of these plants hath long leaves, which are double edged, or sharpe on both sides, with a sharpe crest in the middle, in such manner raised up that it seemeth to be triangle or three-square. The stalks grow among the leaves, and are two or three foot long, being divided into many branches, garnished with many prickly husks or knops of the bignesse of a nut. The root is full of hairy strings.

Sparganium ramosum.
Branched Burre Reed.

2   The great water Burre differeth not in any thing from the first kinde in roots or leaves, save that the first hath his leaves rising immediately from the tuft or knop of the root; but this kinde hath a long stalke comming from the root, whereupon a little above the root the leaves shoot out round about the stalke successively, some leaves still growing above others, even to the top of the stalke, and from the top thereof downward by certaine distances. It is garnished with many

round wharles or rough coronets, having here and there among the said wharles one single short leafe of a pale greene colour.

¶ *The Place.*

Both these are very common, and grow in moist medowes and neere unto water courses. They plentifully grow in the fenny grounds of Lincolnshire and such like places; in the ditches about S. *Georges* fields, and in the ditch right against the place of execution at the end of Southwark, called S. *Thomas* Waterings.

¶ *The Time.*

They bring forth their burry bullets or seedy knots in August.

¶ *The Vertues.*

Some write, that the knops or rough burres of these plants boiled in wine, are good against the bitings of venomous beasts, if they be either drunke, or the wound washed therewith.

(37)

Chap. 8. *Of Cats-taile.*

¶ *The Description.*

CAts-taile hath long and flaggy leaves full of a spongeous matter or pith, amongst which leaves groweth up a long smooth naked stalke without knot, fashioned like a speare, of a firm or sollid substance, having at the top a browne knop or eare, soft, thick, and smooth, seeming to be nothing else but a deale of flocks thicke set and thrust together, which being ripe turns into a downe and is carried away with the winde. The roots be hard, thicke, and white, full of strings, and good to burne, where there is plenty thereof to be had.

¶ *The Place.*

It groweth in pooles and such like standing waters, and sometimes in running streames.

I have found a smaller kinde hereof growing in the ditches and marishie grounds in the Isle of Shepey, going from Sherland house to Feversham.

¶ The Time.

They floure and beare their mace or torch in July and August.

¶ The Names.

It is called in English, Cats-taile or Reed-mace. Of this Cats-taile *Aristophanes* makes mention in his Comedy of Frogs, where he bringeth them forth one talking with another, being very glad that they had spent the whole day in skipping and leaping *inter Cyperum & Phleum*, among Galingale and Cats-taile.

¶ The Vertues.

The soft downe stamped with Swines grease wel washed, healeth burnes or scalds with fire or water.

This downe in some places of the Isle of Ely and the Low-countries adjoyning thereto, is gathered and well sold to make mattresses thereof for plow-men and poore people.

It hath been also often proved to heale kibed or humbled heeles, (as they are termed) being applied to them either before or after the skin is broken.

---

(38)   CHAP. 9. *Of Stitch-wort.*

¶ The Description.

STitch-wort, or as *Ruellius* termeth it, *Holosteum*, is of two kindes, and hath round tender stalks full of joints leaning toward the ground: at every joynt grow two leaves one against another. The floures be white, consisting of many small leaves set in the manner of a star. The roots are small, joynted, and threddy. The seed is contained in small heads somewhat long, and sharp at the upper end; and when it is ripe, it is very small, and browne.

¶ The Place.

They grow in the borders of fields upon banke sides and hedges almost every where.

¶ *The Time.*

They flourish all the Summer, especially in May and June.

¶ *The Names.*

In Latine, *Tota ossea*: in English, All-bone. Wherof I see no reason, unlesse it be by the figure *Antonomia*; as when we say in English, he is an honest man, our meaning is, he is a knave: for this is a tender herbe, having no such bony substance.

¶ *The Vertues.*

They are wont to drinke it in wine with the pouder of Acornes, against the paine in the side, stitches, and such like.

---

(40)

CHAP. 10. *Of the Floure de-luce.*

¶ *The Kindes.*

THere be many kindes of Iris or Floure de-luce, whereof some are tall and great, some little, small, and low; some smell exceeding sweet in the root, some have no smell at all. Some floures are sweet in smell, and some without: some of one colour, some of many colours mixed: vertues attributed to some, others not remembred; some have tuberous or knobby roots, others bulbous or Onion roots; some have leaves like flags, others like grasse or rushes.

¶ *The Description.*

1   THe common Floure de-luce hath long and large flaggy leaves like the blade of a sword with two edges, amongst which spring up smooth and plaine stalks two foot long, bearing floures toward the top compact of six leaves joyned together, wherof three that stand upright are bent inward one toward another; and in those leaves that hang downeward there are certaine rough or hairy welts, growing or rising from the nether part of the leafe upward, almost of a yellow colour. The roots be thicke, long, and knobby, with many hairy threds hanging thereat.

2   The water Floure de-luce, or water Flag, or *Acorus*, is like

unto the garden Floure de-luce in roots, leaves, and stalkes, but the leaves are much longer, sometimes of the height of foure cubits, and altogether narrower. The floure is of a perfect yellow colour, and the root knobby like the other; but being cut, it seemes to be of the colour of raw flesh.

Iris Chalcedonica.
Turky Floure de-luce.

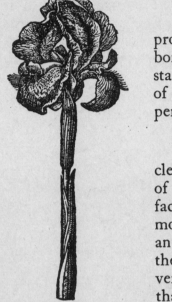

¶ *The Place.*

The water Floure de-luce or yellow Flag prospereth well in moist medowes, and in the borders and brinks of Rivers, ponds, and standing lakes. Although it be a watery plant of nature, yet being planted in gardens it prospereth well.

¶ *The Vertues.*

The root of the common Floure de-luce cleane washed, and stamped with a few drops of Rose-water, and laid plaisterwise upon the face of man or woman, doth in two daies at the most take away the blacknesse or blewnesse of any stroke or bruse: so that if the skinne of the same woman or any other person be very tender and delicate, it shall be needfull that ye lay a piece of silke, sindall, or a piece of fine laune betweene the plaister and the skinne; for otherwise in such tender bodies it often causeth heat and inflammation.

---

(44)

Chap. 11. *Of Ginger.*

¶ *The Description.*

Ginger is most impatient of the coldnesse of these our Northerne regions, as my selfe have found by proofe, for that there have beene brought unto me at severall times sundry plants thereof, fresh, greene, and full of juice, as well from the West Indies, as from Barbary and other places; which have sprouted and budded forth greene leaves in my garden in the heate of Summer, but as soone as it hath beene but touched with the first sharpe blast of Winter, it hath presently perished both blade and root. The true forme or picture hath not before this time been set forth by any that hath written; but the world hath beene deceived by a counterfeit figure, which the reverend and learned Herbarist *Matthias Lobel* did set forth in his Observations.   The forme whereof notwithstanding I have here expressed, with the true and undoubted picture also, which I received from *Lobels* owne hands at the impression hereof. The cause of whose former error, as also the meanes whereby he got the knowledge of the true Ginger, may appeare by his own words sent unto me in Latine, which I have here thus Englished :

Zinziberis verior icon.
The true figure of Ginger.

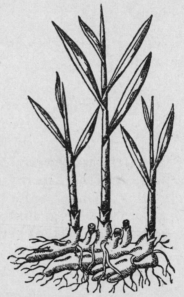

How hard and uncertaine it is to describe in words the true proportion of Plants (having none other guide than skilfull, but yet deceitfull formes of them, sent from friends or other means) they best do know who have deepliest waded in this sea of Simples. About thirty yeares past or more, an honest and expert Apothecarie *William Dries*, to satisfie my desire, sent me from Antwerpe to London the picture of Ginger, which he held to be truly and lively drawne. I my selfe gave him credit easily, because I was not ignorant, that there had beene often Ginger roots brought greene, new, and full of juice, from the Indies to Antwerp: and further, that the same had budded & grown in the said *Dries* garden. But not many yeares after I perceived, that the picture which was sent me by my friend was a counterfeit, and before that time had been drawne and set forth by an old Dutch Herbarist. Therefore not suffering this error any further to spread abroad (which I discovered not many yeares past at Flushing in Zeeland, in the garden of *William* of Nassau Prince of Orange, of famous memorie), I thought it convenient to impart thus much unto M^r. *John Gerrard* an expert Herbarist, and master of happy successe in Surgerie, to the end he might let posteritie know thus much, in the painfull and long laboured travels which now he hath in hand, to the great good and benefit of his countrey.

Thus much have I set downe, truly translated out of his owne words in Latine; though too favourably by him done to the commendation of my mean skill.

¶ *The Place.*

Ginger groweth in Spaine, Barbary, in the Canarie Islands, and the Azores. Our men who sacked Domingo in the Indies, digged it up there in sundry places wilde.

¶ *The Time.*

Ginger flourisheth in the hot time of Sommer, and loseth his leaves in Winter.

¶ *The Names.*

Ginger is called in Latine *Zinziber*, and *Gingiber*.

¶ *The Vertues.*

Ginger, as *Dioscorides* reporteth, is right good with meat in sauces, or otherwise in conditures; for it is of an heating and digesting qualitie, and is profitable for the stomacke, and effectually opposeth it selfe against all darknesse of the sight; answering the qualities and effects of Pepper.

---

(46)

CHAP. 12. *Of Corne.*

THus far have I discoursed upon Grasses, Rushes, Spartum, Flags, and Floure de-luces: my next labor is to set downe for your better instruction the historie of Corne, and the kinds therof, under the name of Graine. And beginning with corne, we will first speake of wheat, and describe it in the first place, because it is preferred before all other corne.

¶ *The Description.*

1 THis kinde of Wheate is the most principall of all other, whose eares are altogether bare or naked, without awnes or chaffie beards. The stalke riseth from a threddy root, compact of many strings, joynted or kneed at sundry distances; from whence shoot forth grassie blades and leaves like unto Rie,

but broader. The plant is so well knowne to many, and so profitable to all, that the meanest and most ignorant need no larger description to know the same by.

¶ *The Place.*

Wheat groweth almost in all the countries of the world that are inhabited and manured, and requireth a fruitfull and fat soile, and rather Sunny and dry, than watery grounds and shadowie: for in dry ground (as *Columella* reporteth) it groweth harder and better compact: in a moist and darke soile it degenerateth sometime to be of another kinde.

Triticum lucidum.
Bright Wheat.

¶ *The Time.*

They are most commonly sowen in the fall of the leafe, or Autumne: sometime in the Spring.

¶ *The Nature.*

Wheat (saith *Galen*) is very much used of men, and with greatest profit. Those Wheats do nourish most that be hard, and have their whole substance so closely compact as they can scarsely be bit asunder; for such do nourish very much: and the contrary but little.

¶ *The Vertues.*

The fine floure mixed with the yolke of an egge, honey, and a little saffron, doth draw and heale byles and such like sores, in children and in old people, very well and quickly. Take crums of wheaten bread one pound and an halfe, barley meale ℥ij. Fennigreeke and Lineseed of each an ounce, the leaves of Mallowes, Violets, Dwale, Sengreene, and Cotyledon, *ana* one handfull: boyle them in water and oyle untill they be tender: then stampe them very small in a stone morter, and adde thereto to the yolke of three egges, oyle of Roses, and oyle of Violets, *ana* ℥ij. Incorporate them altogether; but if the inflammation grow to an Erysipelas, then adde thereto the juice of Nightshade, Plantaine, and

Henbane, *ana* ʒij. it easeth an Erysipelas, or Saint *Anthonies* fire, and all inflammations very speedily.

Slices of fine white bread laid to infuse or steepe in Rose water, and so applied unto sore eyes which have many hot humours falling into them, doe easily defend the humour, and cease the paine.

The oyle of wheat pressed forth betweene two plates of hot iron, healeth the chaps and chinks of the hands, feet, and fundament, which come of cold, making smooth the hands, face or any other part of the body.

(54)

CHAP. 13. *Of Otes.*

¶ *The Description.*

1   A*Vena Vesca*, common Otes, is called *Vesca, a Vescendo*, because it is used in many countries to make sundry sorts of bread, as in Lancashire, where it is their chiefest bread corne for Jannocks, Haver cakes, Tharffe cakes, and those which are called generally Oten cakes; and for the most part they call the graine Haver, whereof they do likewise make drinke for want of Barley.

2   *Avena Nuda* is like unto the common Otes; differing in that, that these naked Otes immediately as they be threshed, without helpe of a Mill become Otemeale fit for our use. In consideration whereof in Northfolke and Southfolke they are called unhulled or naked Otes. Some of those good house-wives that delight not to have any thing but from hand to mouth, according to our English proverbe, may (while their pot doth seeth) go to the barne, and rub forth with their hands sufficient for that present time, not willing to provide for to morrow, according as the scripture speaketh, but let the next day bring it forth.

¶ *The Vertues.*

Common Otes put into a linnen bag, with a little bay salt quilted handsomely for the same purpose, and made hot in a frying pan, and applied very hot, easeth the paine in the side called the stitch.

Otemeale is good for to make a faire and wel coloured maid to looke like a cake of tallow, especially if she take next her stomacke a good draught of strong vinegre after it.

Chap. 14. *Of Turkie Corne.*

¶ *The Place.*

THese kinds of grain were first brought into Spaine, and then into other provinces of Europe: not (as some suppose) out of Asia *minor*, which is the Turks dominions; but out of America and the Islands adjoining, as out of Florida, and Virginia or Norembega, where they use to sow or set it to make bread of it, where it growes much higher than in other countries. It is planted in the gardens of these Northern regions, where it commeth to ripenesse

The forme of the eares of Turky Wheat.

Frumenti Indici ſpica.

Turky Wheat in the huske, as alſo naked or bare.

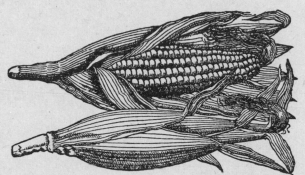

when the summer falleth out to be faire and hot; as my selfe have seen by proof in myne owne garden.

¶ *The Time.*

It is sowen in these countries in March and Aprill, and the fruit is ripe in September.

¶ *The Names.*

† Turky wheat is called of some *Frumentum Turcicum*, and *Milium Indicum*, as also *Maizum*, and *Maiz*, or *Mays*. It in all probabilitie was unknowne to the antient both Greeke and Latine Authors. In English it is called, Turky corne, and Turky wheat. The Inhabitants of America and the Islands adjoyning, as also of the East and West Indies, do call it *Mais*: the Virginians, *Pagatowr*.

¶ *The Temperature and Vertues.*

Turky wheat doth nourish far lesse than either wheat, rie, barly, or otes. The bread which is made thereof is meanely white, without bran: it is hard and dry as Bisket is, and hath in it no clamminesse at all; for which cause it is of hard digestion, and yeeldeth to the body little or no nourishment. Wee have as yet no certaine proofe or experience concerning the vertues of this kinde of Corne; although the barbarous Indians, which know no better, are constrained to make a vertue of necessitie, and thinke it a good food: whereas we may easily judge, that it nourisheth but little, and is of hard and evill digestion, a more convenient food for swine than for man.

---

(79) **Chap. 15.** *Of the English Jacinth, or Hare-bells.*

¶ *The Description.*

1 THe blew Hare-bells or English Jacinth is very common throughout all England. It hath long narrow leaves leaning towards the ground, among the which spring up naked or bare stalks loden with many hollow blew floures, of a strong sweet smell somewhat stuffing the head: after which come the cods or round knobs, containing a great quantitie of small blacke shining seed. The root is bulbous, full of a slimie glewish juice, which will serve to set feathers upon arrowes in stead of glew, or to paste bookes with: hereof is made the best starch next unto that of Wake-robin roots.

Hyacinthus stellatus latifolius cum flore & semine.
The Lilly leaued starry Iacinth in floure and se

2 The white English Jacinth is altogether like unto the precedent, saving that the leaves of this are somewhat broader, the floures more open, and very white of colour.

3   There is found wilde in many places of England another sort, having floures of a faire Carnation colour, which maketh a difference from the other.

The blew Hare-bels grow wilde in woods, Copses, and in the borders of fields every where thorow England.

¶ *The Time.*

They floure from the beginning of May unto the end of June.

¶ *The Names.*

The first of our English Hyacinths is called *Hyacinthus Anglicus*, for that it is thought to grow more plentifully in England than elsewhere: of *Dodonæus*, *Hyacinthus non scriptus*, or the unwritten Hyacinth.

¶ *The Vertues.*

The roots, after the opinion of *Dioscorides*, being beaten and applied with white Wine, hinder or keepe backe the growth of haires.

---

(83)

CHAP. 16. *Of two feigned Plants.*

¶ *The Description.*

1   I Have thought it convenient to conclude the historie of the Hyacinths with these two bulbous Plants, received by tradition from others, though generally holden for feigned and adulterine. Their pictures I could willingly have omitted in this historie, if the curious eye could elsewhere have found them drawne and described in our English Tongue: but because I finde them in none, I will lay them downe here, to the end that it may serve for excuse to others who shall come after, which list not to describe them, being as I said condemned for feined and adulterine nakedly drawne onely. The floures (saith the Author) are no lesse strange than wonderfull. The leaves and roots are like to those of Hyacinths. The floures resemble the Daffodils or Narcissus. The whole plant consisteth of a woolly or flockie matter : which description with the Picture was sent unto *Dodonæus* by *Johannes Aicholzius*.

2 The second feigned picture hath beene taken of the Discoverer and others of late time, to be a kinde of Dragons not seene by any that have written thereof; which hath moved them to thinke it a feigned picture likewise; notwithstanding you shall receive the description thereof as it hath come to my hands. The root (saith my Author) is bulbous or Onion fashion, outwardly blacke; from the which spring up long leaves, sharpe pointed, narrow, and of a

Bulbus Bombicinus Commentitius.
Falſe bumbaſt Iacinth.

Tigridis flos.
The floure of Tygris.

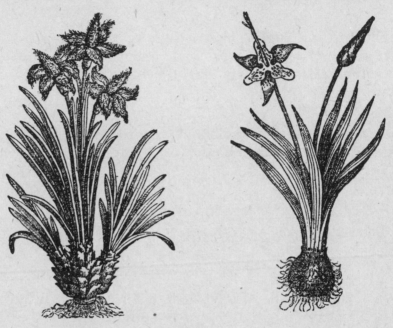

fresh greene colour: in the middest of which leaves rise up naked or bare stalkes, at the top whereof groweth a pleasant yellow floure, stained with many small red spots here and there confusedly cast abroad: and in the middest of the floure thrusteth forth a long red tongue or stile, which in time groweth to be the cod or seed-vessell, crooked or wreathed, wherein is the seed. The vertues and temperature are not to be spoken of, considering that we assuredly persuade our selves that there are no such plants, but meere fictions and devices, as we terme them, to give his friend a gudgeon.

(84)

Chap. 17. *Of Daffodils.*

¶ *The Description.*

1   THe first of the Daffodils is that with the purple crowne or circle, having small narrow leaves, thicke, fat, and full of slimie juice; among the which riseth up a naked stalke smooth and hollow, of a foot high, bearing at the top a faire milke white floure growing forth of a hood or thin filme such as the flours of onions are wrapped in: in the midst of which floure is a round circle or small coronet of a yellowish colour, purfled or bordered about the edge of the said ring or circle with a pleasant purple colour; which being past, there followeth a thicke knob or button, wherein is contained blacke round seed. The root is white, bulbous or Onion-fashion.

Narciſſus juncifolius reflexus flore albo.
The white reflex *Iunquilia.*

2   The second kinde of Daffodill is that sort of *Narcissus* or Primrose peere-lesse that is most common in our country gardens, generally knowne everie where. It hath long fat and thick leaves, full of a slimie juice; among which riseth up a bare thicke stalke, hollow within and full of juice. The floure groweth at the top, of a yellowish white colour, with a yellow crowne or circle in the middle, and floureth in the moneth of Aprill, and sometimes sooner. The root is bulbous fashion.

3   There are three or foure reflex *Junquilia's,* whose cups hang downe, and the six incompassing leaves turne up or backe, whence they take their names.

¶ *The Place.*

The Daffodils with purple coronets grow wilde in sundry places, chiefly in Burgondie, and in Switzerland in medowes.

Theocritus affirmeth the Daffodils to grow in medowes, in his 19 Eidyl, or 20 according to some editions: where he writeth, That the faire Lady *Europa* entring with her Nymphs into the medowes, did gather the sweet smelling daffodils; in these verses: Which we may English thus:

> *But when the Girles were come into*
> *The medowes flouring all in sight,*
> *That Wench with these, this Wench with those*
> *Trim floures, themselves did all delight:*
> *She with the Narcisse good in sent,*
> *And she with Hyacinths content.*

But it is not greatly to our purpose, particularly to seeke out their places of growing wilde, seeing we have them all & everie one of them in our London gardens, in great aboundance. The common wilde Daffodill groweth wilde in fields and sides of woods in the West parts of England.

¶ *The Time.*

They floure for the most part in the Spring, that is, from the beginning of February unto the end of Aprill.

¶ *The Vertues.*

Galen saith, That the roots of Narcissus have such wonderfull qualities in drying, that they consound and glew together very great wounds, yea and such gashes or cuts as happen about the veins, sinues, and tendons. They have also a certaine clensing facultie.

The root of Narcissus stamped with hony and applied plaister-wise, helpeth them that are burned with fire, and joineth together sinues that are cut in sunder.

Being used in manner aforesaid it helpeth the great wrenches of the ancles, the aches and pains of the joints.

The same applied with hony and nettle seed helpeth Sun burning.

Being stamped with the meale of Darnel and hony, it draweth forth thorns and stubs out of any part of the body.

(87)   Chap. 18. *Of Tulipa, or the Dalmatian Cap.*

¶ *The Kindes.*

TUlipa or the Dalmatian Cap is a strange and forrein floure, one of the number of the bulbed floures, whereof there be sundry sorts, some greater, some lesser, with which all studious and painefull Herbarists desire to be better acquainted, because of that excellent diversitie of most brave floures which it beareth. Of this there be two chiefe and generall kindes, *viz.* *Præcox,* and *Serotina*; the one doth beare his floures timely, the other later. To these two we will adde another sort called *Media,* flouring betweene both the others. And from these three sorts, as from their heads, all other kindes doe proceed, which are almost infinite in number. Notwithstanding, my loving friend Mr *James Garret,* a curious searcher of Simples, and learned Apothecarie of London, hath undertaken to finde out, if it were possible, their infinite sorts, by diligent sowing of their seeds, and by planting those of his owne propagation, and by others received from his friends beyond the seas for the space of twenty yeares, not being yet able to attaine to the end of his travel, for that each new yeare bringeth forth new plants of sundry colours not before seen; all which to describe particularly were to rolle *Sisiphus* stone, or number the sands. So that it shall suffice to speake of and describe a few, referring the rest to some that meane to write of Tulipa a particular volume.

¶ *The Description.*

1   THe Tulipa of Bolonia hath fat thicke and grosse leaves, hollow, furrowed or chanelled, bended a little backward, and as it were folded together: which at their first comming up seeme to be of a reddish colour, and being throughly growne turne into a whitish greene. In the midst of those leaves riseth up a naked fat stalke a foot high, or somthing more; on the top whereof standeth one or two yellow floures, somtimes three or more, consisting of six smal leaves, after a sort like to a deepe wide open cup, narrow above, and wide in the bottome. After it hath been some few dayes floured, the points and brims of the floure turn backward, like a Dalmatian or Turkish Cap,

called Tulipan, Tolepan, Turban, and Turfan, whereof it tooke his name. The chives or threds in the middle of the floure be somtimes yellow, otherwhiles blackish or purplish, but commonly of one overworne colour or other, Nature seeming to play more with this floure than with any other that I do know. This floure is of a reasonable pleasant smell, and the other of his kinde have little or no smel

Tulipa ſerotina polyclados major flo. flano fundo nigro, Cluſij.
Cluſius his greater many branched Tulip with a yellow floure, and blacke bottome.

at all. The root is bulbous, and very like to a common onion of S. *Omers.*

2 We have likewise another of greater beautie, and very much desired of all, with white floures dasht on the backside, with a light wash of watchet colour.

¶ *The Place.*

Tulipa groweth wilde in Thracia, Cappadocia, and Italy; in Bizantia about Constantinople; at Tripolis and Aleppo in Syria. They are now common in all the English gardens of such as affect floures.

¶ *The Time.*

They floure from the end of Februarie unto the beginning of May, and somwhat after: although *Augerius Busbequius* in his journey to Constantinople, saw betweene Hadrianople and Constantinople, great aboundance of them in floure everie where, even in the midst of Winter, in the moneth of Januarie, which that warme and temperat clymat may seeme to performe.

¶ *The Names.*

The later Herbarists by a Turkish or strange name call it Tulipa, of the Dalmatian cap called Tulipa, the forme whereof the floure when it is open seemeth to represent.

It is called in English after the Turkish name Tulipa, or it may be called Dalmatian Cap, or the Turks Cap. What name the antient Writers gave it is not certainly knowne.

‡ I do verily thinke that these are the Lillies of the field mentioned by our Saviour, *Mat.* 6. 28, 29. for he saith, That *Solomon* in all his royaltie was not arrayed like one of these. The reasons that induce me to thinke thus, are these; First, their shape: for their floures resemble Lillies; and in these places whereas our Saviour was conversant they grow wilde in the fields. Secondly, the infinite varietie of colour, which is to be found more in this than any other sort of floure. And thirdly, the wondrous beautie and mixtures of these floures. This is my opinion, and these my reasons, which any may either approve of or gainsay, as he shall thinke good.   ‡

¶ *The Temperature and Vertues.*

There hath not been any thing set downe of the antient or later Writers, as touching the Nature or Vertues of the Tulipa, but they are esteemed specially for the beauty of their floures.

‡ The roots preserved with sugar, or otherwise dressed, may be eaten, and are no unpleasant nor any way offensive meat, but rather good and nourishing.   ‡

(89)   Chap. 19. *Of Turkie or Ginny-hen Floure.*

¶ *The Description.*

1 THe Checquered Daffodill, or Ginny-hen Floure, hath small narrow grassie leaves; among which there riseth up a stalke three hands high, having at the top one or two floures, and sometimes three, which consisteth of six small leaves checquered most strangely: wherein Nature, or rather the Creator of all things, hath kept a very wonderfull order, surpassing (as in all other things) the curiousest painting that Art can set downe. One square is of a greenish yellow colour, the other purple, keeping the same order as well on the backside of the floure as on the inside, although they are blackish in one square, and of a Violet colour in an other; insomuch that every leafe seemeth to be the feather of a Ginny hen, whereof it tooke his name. The root is small, white, and of the bignesse of halfe a garden beane.

2 The second kinde of Checquered Daffodill is like unto the

former in each respect, saving that this hath his floure dasht over with a light purple, and is somewhat greater than the other, wherein consisteth the difference.

¶ *The Names.*

The Ginny hen floure is called of *Dodonæus, Flos Meleagris*: of *Lobelius, Lilio-narcissus variegata*, for that it hath the floure of a Lilly, and the root of *Narcissus*: it hath beene called *Fritillaria*, of the table or boord upon which men play at Chesse, which square checkers the floure doth very much resemble; some thinking that it was named *Fritillus*: whereof there is no certainty; for *Martial* seemeth to call *Fritillus, Abacus*, or the Tables whereon men play at Dice, in the fifth booke of his Epigrams, writing to *Galla*.

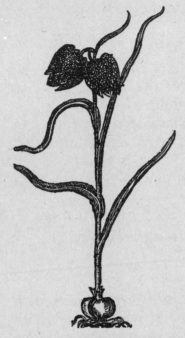

Fritillaria.
Checquered Daffodill.

> The sad Boy now his nuts cast by,
> Is call'd to Schoole by Masters cry:
> And the drunke Dicer now betray'd
> By flattering Tables as he play'd,
> Is from his secret tipling house drawne out,
> Although the Officer he much besought, &c.

In English we may call it Turky-hen or Ginny-hen Floure, and also Checquered Daffodill, and Fritillarie, according to the Latine.

¶ *The Temperature and Vertues.*

Of the facultie of these pleasant floures there is nothing set downe in the antient or later Writer, but are greatly esteemed for the beautifying of our gardens, and the bosoms of the beautifull.

Chap. 20. *Of true Saffron, and the wilde or Spring Saffron.*

¶ *The Description.*

HIs floure doth first rise out of the ground nakedly in September, and his long smal grassie leaves shortly after the floure, never bearing floure and leafe at once. The floure consisteth of six small blew leaves tending to purple, having in the middle many small yellow strings or threds; among which are two, three, or more thicke fat chives of a fierie colour somewhat reddish, of a strong smell when they be dried, which doth stuffe and trouble the head.

¶ *The Place.*

Common or best knowne Saffron groweth plentifully in Cambridge-shire, Saffron-Waldon, and other places thereabout, as corne in the fields.

¶ *The Time.*

Saffron beginneth to floure in September, and presently after spring up the leaves, and remaine greene all the Winter long.

¶ *The Names.*

Saffron is called in Latine, *Crocus*: in Mauritania, *Saffaran*: in Spanish, *Açafron*: in English, Saffron: in the Arabicke tongue, *Zahafaran*.

¶ *The Vertues.*

Avicen affirmeth, That it causeth head-ache, and is hurtfull to the braine, which it cannot do by taking it now and then, but by too much using of it; for the too much using of it cutteth off sleep, through want whereof the head and sences are out of frame. But the moderat use thereof is good for the head, and maketh the sences more quicke and lively, shaketh off heavy and drowsie sleepe, and maketh a man merry.

Also Saffron strengthneth the heart, concocteth crude and raw humors of the chest, opens the lungs, and removeth obstructions.

It is also such a speciall remedie for those that have consumption of the lungs, and are, as wee terme it, at deaths doore, and almost past breathing, that it bringeth breath again, and prolongeth life for certaine dayes, if ten or twenty graines at the most be given with new or sweet Wine. For we have found by often experience, that being taken in that sort, it presently and in a moment removeth away difficulty of breathing, which most dangerously and suddenly hapneth.

Dioscorides teacheth, That being given in the same sort it is also good against a surfet.

It is with good successe put into compositions for infirmities of the eares.

The eyes being anointed with the same dissolved in milke or fennel or rose water, are preserved from being hurt by the small pox or measels, and are defended thereby from humors that would fal into them.

The chives steeped in water serve to illumine or (as we say) limne pictures and imagerie, as also to colour sundry meats and confections.

The weight of ten grains of Saffron, the kernels of Walnuts two ounces, Figs two ounces, Mithridate one dram, and a few Sage leaves stamped together with a sufficient quantitie of Pimpernel water, and made into a masse or lumpe, and kept in a glasse for your use, and thereof 12 graines given in the morning fasting, preserveth from the pestilence, and expelleth it from those that are infected.

¶ *The Place.*

All the wilde Saffrons we have growing in our London gardens. Those which doe floure in Autumne do grow upon certaine craggy rocks in Portugall, not farre from the sea side. The other have been sent over unto us, some out of Italy, and some out of Spaine, by the labour and diligence of that notable learned Herbarist *Carolus Clusius*; out of whose Observations, and partly by seeing them in our owne gardens, we have set downe their description.

That pleasant plant that bringeth forth yellow floures was sent unto me from *Robinus* of Paris, that painfull and most curious searcher of Simples.

¶ *The Time.*

They floure for the most part in Januarie and Februarie; that of the mountain excepted, which floureth in September.

¶ *The Names.*

All these Saffrons are unprofitable, and therefore they be truly

said to be *Croci sylvestres*, or wild Saffrons: in English, Spring
Saffrons, and vernall Saffrons.

¶ *The Nature and Vertues.*

Of the faculties of these we have nothing to set downe, for that
as yet there is no knowne use of them in Physicke.

(91)   CHAP. 21. *Of Medow Saffron.*

¶ *The Kindes.*

THere be sundry sorts of medow Saffrons, differing very
notably as well in the colour of their floures, as also in nature
and country from whence they had their being, as shall be
declared.

¶ *The Description.*

1 MEdow Saffron hath three or foure leaves rising immediately forth of the ground, long, broad, smooth,
fat, much like to the leaves of the white Lillie in
forme and smoothnesse: in the middle whereof spring up three or
foure thicke cods of the bignesse of a small Wall-nut, standing upon
short tender foot-stalkes, three square, and opening themselves
when they be ripe, full of seed something round, and of a blackish
red colour: and when this seed is ripe, the leaves together with the
stalkes doe fade and fall away. In September the floures bud forth,
before any leaves appeare, standing upon short tender and whitish
stemmes, like in forme and colour to the floures of Saffron, having
in the middle small chives or threds of a pale yellow colour, altogether
unfit for meat or medicine.

2 The second kinde of Mede Saffron is like the precedent,
differing onely in the colour of the floures, for that this plant doth
bring forth white leaves, which of some hath beene taken for the
true *Hermodactylus*; but in so doing they have committed the
greater error.

3 In the Spring of the yeare it bringeth forth his leaves, thicke,
fat, shining, and smooth, not unlike the leaves of Lillies, which doe
continue greene unto the end of June; at which time the leaves do
wither away, but in the beginning of September there shooteth

forth of the ground naked milke white floures without any greene leafe at all: but so soone as the Plant hath done bearing of floures, the root remaines in the ground, not sending forth any thing untill Februarie in the yeare following.

¶ *The Place.*

Medow Saffron, or *Colchicum*, groweth in Messinia, and in the Isle of Colchis, whereof it tooke his name. The titles of the rest do set forth their native countries; notwithstanding our London gardens are possessed with the most part of them.

Colchicum biflorum.
Twice flouring Mede Saffron.

The two first do grow in England in great aboundance in fat and fertile medowes, as about Vilford and Bathe, as also in the medowes neere to a small village in the West part of England, called Shepton Mallet, in the medowes about Bristoll, in Kingstrop medow neere unto a water mil as you go from Northampton to Holmby house, upon the right hand of the way, and likewise in great plenty in Nobottle wood two miles from Northampton, and in many other places.

‡ The rest for the most part may be found in the gardens of the Florists among us. ‡

¶ *The Time.*

The leaves of all the kindes of Mede Saffron doe begin to shew themselves in Februarie. The seed is ripe in June. The leaves, stalks, and seed do perish in July, and their pleasant floures do come forth of the ground in September.

¶ *The Names.*

Divers name it in Latine *Bulbus agrestis*, or wild Bulbe: in French, *Mort au chien*. Some have taken it to be the true Hermodactyl, yet falsely. Other some call it *Filius ante patrem*, although there is a kinde of *Lysimachia* or Loose-strife so called, because it first bringeth forth his long cods with seed, and then the floure

after, or at the same time at the end of the said cod.   But in this
Mede Saffron it is far otherwise, because it bringeth forth leaves
in Februarie, seed in May, and floures in September; which is a
thing cleane contrarie to all other plants whatsoever, for that they
doe first floure, and after seed: but this Saffron seedeth first, and
foure moneths after brings forth floures: and therefore some have
thought this a fit name for it, *Filius ante Patrem*: and we accord-
ingly may call it, The Sonne before the Father.

¶ *The Vertues of Hermodactyls.*

† The roots of Hermodactyls are properly given (saith *Paulus*)
to those that have the Gout.

The same stamped, and mixed with the whites of egges, barley
meale, and crums of bread, and applied plaisterwise, ease the paine
of the Gout, swellings and aches about the joynts.

¶ *The Correction.*

The pouder of Ginger, long Pepper, Annise seed or Cumine
seed, and a little Masticke, correct the churlish working of that
Hermodactyll which is used in Shops.   But those which have eaten
of the common Medow Saffron must drinke the milke of a cow, or
else death presently ensueth.

¶ *The Danger.*

The roots of all the sorts of Mede Saffrons are very hurtfull to
the stomacke, and being eaten they kill by choaking as Mushromes
do, according unto *Dioscorides*; whereupon some have called it
Colchicum strangulatorium.

(92)   CHAP. 22. *Of Star of Bethlem.*

¶ *The Kindes.*

THere be sundry kindes of wilde field Onions called Stars of
Bethlem, differing in stature, tast and smell.

¶ *The Description.*

1 OUr common Starre of Bethlehem hath many narrow leaves, thicke, fat, full of juice, and of a very greene colour, with a white streake downe the middle of each leafe: among the which rise up small naked stalkes, at the top whereof grow floures compact of six little leaves, stripped on the backe side with lines of greene, the inside being milke-white. These floures open themselves at the rising of the Sunne, and shut againe at the Sun-setting; whereupon this plant hath been called by some, *Bulbus Solsequius*. The floures being past, the seed doth follow, inclosed in three cornered huskes. The root is bulbous, white both within and without.

¶ *The Place.*

Stars of Bethlehem, or Star-floures, grow in sundry places that lie open to the aire, not onely in Germany and the Low-countries, but also in England, and in our gardens very common. The yellow kinde *Lobel* found in Somerset-shire in the corne fields. The rest are strangers in England; yet we have most of them in some of our choice gardens.

¶ *The Time.*

These kindes of bulbed plants do floure from Aprill to the end of May.

¶ *The Vertues.*

The roots, saith *Dioscorides*, are eaten both raw and boiled.

---

(93)

CHAP. 23. *Of Onions.*

¶ *The Kindes.*

THere be, saith *Theophrastus*, divers sorts of Onions, which have their syr-names of the places where they grow: some also lesser, others greater; some be round, and divers long, but none wilde, as *Pliny* writeth.

¶ *The Description.*

1   THe Onion hath narrow leaves, and hollow within; the stalke is single, round, biggest in the middle, on the top whereof groweth a round head covered with a thin skin or film, which being broken, there appeare little white floures made up in form of a ball, and afterward blacke seed three cornered, wrapped in thin white skins. In stead of the root there is a bulbe or round head compact of many coats, which oftentimes becommeth great in manner of a Turnep, many times long like an egge. To be briefe, it is covered with very fine skins for the most part of a whitish colour.

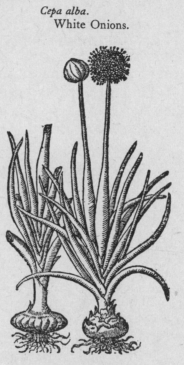

Cepa alba.
White Onions.

¶ *The Place.*

The Onion requireth a fat ground well digged and dunged, as *Palladius* saith. It is cherished everie where in kitchen gardens, now and then sowne alone, and many times mixed with other herbs, as with Lettuce, Parseneps, and Carrets. *Palladius* liketh well that it should be sowne with Savorie, because, saith *Pliny*, it prospereth the better, and is more wholesome.

¶ *The Time.*

It is sowne in March or Aprill, and somtimes in September.

¶ *The Vertues.*

The Onions do bite, attenuate or make thin, and cause drynesse: being boiled they do lose their sharpnesse, especially if the water be twice or thrice changed, and yet for all that they doe not lose their attenuating qualitie.

The juice of Onions snuffed up into the nose, purgeth the head, and draweth forth raw flegmaticke humors.

Stamped with Salt, Rue, and Honey, and so applied, they are good against the biting of a mad Dog.

Rosted in the embers and applied, they ripen and breake cold Apostumes, Biles, and such like.

The juice of Onions mixed with the decoction of Penniroyall, and anointed upon the goutie member with a feather, or a cloath wet therein, and applied, easeth the same very much.

The juice anointed upon a pild or bald head in the Sun, bringeth the haire againe very speedily.

The juice taketh away the heat of scalding with water or oile, as also burning with fire & gunpouder, as is set forth by a very skilfull Surgeon Mr *William Clowes* one of the Queens Surgeon; and before him by *Ambrose Parey*, in his treatise of wounds made by gun-shot.

Onions sliced and dipped in the juice of Sorrell, and given unto the Sicke of a tertian Ague, to eat, takes away the fit in once or twice so taking them.

¶ *The Hurts.*

The Onion being eaten, yea though it be boiled, causeth head-ache, hurteth the eyes, and maketh a man dim sighted, dulleth the sences, and provoketh overmuch sleep, especially being eaten raw.

---

(102)   ## CHAP. 24. *Of White Lillies.*

¶ *The Kindes.*

THere be sundry sorts of Lillies, whereof some be wilde or of the field, others tame or of the garden; some white, others red; some of our own countries growing, others from beyond the seas: and because of the variable sorts, we wil divide them into chapters, beginning with the two white Lillies, which differ little but in the native place of growing.

¶ *The Description.*

1   THe white Lilly hath long smooth and full bodied leaves of a grassie or light green colour. The stalks be two cubits high, and somtimes more, set or garnished with the like leaves, but growing smaller and smaller toward the top; and upon them do grow faire white floures strong of smell, narrow toward the foot of the stalke whereon they do grow, wide or open

in the mouth like a bell. In the middle part of them doe grow small
tender pointals tipped with a dusty yellow colour, ribbed or chamfered on the back side, consisting of six small leaves thicke and fat.
The root is a bulb made of scaly cloves, full of tough and clammy
juice, wherewith the whole plant doth generally abound.

2 The white Lilly of Constantinople hath very large & fat
leaves like the former, but narrower and lesser. The stalke riseth
up to the height of three cubits, set and garnished with leaves also
like the precedent, but much lesse. Which stalke oftentimes doth
alter and degenerat from his naturall roundnesse to a flat forme, as
it were a lath of wood furrowed or chanelled alongst the same, as
it were ribs or welts. The floures grow at the top like the former,
saving that the leaves doe turne themselves more backward like the
Turks cap, and beareth many more floures than our English white
Lilly doth.

¶ *The Place.*

Our English white Lilly groweth in most gardens of England.
The other groweth naturally in Constantinople and the parts
adjacent, from whence we had plants for our English gardens,
where they flourish as in their owne countrey.

¶ *The Time.*

The Lillies floure from May to the end of June.

¶ *The Names.*

The Lilly is called in Latine, *Rosa Junonis*, or *Juno's* Rose,
because as it is reported it came up of her milke that fell upon the
ground. But the Poets feign, That *Hercules*, who *Jupiter* had by
Alcumena, was put to *Juno's* breasts whilest shee was asleepe; and
after the sucking there fell away aboundance of milk, and that one
part was spilt in the heavens, and the other upon the earth; and
that of this sprang the Lilly, and of the other the circle in the
heavens called *Lacteus Circulus*, or the Milky way, or otherwise in
English Watling street. S. *Basil* in the explication of the 44 Psalm
saith, That no floure so lively sets forth the frailty of mans life as
the Lilly.

The other is called *Lilium album Byzantinum*: in English, the
white Lilly of Constantinople.

¶ *The Vertues.*

The root of the garden Lilly stamped with hony gleweth together sinues that be cut in sunder.

Florentinus a writer of Husbandry saith, That if the root be curiously opened, and therein be put some red, blew, or yellow colour that hath no causticke or burning qualitie, it will cause the floure to be of the same colour.

---

(103)

CHAP. 25. *Of Red Lillies.*

¶ *The Kindes.*

THere be likewise sundry sorts of Lillies, which we do comprehend under one generall name in English, Red Lillies, whereof some are of our owne countries growing, and others of beyond the seas, the which shall be distinguished severally.

¶ *The Description.*

1　THe gold-red Lilly groweth to the height of two, and somtimes three cubits, and often higher than those of the common white Lilly. The leaves be blacker and narrower, set very thicke about the stalke. The floures in the top be many, from ten to thirty, according to the age of the plant, and fertilitie of the soile, like in forme and greatnesse to those of the white Lilly, but of a white colour tending to a Saffron, sprinckled or poudred with many little blacke specks, like to rude unperfect draughts of certaine letters. The roots be great bulbs, consisting of many cloves, as those of the white Lilly.

¶ *The Place.*

These Lillies do grow wilde in the plowed fields of Italy and Languedocke, in the mountaines and vallies of Hetruria and those places adjacent. They are common in our English gardens, as also in Germanie.

¶ *The Names.*

‡ I have thought good here also to give you that discourse touching the Poets Hyacinth, which being translated out of *Dodonæus*, was formerly unfitly put into the chapter of Hyacinths, which therefore I there omitted, and have here restored to his due place. ‡

† There is a Lilly which *Ovid, Metamorph. lib.* 10. calls *Hyacinthus*, of the boy *Hyacinthus*, of whose bloud he feigned that this floure sprang, when hee perished as he was playing with *Apollo*: for whose sake he saith that *Apollo* did print certain letters and notes of his mourning. These are his words, which lately were elegantly thus rendered in English by Mr *Sands*:

Behold! the bloud which late the grasse had dy'de
Was now no bloud: from whence a floure full blowne,
Far brighter than the Tyrian skarlet shone:
Which seem'd the same, or did resemble right
A Lilly, changing but the red to white.
Nor so contented, (for the youth receiv'd
That grace from *Phœbus*) in the leaves he weav'd
The sad impression of his sighs, Ai, Ai,
They now in funerall characters display.

But let us return to the proper names from which we have digressed. Most of the later herbarists call this plant *Hyacinthus Pöeticus*, or the Poets Jacinth. *Pausanias* in his second booke of Corinthiacks hath made mention of *Hyacinthus* called of the Hermonians *Comosandalos*, setting down the ceremonies done by them on their festivall dayes in honor of the goddesse *Chthonia*. The Priests (saith he) and the magistrats for that yeare do leade the troupe of the pomp; the women & men follow after; the boyes solemnly leade forth the goddesse with a stately shew: they go in white vestures, with garlands on their heads made of a floure which the inhabitants call *Comosandalos*, which is the blew or sky-coloured Hyacinth, having the marks and letters of mourning as aforesaid.

¶ *The Vertues.*

The leaves of the herbe applied are good against the stinging of Serpents.

The same boiled and tempered with vineger are good against burnings, and heale green wounds and ulcers.

The root rosted in the embers, and pouned with oile of Roses, cureth burnings.

The same stamped with honey cureth the wounded sinewes and members out of joint. It takes away the wrinkles, and deformities of the face.

The roots boiled in Wine, saith *Pliny*, causeth the cornes of the feet to fall away within few dayes, with removing the medicine untill it have wrought his effect.

(104)   CHAP. 26. *Of Mountaine Lillies.*

§ *The Description.*

1   THe great mountain Lilly hath a cloved bulb or scaly root like those of the red Lilly, yellow of colour, very small in respect of the greatnesse of the plant; from the which riseth up a stalke, somtimes two or three, according to the age of the plant, whereof the middle stalke commonly turneth from his roundnesse into a flat forme, as those of the white Lilly of Constantinople. Upon these stalks do grow faire leaves of a blackish greene colour, in roundles and spaces as the leaves of Woodroofe, not unlike to the leaves of white Lilly, but smaller at the top of the stalkes. The floures be in number infinite, or at the least hard to be counted, very thicke set or thrust together, of an overworne purple, spotted on the inside with many smal specks of the colour of rusty iron. The whole floure doth turne it selfe backward at such time as the sun hath cast his beames upon it, like unto the Tulipa or Turks cap, as the Lilly or Martagon of Constantinople doth; from the middle whereof do come forth tender pendants hanging thereat, of the colour the floure is spotted with.

Lilium montanum majus.
The great mountaine Lilly.

2   The small mountain Lilly is very like unto the former in root, leafe, stalk, and floures: differing in these points, The whole plant is lesse, the stalke never leaveth his round forme, and beareth fewer floures.

The small sort I have had many yeares growing in my garden, but the greater I have not had til of late, given me by my loving friend Mr *James Garret* Apothecarie of London.

There hath not bin any thing left in writing either of the nature or vertues of these plants: notwithstanding we may deem, that God which gave them such seemely and beautifull shape, hath not left them without their peculiar vertues, the finding out whereof we leave to the learned and industrious searcher of Nature.

---

(107)   CHAP. 27. *Of the Persian Lilly.*

¶ *The Description.*

THe Persian Lilly hath for his root a great white bulbe, differing in shape from the other Lillies, having one great bulbe firme or solid, full of juice, which commonly each yere setteth off or encreaseth one other bulbe, and sometimes more, which the next yere after is taken from the mother root, and so bringeth forth such floures as the old plant did. From this root riseth up a fat thicke and straight stem of two cubits high, whereupon is placed long narrow leaves of a greene colour, declining to blewnesse as doe those of the woad. The floures grow alongst the naked part of the stalk like little bels, of an overworn purple colour, hanging down their heads, every one having his own footstalke of two inches long, as also his pestell or clapper from the middle part of the floure; which being past and withered, there is not found any seed at all, as in other plants, but is encreased only in his root.

¶ *The Place.*

This Persian Lilly groweth naturally in Persia and those places adjacent, whereof it tooke his name, and is now (by the industry of Travellers into those countries, lovers of plants) made a denizon in some few of our London gardens.

¶ *The Time*.

This plant floureth from the beginning of May to the end of June.

There is not any thing known of the nature or vertues of this Persian Lilly, esteemed as yet for his rarenesse and comely proportion; although (if I might bee so bold with a stranger that hath vouchsafed to travell so many hundreds of miles for our acquaintance) wee have in our English fields many scores of floures in beauty far excelling it.

---

(108)   CHAP. 28. *Of the Crowne Imperiall*.

¶ *The Description*.

THe Crowne Imperiall hath for his root a thicke firme and solid bulbe, covered with a yellowish filme or skinne, from the which riseth up a great thicke fat stalke two cubits high, in the bare and naked part of a darke overworne dusky purple colour. The leaves grow confusedly about the stalke like those of the white Lilly, but narrower: the floures grow at the top of the stalke, incompassing it round, in forme of an Imperiall Crowne, (whereof it tooke his name) hanging their heads downward as it were bels; in colour it is yellowish; or to give you the true colour, which by words otherwise cannot be expressed, if you lay sap berries in steep in faire water for the space of two houres, and mix a little saffron in that infusion, and lay it upon paper, it sheweth the perfect colour to limne or illumine the floure withall. The back side of the said floure is streaked with purplish lines, which doth greatly set forth the beauty therof. In the bottom of each of these bels there is placed sixe drops of most cleare shining sweet water, in taste like sugar, resembling in shew faire orient pearles; the which drops if you take away, there do immediatly appeare the like: notwithstanding if they may be suffered to stand still in the floure according to his own nature, they will never fall away, no not if you strike the plant untill it be broken. Among these drops there standeth out a certain pestel, as also sundry small chives tipped with small pendants like those of the Lilly: above the whole floures there groweth a tuft of green leaves like those upon the stalke, but smaller. After the floures be faded, there follow cods or seed-vessels six square, wherein is contained flat seeds tough & limmer, of the colour of Mace: the whole plant, as wel roots as floures do savor or smell very like a fox. As the plant groweth old, so doth it wax rich, bringing forth a Crowne of floures amongst the uppermost green leaves, which some make a second kinde, although in truth they are but one and the selfe. same, which in time is thought to grow to a triple crowne, which hapneth by the age of the root, and fertilitie of the soile.

Corona Imperialis.
The Crowne Imperiall.

¶ *The Place.*

This plant likewise hath been brought from Constantinople amongst other bulbous roots, and made denizons in our London gardens, whereof I have great plenty.

¶ *The Time.*

It floureth in Aprill, and sometimes in March, when as the weather is warme and pleasant. The seed is ripe in June.

¶ *The Names.*

This rare and strange Plant is called in Latine, *Corona Imperialis,* & *Lilium Byzantinum.*

¶ *The Temperature and Vertues.*

The vertue of this admirable plant is not yet knowne, neither his faculties or temperature in working.

---

(113)

CHAP. 29. *Of Fox Stones.*

¶ *The Kindes.*

THere be divers kindes of Fox-stones, differing very much in shape of their leaves, as also in floures: some have floures, where-in is to be seen the shape of sundry sorts of living creatures; some the shape and proportion of flies, in other gnats, some humble bees,

others like unto honey Bees; some like Butter-flies, and others like
Waspes that be dead; some yellow of colour, others white; some
purple mixed with red, others of a brown overworne colour: the
which severally to distinguish, as well those here set downe, as
also those that offer themselves daily to our view and consideration,
would require a particular volume; for there is not any plant which
doth offer such varietie unto us as these kinds, except the Tulipa's,
which go beyond all account: for that the most singular Simplest
that ever was in these later ages, *Carolus Clusius* (who for his singular
industry and knowledge herein is worthy triple honor) hath spent
at the least 35 yeares, sowing the seeds of Tulipa's from yeare to
yeare, and to this day he could never attain to the end or certainty
of their severall kinds of colours. The greatest reason thereof that
I can yeeld is this, That if you take the seeds of a Tulipa that bare
white floures, and sow them in a pan or tub with earth, you shal
receive from that seed plants of infinite colours. Contrariwise, if
you sow the seeds of a plant that beareth flours of variable colours,
the most of those plants will be nothing like the plant from whence
the seed was taken.

¶ *The Description.*

1   BUtterfly Orchis or Satyrion beares next the root two very
broad leaves like those of the Lilly, seldome three: the
floures be white of colour, resembling the shape of a
Butterfly: the stalke is a foot high.

2   The Waspe Satyrion groweth out of the ground, having
stalks small and tender: the leaves are like the former, but somwhat
greater, declining to a brown or dark colour. The flours be small,
of the colour of a dry oken leafe, in shape resembling the great Bee
called in English an Hornet, or drone Bee.

3   The leaves of Bee Satyrion are longer than the last before mentioned, narrower, turning themselves against the Sun as it were round.
The stalk is round, tender, and very fragile. At the top grow the
floures, resembling in shape the dead carkasse of a Bee. The bulbes
of the roots be smaller and rounder than the last described.

4   The Fly Satyrion is in his leaves like the other, saving that
they be not of so dark a colour: the floures be smaller, and more
plentifully growing about the stalke, in shape like unto Flies, of a
darke greenish colour, even almost blacke.

¶ *The Place.*

These kindes of Orchis grow for the most part in moist medowes and fertile pastures, as also in moist woods.

The Bee, the Fly, and the Butter-fly Satyrions grow upon barren chalky hils, & heathy grounds, upon the hils adjoyning to a village in Kent named Greenhithe, upon Long-field downs by Southfleet, two miles from the same place, and in many other places of Kent: likewise in a field adjoyning to a small grove of trees, halfe a mile from S. Albons, at the South end thereof. They grow likewise at Hatfield neere S. Albons, by the relation of a learned Preacher there dwelling, Mr *Robert Abbot*, an excellent and diligent Herbarist.

That kind which resembleth the white Butter-fly groweth upon the declining of the hill at the end of Hampsted heath, neere to a small cottage there in the way side, as yee goe from London to Henden a village there by. It groweth in the fields adjoyning to the fold or pin-fold without the gate, at a village called High-gate, neere London: and likewise in the wood belonging to a Worshipfull gentleman of Kent named Mr *Sidley*; of Southfleet: where doe grow likewise many other rare and dainty simples, that are not to be found elsewhere in a great circuit.

¶ *The Time.*

They floure for the most part from May to the end of August, and some of them sooner.

¶ *The Names.*

These kindes of Orchis have not bin much written of by the Antients, neither by the late writers to any purpose; so that it may content you for this time to receive the names set down in their severall titles, reserving what else might be said as touching the Greeke, French, or Dutch names, or any generall definition, untill a further consideration.

¶ *The Temperature and Vertues.*

There is no great use of these in physicke, but they are chiefly regarded for the pleasant and beautifull floures wherewith Nature hath seemed to play and disport her selfe.

(118)   Chap. 30. *Of Birdsnest.*

¶ *The Description.*

1   BIrds nest hath many tangling roots platted or crossed one over another very intricately, which resembleth a Crows nest made of sticks; from which riseth up a thicke soft grosse stalk of a browne colour, set with small short leaves of the colour of a dry oken leafe that hath lien under the tree all the winter long. On the top of the stalke groweth a spiky eare or tuft of floures, in shape like unto maimed Satyrion, wherof doubtlesse it is a kinde. The whole plant, as well stickes, leaves, and floures, are of a parched brown colour.

Satyrium abortivum, sive Nidus Avis.
Birds nest.

¶ *The Place.*

This bastard or unkindely Satyrion is very seldome seene in these Southerly parts of England. It is reported, that it groweth in the North parts of England, neere unto a village called Knaesborough. I found it growing in the middle of a wood in Kent two miles from Gravesend, neere unto a worshipfull gentlemans house called Mr *William Swan*, of Howcke green. The wood belongs to one Mr *John Sidley*. Which plant I did never see elsewhere; and because it is very rare, I am the more willing to give you all the markes in the wood for the better finding it, because it doth grow but in one piece of the wood: that is to say, The ground is covered all over in the same place neere about it with the herb Sanicle, as also with the kind of Orchis called *Hermaphroditica*, or Butterfly Satyrion.

¶ *The Time.*

It floureth and flourisheth in June and August. The dusty or mealy seed (if it may bee called seed) falleth in the end of August: but in my judgment it is an unprofitable or barren dust, and no seed at all.

¶ *The Names.*

It is called *Satyrium abortivum*: of some, *Nidus avis*: in French, *Nid d'oiseau*: in English, Birds nest, or Goose nest.

¶ *The Nature and Vertues.*

It is not used in physicke, that I can finde in any authoritie either of the antient or later writers, but is esteemed as a degenerat kind of Orchis, and therefore not used.

THE SECOND BOOKE OF THE HISTORIE OF PLANTS.

Containing the Description, Place, Time, Names, Nature, and Vertues of all sorts of Herbes, for meat, medicine, or sweet-smelling use, &c.

WEE have in our first booke sufficiently described the Grasses, Rushes, Flags, Corne, and bulbous rooted Plants, which for the most part are such as with their brave and gallant floures deck and beautifie gardens, and feed rather the eies than the belly. Now there remain certain other bulbs, whereof the most, though not all, serve for food: of which we will also discourse in the first place in this booke, dividing them in such sort, that those of one kinde shal be separated from another.

---

(1)

Chap. 31. *Of Turneps.*

¶ *The Kindes.*

THere be sundry sorts of Turneps, some wild, some of the garden; some with round roots globe fashion, other ovall or peare-fashion; and another sort longish or somewhat like a Radish: and of all these there are sundry varieties, some being great, and some of a smaller sort.

¶ *The Description.*

1 THe Turnep hath long rough and greene leaves, cut or snipt about the edges with deepe gashes. The stalke divideth it selfe into sundry branches or armes, bearing at the top small floures of a yellow colour, and sometimes of a light purple: which being past, there do succeed long cods full of small blackish seed like Rape seed: the root is round like a bowle, and sometimes a little stretched out in length, growing very shallow in the ground, and often shewing it selfe above the face of the earth.

2 The small Turnep is like unto the first described, saving that it is lesser. The root is much sweeter in taste, as my selfe have often proved.

¶ *The Place.*

The Turnep prospereth well in a light loose and fat earth, and so loose, as *Petrus Crescentius* saith, that it may be turned almost into dust. It groweth in fields and divers vineyards and hop-gardens in most places of England.

The small Turnep growes by Hackney in a sandy ground, and those that are brought to Cheapside market from that village are the best that ever I tasted.

¶ *The Time.*

Turneps are sown in the spring, as also in the end of August. They floure and seed the second yeare after they are sowne: for those that floure the same yeare that they are sown, are a degenerat kind, called in Cheshire about the Namptwich, Madneps, of their evill qualitie in causing frensie and giddinesse of the brain for a season.

¶ *The Names.*

The Turnep is called in Latine, *Rapum*: the name commonly used in shops and every where, is *Rapa*.

¶ *The Temperature and Vertues.*

The bulbous or knobbed root, which is properly called *Rapum* or Turnep, and hath given name to the plant, is many times eaten raw, especially of the poore people in Wales, but most commonly boiled.

The decoction of Turneps is good against the cough and hoarsenesse of the voice, being drunke in the evening with a little sugar, or a quantitie of clarified hony.

Dioscorides writeth, That the Turnep it selfe being stamped, is with good successe applied upon mouldy or kibed heeles, and that also oile of Roses boiled in a hollow turnep under the hot embers doth cure the same.

The seed is mixt with Counterpoisons and Treacles, and beeing drunke it is a remedie against poisons.

(11)

CHAP. 32. *Of Tarragon.*

¶ *The Description.*

TArragon the sallade herbe hath long and narrow leaves of a deep green colour, greater and longer than those of common Hyssope, with slender brittle round stalkes two cubites high: about the branches whereof hang little round floures, never perfectly opened, of a yellow colour mixed with blacke, like those of common Wormewood.

Draco herba.
Tarragon.

¶ *The Place.*

Tarragon is cherished in gardens, and is encreased by the young shoots: *Ruellius* and such others have reported many strange tales hereof scarce worth the noting, saying, that the seed of flax put into a Raddish root or sea Onion, and so set, doth bring forth this herbe Tarragon.

¶ *The Time.*

It is greene all Summer long, and a great part of Autumne, and floureth in July.

¶ *The Names.*

It is called in Latine, *Draco*; in French, *Dragon*; in English, Tarragon.

¶ *The Vertues.*

Tarragon is not to be eaten alone in sallades, but joyned with other herbs, as Lettuce, Purslain, and such like, that it may also temper the coldnesse of them, like as Rocket doth, neither do we know what other use this herbe hath.

(13)

CHAP. 33. *Of Indian Cresses.*

¶ *The Description.*

CResses of India have many weake and feeble branches, rising immediatly from the ground, dispersing themselves far abroad; by meanes whereof one plant doth occupie a great circuit of ground, as doth the great Bindeweede. The tender stalks divide

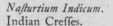
Nasturtium Indicum.
Indian Cresses.

themselves into sundry branches, trailing likewise upon the ground, somewhat bunched or swollen up at every joint or knee, which are in colour of a light red, but the spaces betweene the joints are greene. The leaves are round like wall peniwort, called Cotyledon, the foot-stalke of the leafe commeth forth on the backe-side almost in the middest of the leafe, as those of Frogbit, in taste and smell like the garden Cresses. The flours are dispersed throughout the whole plant, of colour yellow, with a crossed star overthwart the inside, of a deepe Orange colour: unto the backe-part of the same doth hang a taile or spurre, such as hath the Larkes heele, called in Latine *Consolida Regalis*; but greater, and the spur or heele longer; which beeing past there succeed bunched and knobbed coddes or seed vessells, wherein is contained the seed, rough, browne of colour, and like unto the seeds of the beete, but smaller.

¶ *The Place.*

The seeds of this rare and faire plant came from the Indies into Spaine, and thence into France and Flanders, from whence I received seed that bore with mee both floures & seed, especially those I received from my loving friend *John Robin* of Paris.

¶ *The Names.*

This beautifull Plant is called in Latine, *Nasturtium Indicum*: in English, Indian Cresses. Although some have deemed it a kind of *Convolvulus*, or Binde-weed; yet I am well contented that it retaine the former name, for that the smell and taste shew it to be a kinde of Cresses.

¶ *The Nature and Vertues.*

We have no certaine knowledge of his nature and vertues, but are content to referre it to the kindes of Cresses, or to a further consideration.

---

(18)

C<small>HAP</small>. 34. *Of wilde water-Cresses or Cuckow-floures.*

¶ *The Description.*

1 THe first of the Cuckow flours hath leaves at his springing up somwhat round, & those that spring afterward grow jagged like the leaves of Greek Valerian; among which riseth up a stalk a foot long, set with the like leaves, but smaller and more jagged, resembling those of Rocket. The floures grow at the top in small bundles, white of colour, hollow in the middle, resembling the white sweet-John: after which come small chaffie huskes or seed-vessels, wherein the seed is contained. The root is small and threddy.

2 Milk-white Lady-smock hath stalks rising immediatly from the root, dividing themselves into sundry small twiggy and hard branches, set with leaves like those of *Serpillum*. The floures grow at the top, made of foure leaves of a yellowish colour: the root is tough and wooddy, with some fibres anexed thereto. ‡ This is no

other than the first described, differing only therefrom in that the floures are milke white, as our Author truly in the title of his figure made them. Yet forgetting himselfe in his description, he maketh them yellowish, contrary to himselfe and the truth.   ‡

‡ 3   I should be blame-worthy if in this place I omitted that prety conditioned *Sium* which is kept in divers of our London gardens, and was first brought hither by that great Treasurer of Natures rarities, Mr *John Tradescant*. This Plant hath leaves set many on a rib like as the other *Sium* described in the second place hath, but are cut in with two or three pretty deep gashes: The stalke is some cubit high, & divided into many branches, which have small white floures growing upon them: after these floures are past, there follow small long cods containing a smal white seed. Now the nature of this plant is such, that if you touch but the cods when the seed is ripe, though you doe it never so gently, yet will the seed fly al abroad with violence, as disdaining to be touched: whence they usually call it *Noli me tangere*; as they for the like quality name the *Persicaria siliquosa*. The nature of this plant is somewhat admirable, for if the seeds, as I said, be fully ripe, though you put but your hand neere them, as profering to touch them, though you doe not, yet will they fly out upon you, and if you expect no such thing, perhaps make you afraid, by reason of the suddennesse thereof. This herbe is written of only by *Prosper Alpinus*, under the title of *Sium minimum*; and it may be called in English, Impatient Lady-smock, or Cuckow floure. It is an annual, and yearely sowes it selfe by the falling seeds. ‡

¶ *The Place and Time.*

‡ 3   This grows naturally in some places of Italy: also I found it about Bath & other parts of this kingdome.   ‡

These floure for the most part in Aprill and May, when the Cuckow begins to sing her pleasant notes without stammering.

¶ *The Names.*

They are commonly called in Latine *Flos Cuculi*; and also some call them *Nasturtium aquaticum minus*, or lesser water-Cresse: of some, *Cardamine*: in English, Cuckow-flours: in Norfolk, Canturbury bels: at the Namptwich in Cheshire my native country, Lady-smockes; which hath caused me to name it after their fashion.

(25)

Chap. 35. *Of Shepheards purse.*

¶ *The Description.*

1 THe leaves of Shepheards purse grow up at the first long, gashed in the edges like those of Rocket, spred upon the ground: from these spring up very many little weake stalkes divided into sundry branches, with like leaves growing on them, but lesser; at the top whereof are orderly placed small white floures: after these come up little seed vessels, flat, and cornered, narrow at the stemme like to a certaine little pouch or purse, in which lieth the seed. The root is white not without strings.

¶ *The Place.*

These herbes doe grow of themselves for the most part, neere common high waies, in desart and untilled places, among rubbish and old walls.

¶ *The Time.*

They floure, flourish and seed all the Summer long.

¶ *The Names.*

Shepheards purse is called in Latine, *Pastoris bursa*: in French, *Bourse de pasteur ou Curè*: in English, Shepheards purse or scrip: of some, Shepheards pouch, and poore mans Parmacetie: and in the North part of England, Toy-wort, Pick-purse, and Case-weed.

¶ *The Vertues.*

Shepheards purse staieth bleeding in any part of the body, whether the juice or the decoction thereof be drunke, or whether it be used pultesse wise, or in bath, or any other way else.

(27)

Chap. 36. *Of Groundsell.*

¶ *The Description.*

1 THe stalke of Groundsell is round, chamfered and divided into many branches. The leaves be green, long, and cut in the edges almost like those of Succorie, but lesse, like in a manner to the leaves of Rocket. The floures be yellow, and

turn to down, which is caried away with the wind. The root is full of strings and threds.

¶ *The Place.*

These herbs are very common throughout England, and do grow almost every where.

Erigerum.
Groundfell.

¶ *The Time.*

They flourish almost every moneth of the yeare.

¶ *The Names.*

Groundsel is called in Latine, *Senecio*, because it waxeth old quickly.

¶ *The Vertues.*

The leaves of Groundsel boiled in wine or water, and drunke, heale the paine and ach of the stomacke that proceeds of Choler.

The leaves stamped and strained into milke and drunke, helpe the red gums and frets in Children.

Dioscorides saith, That with the fine pouder of Frankincense it healeth wounds in the sinues. The like operation hath the downe of the floures mixed with vineger.

Boiled in ale with a little hony and vineger, it provoketh vomit, especially if you adde thereto a few roots of *Asarabacca.*

---

(28)   CHAP. 37. *Of Saint James his Wort.*

¶ *The Kindes.*

THe herb called Saint *James* his Wort is not without cause thought to be a kind of Groundsel: of which there be sundry sorts, some of the pasture, & one of the sea; some sweet smelling, and some of a loathsome savor.

¶ *The Description.*

1   SAint James his wort or Rag-wort is very well known
every where, and bringeth forth at the first broad leaves
gashed round about like to the leaves of common Wormewood, but broader, thicker, not whitish or soft, of a deep green
colour, with a stalke which riseth up above a cubit high, chamfered,
blackish, and somwhat red withall. The armes or wings are set
with lesser leaves like those of Groundsell or wilde Rocket. The
floures at the top be of a yellow colour like Marigolds, as well the
middle button, as the small floures that stand in a pale round about,
which turne into downe as doth Groundsel. The root is threddy.

¶ *The Place.*

Land Rag-wort groweth every where in untilled pastures and
fields, which are somewhat moist especially, and neare unto the
borders of fields.

¶ *The Time.*

They floure in July and August, at which time they are carried
away with the Down.

¶ *The Names.*

In Latine, *Herba S. Jacobi*: in English, S. *James* his Wort: the
countrey people doe call it Stagger-wort, and Staner-wort, and also
Rag-wort, and Rag-weed. In Holdernesse in York-shire they call it
Seggrum.

¶ *The Vertues.*

It is commended by the later Physitians to bee good for greene
wounds; it also healeth them, with the juyce heereof tempered with
honey and May Butter, and boiled together unto the forme of an
Unguent or salve.

It is much commended, and not without cause, to helpe old aches
and paines in the armes, hips, and legs, boiled in hogs grease to the
forme of an ointment.

Moreover, the decoction hereof gargarised is much set by as a
remedy against swellings and impostumations of the throat, which
it wasteth away and throughly healeth.

The leaves stamped very small, and boiled with some hogs grease
unto the consumption of the juyce, adding thereto in the end of the
boyling a little Masticke and Olibanum, and then strained, taketh
away the old ache in the huckle bones called Sciatica.

CHAP. 38. *Of Dandelion.*

❡ *The Description.*

1 THe hearbe which is commonly called Dandelion doth send forth from the root long leaves deeply cut and gashed in the edges like those of wild Succorie, but smoother: upon every stalke standeth a floure greater than that of Succorie, but double, & thicke set together, of colour yellow, and sweet in smell, which is turned into a round downy blowbal that is carried away with the wind. The root is long, slender, and full of milky juice, when any part of it is broken, as is the Endive or Succorie, but bitterer in tast than Succorie.

Dens Leonis.
Dandelion.

❡ *The Place.*

They are found often in medowes neere unto water ditches, as also in gardens and high wayes much troden.

❡ *The Time.*

They floure most times in the yeare, especially if the winter be not extreme cold.

CHAP. 39. *Of Lettuce.*

❡ *The Kindes.*

THere be according to the opinion of the Antients, of Lettuce two sorts, the one wilde or of the field, the other tame or of the garden: but time, with the industrie of later writers, have found out others both wilde and tame, as also artificiall.

¶ *The Description.*

1   GArden Lettuce hath a long broad leafe, smooth, and of a light greene colour: the stalke is round, thicke set with leaves full of milky juice, bushed or branched at the top: wherupon do grow yellowish floures, which turne into downe that is carried away with the winde. The seed sticketh fast unto the cottony downe, and flieth away likewise, white of colour, and somewhat long: the root hath hanging on it many long tough strings, which being cut or broken, do yeeld forth in like manner as doth the stalke and leaves, a juice like to milke. And this is the true description of the naturall Lettuce, and not of the artificiall; for by manuring, transplanting, and having a regard to the Moone and other circumstances, the leaves of the artificiall Lettuce are oftentimes transformed into another shape: for either they are curled, or else so drawne together, as they seeme to be like a Cabbage or headed Colewort, and the leaves which be within and in the middest are something white, tending to a very light yellow.

¶ *The Place.*

Lettuce delighteth to grow, as *Palladius* saith, in a mannured, fat, moist, and dunged ground: it must be sowen in faire weather in places where there is plenty of water, as *Columella* saith, and prospereth best if it be sowen very thin.

¶ *The Time.*

It is certaine, saith *Palladius*, that Lettuce may well be sowen at any time of the yeare, but especially at every first Spring, and so soone as Winter is done, till Summer be well nigh spent.

¶ *The Names.*

Garden Lettuce is called in Latine, *Lactuca sativa*, of the milky juice which issueth forth of the wounded stalks and roots.

¶ *The Temperature.*

Lettuce is a cold and moist pot-herbe, yet not in the extream degree of cold or moisture, but altogether moderatly; for otherwise it were not to be eaten.

¶ *The Vertues.*

Lettuce cooleth the heat of the stomacke, called the heart-burning; and helpeth it when it is troubled with choler: it quencheth thirst, and causeth sleepe.

Lettuce maketh a pleasant sallad, being eaten raw with vineger, oile, and a little salt: but if it be boiled it is sooner digested, and nourisheth more.

It is served in these daies, and in these countries in the beginning of supper, and eaten first before any other meat: which also *Martiall* testifieth to be done in his time, marvelling why some did use it for a service at the end of supper, in these verses.

Tell me why Lettuce, which our Grandsires last did eate,
Is now of late become, to be the first of meat?

Notwithstanding it may now and then be eaten at both those times to the health of the body: for being taken before meat it doth many times stir up appetite: and eaten after supper it keepeth away drunkennesse which commeth by the wine; and that is by reason that it staieth the vapours from rising up into the head.

---

(40)   CHAP. 40.   *Of Coleworts.*

¶ *The Description.*

1   THe Garden Colewort hath many great broad leaves of a deepe blacke greene colour, mixed with ribs and lines of reddish and white colours: the stalke groweth out of the middest from among the leaves, branched with sundry armes bearing at the top little yellow floures: and after they be past, there do succeed long cods full of round seed like those of the Turnep, but smaller, with a wooddy root having many strings or threds fastned thereto.

2   There is also found a certaine kinde hereof with the leaves wrapped together into a round head or globe, whose head is white of colour, especially toward Winter when it is ripe. The root is hard, and the stalks of a wooddy substance. ‡ This is the great ordinary Cabbage knowne every where, and as commonly eaten all over this kingdome. ‡

¶ *The Place.*

The greatest sort of Colewoorts grow in gardens, and do love a soile which is fat: they doe best prosper being removed, and every of them grow in our English gardens, except the wilde, which growes in fields and new digged ditch banks.

¶ *The Vertues.*

Dioscorides teacheth, that the Colewoort beeing eaten is good for them that have dim eies.

It is reported, that the raw Colewort beeing eaten before meate, doth preserve a man from drunkennesse: the reason is yeelded, for that there is a naturall enmitie betweene it and the vine, which is such, as if it grow neere unto it, forthwith the vine perisheth and withereth away: yea, if wine be poured unto it while it is in boiling, it will not be any more boiled, and the colour thereof quite altered, as *Cassius* and *Dionysius Uticensis* do write in their bookes of tillage: yet doth not *Athenæus* ascribe that vertue of driving away drunkennesse to the leaves, but to the seeds of Colewort.

Moreover, the leaves of Coleworts are good against all inflammations, and hot swellings; beeing stamped with barley meale, and laied upon them with salt: and also to breake carbuncles.

The juyce of Coleworts, as *Dioscorides* writeth, beeing taken with Floure-de-lys and nitre, doth make the body soluble: and being drunke with wine, it is a remedy against the bitings of venomous beasts.

The same being applied with the pouder of Fennugreeke, taketh away the paine of the gout.

Being conveied into the nosthrils, it purgeth the head.

Pliny writeth, that the juice mixed with wine, and dropped into the eares, is a remedy against deafenesse.

The seed, as *Galen* saith, taketh away freckles of the face, sunburning, and what thing soever that need to be gently scoured or clensed away.

They say that the broth wherein the herbe hath bin sodden is marvellous good for the sinewes and joints, and likewise for cankers in the eies, called in Greeke *Carcinomata*, which cannot be healed by any other meanes, if they be washed therewith.

Chap. 41. *Of Beets.*

¶ *The Description.*

1   THe common white Beet hath great broad leaves, smooth, and plain: from which rise thicke crested or chamfered stalks: the floures grow along the stalks clustering together, in shape like little stars, which being past, there succeed round & uneven prickly seed. The root is thicke, hard, and great.

2   There is likewise another sort hereof, that was brought unto me from beyond the seas, by that courteous Merchant master *Lete*, before remembred, the which hath leaves very great, and red of colour, as is all the rest of the plant, as well root, as stalke, and floures full of a perfect purple juyce tending to rednesse: the middle rib of which leaves are for the most part very broad and thicke, like the middle part of the Cabbage leafe, which is equall in goodnesse with the leaves of Cabbage being boyled. It grew with me 1596. to the height of eight cubits, and did bring forth his rough and uneven seed very plentifully: with which plant nature doth seeme to play and sport herselfe: for the seeds taken from that plant, which was altogether of one colour and sowen, doth bring forth plants of many and variable colours, as the worshipfull Gentleman master *John Norden* can very well testifie: unto whom I gave some of the seeds aforesaid, which in his garden brought forth many other of beautifull colours.

¶ *The Place.*

The Beete is sowne in gardens: it loveth to grow in a moist and fertile ground.

¶ *The Vertues.*

Being eaten when it is boyled, it nourisheth little or nothing, and is not so wholesome as Lettuce.

The juyce conveighed up into the nosthrils doth gently draw forth flegme, and purgeth the head.

The great and beautifull Beet last described may be used in Winter for a sallad herb, with vinegre, oyle, and salt, and is not only pleasant to the taste, but also delightfull to the eie.

The greater red Beet or Roman Beet, boyled and eaten with oyle, vinegre and pepper, is a most excellent and delicat sallad: but what might be made of the red and beautifull root (which is to be preferred before the leaves, as well in beautie as in goodnesse) I refer unto the curious and cunning cooke, who no doubt when hee had the view thereof, and is assured that it is both good and wholesome, will make thereof many and divers dishes, both faire and good.

(44)

Chap. 42. *Of Floure-Gentle.*

¶ *The Kindes.*

THere be divers sorts of Floure-gentle, differing in many points very notably, as in greatnesse and smalnesse; some purple, and others of a skarlet colour; and one above the rest wherewith Nature hath seemed to delight her selfe, especially in the leaves, which in variable colours strives with the Parrats feathers for beauty.

¶ *The Description.*

1   PUrple Floure-gentle riseth up with a stalke a cubit high, and somtimes higher, streaked or chamfered alongst the same, often reddish toward the root, and very smooth; which divides it self toward the top into smal branches, about which stand long leaves, broad, sharpe pointed, soft, slipperie, of a greene colour, and sometimes tending to a reddish: in stead of floures come up eares or spoky tufts, very brave to look upon, but without smel, of a shining light purple, with a glosse like Velvet, but far passing it: which when they are bruised doe yeeld a juice almost of the same colour, and being gathered, doe keep their beauty a long time after; insomuch that being set in water, it will revive again as at the time of his gathering, and remaineth so, many yeares; whereupon likewise it hath taken it's name. The seed standeth in the ripe eares, of colour blacke, and much glittering: the root is short and full of strings.

2   It farre exceedeth my skill to describe the beauty and excellencie of this rare plant called *Floramor*; and I thinke the pensil of the most curious painter will be at a stay, when he shall come to set it downe in his lively colours. But to colour it after my best manner, this I say, *Floramor* hath a thicke knobby root, whereon do grow many threddie strings; from which riseth a thicke stalke, but tender

and soft, which beginneth to divide it selfe into sundry branches at the ground and so upward, whereupon doth grow many leaves, wherein doth consist his beauty: for in few words, everie leafe resembleth in colour the most faire and beautifull feather of a Parat especially those feathers that are mixed with most sundry colours, as a stripe of red, and a line of yellow, a dash of white, and a rib of green colour, which I cannot with words set forth, such are the sundry mixtures of colours that Nature hath bestowed in her greatest jolitie, upon this floure. The floure doth grow betweene the foot-stalks of those leaves, and the body of the stalke or trunke, base, and of no moment in respect of the leaves, being as it were little chaffie husks of an overworne tawny colour: the seed is black, and shining like burnished horne.

Amaranthus purpureus.
Purple Floure-Gentle.

¶ *The Place and Time.*

These pleasant floures are sowne in gardens, especially for their great beautie.

They floure in August, and continue flourishing till the frost overtake them, at what time they perish.

¶ *The Vertues.*

It is reported they stop all kindes of bleeding; which is not manifest by any apparant quality in them, except peradventure by the colour onely that the red eares have: for some are of opinion, that all red things stanch bleeding in any part of the body: because some things of red colour doe stop bloud: But *Galen, lib.* 2. & 4. *de simp. facult.* plainly sheweth, that there can be no certainty gathered from the colours, touching the vertues of simple and compound medicines: wherefore they are ill persuaded, that thinke the floure Gentle to stanch bleeding, because of the colour onely, if they had no other reason to induce them thereto.

⁽⁴⁶⁾ ### CHAP. 43. *Of stinking Orach.*

¶ *The Description.*

STinking Orach growes flat upon the ground and is a base and low plant with many weake and feeble branches, whereupon doe grow small leaves of a grayish colour, sprinckled over with a certaine kind of dusty mealinesse, in shape like the leaves of Basill: amongst which leaves here and there confusedly be the seeds dispersed, as it were nothing but dust and ashes. The whole plant is of a most loathsome savour or smell; upon which plant if any should chance to rest and sleepe, hee might very well report to his friends, that he had reposed himselfe among the chiefe of *Scoggins* heires.

¶ *The Place.*

It groweth in the most filthy places that may bee found. Sometime it is found in places neere Bricke kilns and old walls, which doth somwhat alter his smell, which is like tosted cheese: but that which groweth in his natural place smels like stinking salt-fish, whereof it tooke his name *Garosmus*.

¶ *The Time.*

It is an hearbe for a yeare, which springeth up, and when the seed is ripe it perisheth, and recovereth it selfe againe of his owne seed; so that if it be gotten into a ground, it cannot bee destroyed.

¶ *The Names.*

Stinking Orach is called of *Cordus*, *Garosmus*, because it smelleth like stinking fish: for it smelleth more stinking than the rammish male Goat: whereupon some by a figure have called it *Vulvaria*: and it may be called in English, stinking Mother-wort.

¶ *The Nature and Vertues.*

There hath bin nothing set downe by the Antients, either of his nature or vertues.

(54)

CHAP. 44. *Of Scorpion Grasse.*

¶ *The Description.*

1   SCorpion grasse hath many smooth, plaine, even leaves, of a darke greene colour; stalkes small, feeble and weake, trailing upon the ground, and occupying a great circuit in respect of the plant. The floures grow upon long and slender foot-

Scorpioides Bupleurifolio. Penæ & L'Obelij.
Scorpion graſſe, or Caterpillers.

Myoſotis ſcorpioides aruenſis hirſuta.
Mouſe-eare Scorpion graſſe.

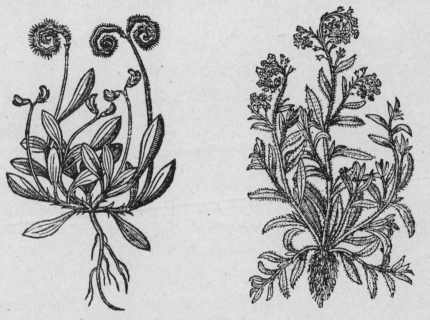

stalks, of colour yellow, in shape like to the floures of broome; after which succeed long, crooked, rough cods, in shape and colour like unto a Caterpiller; wherein is contained yellowish seed like unto a kidney in shape. The root is small and tender: the whole plant perisheth when the seed is ripe.

2   There is another sort almost in every shallow gravelly running streame, having leaves like to *Becabunga* or Brooklime. The floures grow at the top of tender fat greene stalkes, blew of colour, and sometimes with a spot of yellow among the blew; the whole branch of floures do turne themselves likewise round like the scorpions taile.

3   There is likewise another sort growing upon most dry gravelly and barren ditch bankes, with leaves like those of Mouse-eare: this is called *Myosotes scorpioides*; it hath rough and hairy leaves, of an overworne russet colour: the floures doe grow upon weake, feeble, and rough branches, as is all the rest of the plant. They likewise grow for the most part at one side of the stalke, blew of colour, with a like little spot of yellow as the others, turning themselves backe againe like the taile of a Scorpion.

¶ *The Place.*

1   These Scorpion grasses grow not wilde in England, notwithstanding I have received seed of the first from beyond the seas, and have dispersed them through England, which are esteemed of gentlewomen for the beautie and strangnesse of the crooked cods resembling Caterpillers.

The others do grow in waters and streames, as also on dry and barren bankes.

¶ *The Time.*

The first floureth from May to the end of August: the others I have found all the Summer long.

¶ *The Nature and Vertues.*

Dioscorides saith, that the leaves of Scorpion grasse applyed to the place, are a present remedy against the stinging of Scorpions: and likewise boyled in wine and drunke, prevaile against the said bitings, as also of addars, snakes, and such venomous beasts: being made in an unguent with oile, wax, and a little gum *Elemni*, they are profitable against such hurts as require an healing medicine.

(56)

Chap. 45. *Of sleepy Nightshade.*

¶ *The Description.*

DWale or sleeping Nightshade hath round blackish stalkes six foot high, whereupon do grow great broad leaves of a dark green colour: among which grow smal hollow floures belfashion, of an overworn purple colour; in the place whereof come forth great round berries of the bignesse of the black chery, green at the first, but when they be ripe of the colour of black jet or burnished horne, soft, and ful of purple juice; among which juice lie the seeds, like the berries of Ivy: the root is very great, thick, and long lasting.

¶ *The Place.*

It growes in untoiled places neere highwaies and the sea marishes, and in such like places.

It groweth very plentifully in Holland in Lincolneshire, and in the Isle of Ely at a place called Walsoken, neere unto Wisbitch.

I found it growing without Highgate, neere unto a pound or pinfold on the left hand.

¶ *The Time.*

This flourisheth all the Spring and Summer, bearing his seed and floure in July and August.

¶ *The Names.*

In English, Dwale, or sleeping Nightshade: the Venetians and Italians call it *Bella dona:* in French, *Morelle mortelle.*

¶ *The Vertues.*

This kinde of Nightshade causeth sleep, troubleth the mind, bringeth madnesse if a few of the berries be inwardly taken, but if moe be given they also kill and bring present death. *Theophrastus* in his sixth booke doth likewise write of Mandrake in this manner; Mandrake causeth sleepe, and if also much of it be taken it bringeth death.

The greene leaves of deadly Nightshade may with great advice be used in such cases as Pettimorell: but if you will follow my counsell, deale not with the same in any case, and banish it from your gardens and the use of it also, being a plant so furious and deadly: for it bringeth such as have eaten thereof into a dead sleepe wherein many have died, as hath beene often seene and proved by experience both in England and elsewhere. But to give you an example hereof it shall not be amisse: It came to passe that three boies of Wisbich in the Isle of Ely did eate of the pleasant and beautifull fruit hereof, two whereof died in lesse than eight houres after that they had eaten of them. The third child had a quantitie of honey and water mixed together given him to drinke, causing him to vomit often: God blessed this meanes and the child recovered.

Banish therefore these pernitious plants out of your gardens, and all places neere to your houses, where children or women with child do resort, which do oftentimes long and lust after things most vile and filthie; and much more after a berry of a bright shining blacke colour, and of such great beautie, as it were able to allure any such to eate thereof.

The leaves hereof laid unto the temples cause sleepe, especially if they be imbibed or moistened in wine vinegre. It easeth the intollerable paines of the head-ache proceeding of heat in furious agues, causing rest being applied as aforesaid.

(58)   ## CHAP. 46. *Of the Marvell of the World.*

¶ *The Description.*

THis admirable Plant, called the Marvell of Peru, or the Marvell of the World, springs forth of the ground like unto Basil in leaves; among which it sendeth out a stalke two cubits and a halfe high, of the thicknesse of a finger, full of juice, very firme, and of a yellowish green colour, knotted or kneed with joints somewhat bunching forth, of purplish colour, as in the female Balsamina: which stalke divideth it selfe into sundry branches or boughes, and those also knottie like the stalke. His branches are decked with leaves growing by couples at the joints like the leaves of wilde Peascods, greene, fleshy, and full of joints; which being rubbed doe yeeld the like unpleasant smell as wilde Peascods do, and are in taste also very unsavory, yet in the later end they leave a tast and sharp smack of Tabaco. The stalks toward the top are garnished with long hollow single floures, folded as it were into five parts before they be opened; but being fully blown, do resemble the floures of Tabaco, not ending in sharp corners, but blunt & round as the flours of Bindweed, and larger than the floures of Tabaco, glittering oft times with a fine purple or crimson colour, many times of an horse-flesh, sometimes yellow, sometimes pale, and somtime resembling an old red or yellow colour; sometime whitish, and most commonly two colours occupying half the floure, or intercoursing the whole floure with streaks or orderly streames, now yellow, now purple, divided through the whole, having sometime great, somtime little spots of a purple colour, sprinkled and scattered in a most variable order and brave mixture. The ground or field of the whole floure is either pale, red, yellow, or white, containing in the middle of the hollownesse a pricke or pointal set round about with six small strings or chives. The floures are very sweet and pleasant, resembling the Narcisse or white Daffodill, and are very suddenly fading; for at night they are floured wide open, and so continue untill eight of the clocke the next morning, at which time they begin to close (after the maner of Bindweed) especially if the weather be very hot: but the aire being temperat, they remain open the whole day, and are closed only at night, and so perish, one floure lasting but onely one day, like the true Ephemerum or Hemerocallis. This marvellous variety doth not without cause bring admiration to all that observe it. For if the floures be gathered and reserved in severall papers, and compared with those floures that will spring and flourish the next day, you shall easily perceive that one is not like another in colour, though you shall compare one hundred which floure one day, and another hundred which you gather the next day, and so from day to day during the time of their flouring. The cups and huskes which containe and embrace the floures are divided into five pointed sections, which are green, and as it were, consisting of skinnes, wherein is conteined one seed and no more, covered with a blackish skinne, having a blunt point whereon the floure groweth; but on the end next the cup or huske it is adorned with a little five cornered crowne. The seed is as big as a pepper corne, which of it selfe fadeth with any light motion. Within this seed is contained a white kernell, which being bruised, resolveth into a very white pulpe like starch. The root is thicke and like unto a great raddish, outwardly black, and within white, sharpe in taste, wherewith is mingled a superficiall sweetnesse. It bringeth new floures from July unto October in infinite number, yea even

Mirabilia Peruviana flore albo.
The Maruell of Peru with white floures.

untill the frosts doe cause the whole plant to perish: notwithstanding it may be reserved in pots, and set in chambers and cellars that are warme, and so defended from the injurie of our cold climate; provided alwaies that there be not any water cast upon the pot, or set forth to take any moisture in the aire untill March following; at which time it must be taken forth of the pot and replanted in the garden. By this meanes I have preserved many (though to small purpose) because I have sowne seeds that have borne floures in as ample manner and in as good time as those reserved plants.

Of this wonderfull herbe there be other sorts, but not so amiable or so full of varietie, and for the most part their floures are all of one color. But I have since by practise found out another way to keepe the roots for the yere following with very little difficultie, which never faileth. At the first frost I dig up the roots and put up or rather hide the roots in a butter ferkin, or such like vessell, filled with the sand of a river, the which I suffer still to stand in some corner of an house where it never receiveth moisture untill Aprill or the midst of March, if the weather be warme; at which time I take it from the sand and plant it in the garden, where it doth flourish exceeding well and increaseth by roots; which that doth not which was either sowne of seed the same yeere, nor those plants that were preserved after the other manner.

¶ *The Place.*

The seed of this strange plant was brought first into Spaine, from Peru, whereof it tooke his name *Mirabilia Peruana*, or *Peruviana:* and since dispersed into all the parts of Europe: the which my selfe have planted many yeeres, and have in some temperate yeeres received both floures and ripe seed.

¶ *The Time.*

It is sowne in the midst of Aprill, and bringeth forth his variable floures in September, and perisheth with the first frost, except it be kept as aforesaid.

¶ *The Names.*

It is called in Peru of those Indians there, *Hachal.* Of others after their name *Hachal Indi:* of the high and low Dutch, *Solanum Odoriferum:* of some, *Jasminum Mexicanum:* and of *Carolus Clusius, Admirabilia Peruviana:* in English rather the Marvell of the World, than of Peru alone.

¶ *The Nature and Vertues.*

We have not as yet any instructions from the people of India, concerning the nature or vertues of this plant: the which is esteemed as yet rather for his rarenesse, beautie, and sweetnesse of his floures, than for any vertues knowne; but it is a pleasant plant to decke the gardens of the curious. Howbeit *Jacobus Antonius Cortusus* of Padua hath by experience found out, that two drams of the root thereof taken inwardly doth very notably purge waterish humours.

(59)   Chap. 47. *Of Madde Apples.*

¶ *The Description.*

Raging Apples hath a round stalke of two foot high, divided into sundry branches, set with broad leaves somewhat indented about the edges, not unlike the leaves of white Henbane, of a darke browne greene colour, somewhat rough. Among the which come the floures of a white colour, and somtimes changing into purple, made of six parts wide open like a star, with certain yellow chives or thrums in the middle: which being past, the fruit comes in place, set in a cornered cup or huske after the manner of great Nightshade, great and somewhat long, of the bignesse of a Swans egge, and some-times much greater, of a white colour, somtimes yellow, and often brown, wherein is contained small flat seed of a yellow colour. The root is thick, with many threds fastned thereto.

¶ *The Place.*

This Plant growes in Egypt almost every where in sandy fields even of it selfe, bringing forth fruit of the bignesse of a great Cucumber, as *Petrus Bellonius* writeth, *lib.* 2. of his singular ob-servations.

We had the same in our London gardens, where it hath borne floures; but Winter approaching before the time of ripening, it perished: neverthelesse it came to beare fruit of the bignes of a goose egg one extraordinarie temperate yeare, as I did see in the garden of a worshipfull merchant Mr *Harvy* in Limestreet; but never to the full ripenesse.

¶ *The Use, and Danger.*

The people of Toledo eat them with great devotion, being boiled with fat flesh, putting to it some scraped cheese, which they do keep in vineger, hony, or salt pickle all winter.

Petrus Bellonius and *Hermolaus Barbarus* report, That in Egypt & Barbary they use to eat the fruit of *Mala insana* boiled or rosted under ashes, with oile, vineger, and pepper, as people use to eat Mushroms. But I rather wish English men to content themselves with the meat and sauce of our owne country, than with fruit and sauce eaten with such perill; for doubtlesse these Apples have a mischievous qualitie, the use whereof is utterly to bee forsaken. As wee see and know many have eaten and do eat Mushroms more for wantonnesse than for need; for there are two kinds therof deadly, which being dressed by an unskilfull cooke may procure untimely death: it is therefore better to esteem this plant and have it in the garden for your pleasure and the rarenesse thereof, than for any vertue or good qualities yet knowne.

(60)

Chap. 48. *Of Apples of Love.*

¶ *The Description.*

THe Apple of Love bringeth forth very long round stalkes or branches, fat and full of juice, trailing upon the ground, not able to sustain himselfe upright by reason of the tendernesse of the stalkes, and also the great weight of the leaves and fruit wherewith it is surcharged. The leaves are great, and deeply cut or jagged about the edges, not unlike to the leaves of Agrimonie, but greater, and of a whiter greene colour: Amongst which come forth yellow floures growing upon short stems or footstalkes, clustering together in bunches: which being fallen there doe come in place faire and goodly apples, chamfered, uneven, and bunched out in many places; of a bright shining red colour, and the bignesse of a goose egge or a large pippin. The pulpe or meat is very full of moisture, soft, reddish, and of the substance of a wheat plumme. The seed is small, flat and rough: the root small and threddy: the whole plant is of a ranke and stinking savour.

There hath happened unto my hands another sort, agreeing very notably with the former, as well in leaves and stalkes as also in floures and roots, onely the fruit hereof was yellow of colour, wherein consisteth the difference.

¶ The Place.

Apples of Love grow in Spaine, Italie, and such hot Countries, from whence my selfe have received seeds for my garden, where they doe increase and prosper.

Poma amoris.
Apples of loue.

¶ The Time.

It is sowne in the beginning of Aprill in a bed of hot horse-dung, after the maner of muske Melons and such like cold fruits.

¶ The Names.

The Apple of Love is called in Latine *Pomum Aureum*, *Poma Amoris*, and *Lycopersicum*: of some, *Glaucium*: in English, Apples of Love, and Golden Apples: in French, *Pommes d'amours*. Howbeit there be other golden Apples whereof the Poëts doe fable, growing in the Gardens of the daughters of *Hesperus*, which a Dragon was appointed to keepe, who, as they fable, was killed by *Hercules*.

¶ The Temperature.

The Golden Apple, with the whole herbe it selfe is cold, yet not fully so cold as Mandrake, after the opinion of *Dodonæus*. But in my judgement it is very cold, yea perhaps in the highest degree of coldnesse: my reason is, because I have in the hottest time of Summer cut away the superfluous branches from the mother root, and cast them away carelesly in the allies of my Garden, the which (notwithstanding the extreme heate of the Sun, the hardnesse of the trodden allies, and at that time when no rain at all did fal) have growne as fresh where I cast them, as before I did cut them off; which argueth the great coldnesse contained therein. True it is, that it doth argue also a great moisture wherewith the plant is possessed, but as I have said, not without great cold, which I leave to every mans censure.

¶ *The Vertues.*

In Spaine and those hot Regions they use to eate the Apples prepared and boiled with pepper, salt, and oyle: but they yeeld very little nourishment to the body, and the same naught and corrupt.

Likewise they doe eate the Apples with oile, vinegre and pepper mixed together for sauce to their meat, even as we in these cold countries doe Mustard.

(47)   CHAP. 49. *Of Thornie Apples.*

¶ *The Description.*

1   THe stalkes of Thorny-apples are oftentimes above a cubit and a halfe high, seldome higher, an inch thicke, upright and straight, having very few branches, sometimes none at all, but one upright stemme; whereupon doe grow leaves smooth and even, little or nothing indented about the edges, longer and broader than the leaves of Nightshade, or of the mad Apples. The floures come forth of long toothed cups, great, white, of the forme of a bell, or like the floures of the great Withwinde that rampeth in hedges; but altogether greater and wider in the mouth, sharpe cornered at the brimmes, with certaine white chives or threds in the middest, of a strong ponticke savour, offending the head when it is smelled unto: in the place of the floure commeth up round fruit full of short and blunt prickles of the bignesse of a green Wallnut when it is at the biggest, in which are the seeds of the bignesse of tares or of the seed of Mandrakes, and of the same forme. The herbe it selfe is of a strong savor, and doth stuffe the head, and causeth drowsinesse. The root is small and threddy.

2   There is another kinde hereof altogether greater than the former, whose seeds I received of the right honourable the Lord *Edward Zouch*; which he brought from Constantinople, and of his liberalitie did bestow them upon me, as also many other rare and strange seeds; and it is that Thorn-apple that I have dispersed through this land, whereof at this present I have great use in

Surgery; as well in burnings and scaldings, as also in virulent and maligne ulcers, apostumes, and such like. The which plant hath a very great stalke in fertile ground, bigger then a mans arme, smooth and greene of colour, which a little above the ground divideth it selfe into sundry branches or armes in manner of an hedge tree; whereupon are placed many great leaves cut and indented deepely about the edges, with many uneven sharpe corners: among these leaves come white round floures made of one piece in manner of a bell, shutting it selfe up close toward night, as doe the floures of the great Binde-weed, whereunto it is very like, of a sweet smell, but so strong, that it offends the sences. The fruit followeth round, sometimes of the fashion of an egge, set about on every part with most sharpe prickles; wherein is contained very much seed of the bignesse of tares, and of the same fashion. The root is thicke, made of great and small strings: this plant is sowen, beareth his fruit, and perisheth the same yeare.

¶ *The Place.*

1   This plant is rare and strange as yet in England: I received seeds thereof from *John Robin* of Paris, an excellent Herbarist; which do grow and bare floures, but perished before the fruit came to ripenesse.

¶ *The Time.*

The first is to be sowne in a bed of horse-dung, as we do Cucumbers and Muske-melons.

The other may be sowne in March and Aprill, as other seeds are.

¶ *The Names.*

Anguillara suspected it to be *Hippomanes* which *Theocritus* mentioned, wherewith in his second *Eclog* he sheweth that horses are made mad: for *Cratevas*, whom *Theocritus* his Scholiast doth cite, writeth, That the plant of *Hippomanes* hath a fruit full of prickles, as hath the fruit of wild Cucumber. In English it may be called Thorn-Apple, or the Apple of Peru.

‡   The words of *Theocritus* are in English:

> *Hippomanes 'mongst th'Arcadians springs, by which ev'n all*
> *The Colts and agile Mares in mountaines mad do fall.*

There is no plant at this day known, in mine opinion, whereunto *Cratevas* his description may more fitly be referred, than to the

Papaver spinosum, or *Ficus infernalis*, which we shall hereafter describe.   ‡

¶ *The Vertues*.

The juice of Thorn-apples boiled with hogs grease to the form of an unguent or salve, cures all inflammations whatsoever, all manner of burnings or scaldings, as well of fire, water, boiling lead, gunpouder, as that which comes by lightning, and that in very short time, as my selfe have found by my daily practise, to my great credit and profit. The first experience came from Colchester, where Mistresse *Lobel* a merchants wife there being most grievously burned by lightning, and not finding ease or cure in any other thing, by this found helpe and was perfectly cured when all hope was past, by the report of Mr *William Ram* publique Notarie of the said towne.

The leaves stamped small and boiled with oile Olive untill the herbs be as it were burnt, then strained and set to the fire again, with some wax, rosin, and a little turpentine, and made into a salve, doth most speedily cure new and fresh wounds.

---

(63) CHAP. 50. *Of Bitter-sweet, or wooddy Nightshade*.

¶ *The Description*.

Bitter-sweet bringeth forth wooddy stalks as doth the Vine, parted into many slender creeping branches, by which it climeth and taketh hold of hedges and shrubs next unto it. The barke of the oldest stalks are rough and whitish, of the colour of ashes, with the outward rind of a bright green colour, but the yonger branches are green as are the leaves: the wood brittle, having in it a spongie pith: it is clad with long leaves, smooth, sharp pointed, lesser than those of the Bindweed. At the lower part of the same leaves doth grow on either side one smal or lesser leafe like unto two eares. The floures be small, and somewhat clustered together, consisting of five little leaves apiece of a perfect blew colour, with a certain pricke or yellow pointal in the middle: which being past, there do come in place faire berries more long than round, at the first green, but very red when they be ripe; of a sweet taste at the first, but after very unpleasant, of a strong savor, growing together in clusters like burnished coral. The root is of a mean bignesse, and full of strings.

I have found another sort which bringeth forth most pleasant white flours, with yellow pointals in the middle: in other respects agreeing with the former.

¶ *The Place.*

Bitter-sweet growes in moist places about ditches, rivers, and hedges, almost everie where.

Amara-dulcis.
Bitter-sweet.

The other sort with the white floures I found in a ditch side, against the right honourable the Earle of Sussex his garden wall, at his house in Bermondsey street by London, as you go from the court which is full of trees, unto a ferm house neere thereunto.

¶ *The Time.*

The leaves come forth in the spring, the flours in July, the berries are ripe in August.

¶ *The Names.*

The later Herbarists have named this plant *Dulcamara, Amarodulcis,* & *Amara-dulcis*; *Pliny* calleth it *Melortum*: *Theophrastus, Vitis sylvestris*: in English we call it Bitter-sweet, and wooddy Nightshade. But every Author must for his credit say something, although but to smal purpose; for *Vitis sylvestris* is that which wee call our Ladies Seale, which is no kinde of Nightshade.

¶ *The Vertues.*

The juice is good for those that have fallen from high places, and have been thereby bruised, or dry-beaten.

(65)

Chap. 51. *Of Mandrake.*

¶ *The Description.*

THe male Mandrake hath great broad long smooth leaves of a darke greene colour, flat spred upon the ground: among which come up the floures of a pale whitish colour, standing every one upon a single small and weake foot-stalke of a whitish greene colour: in their places grow round Apples of a yellowish colour, smooth, soft, and glittering, of a strong smell: in which are contained flat and smooth seeds in fashion of a little kidney, like those of the Thorne-apple. The root is long, thicke, whitish, divided many times into two or three parts resembling the legs of a man, as it hath been reported; whereas in truth it is no otherwise than in the roots of carrots, parseneps, and such like, forked or divided into two or more parts, which Nature taketh no account of. There hath beene many ridiculous tales brought up of this plant, whether of old wives, or some runnagate Surgeons or Physicke-mongers I know not, (a title bad enough for them) but sure some one or moe that sought to make themselves famous and skilfull above others, were the first brochers of that errour I speake of. They adde further, That it is never or very seldome to be found growing naturally but under a gallowes, where the matter that hath fallen from the dead body hath given it the shape of a man; and the matter of a woman, the substance of a female plant; with many other such doltish dreames. They fable further and affirme, That he who would take up a plant thereof must tie a dog therunto to pull it up, which will give a great shreeke at the digging up; otherwise if a man should do it, he should surely die in short space after. Besides many fables of loving matters, too full of scurrilitie to set forth in print, which I forbeare to speake of. All which dreames and old wives tales you shall from henceforth cast out of your bookes and memory; knowing this, that they are all and everie part of them false and most untrue: for I my selfe and my servants also have digged up, planted, and replanted very many, and yet never could either perceive shape of man or woman, but sometimes one streight root, sometimes two, and often six or seven branches comming from the maine great root, even as Nature list to bestow upon it, as to other plants. But the idle drones that have little or nothing to do but eate and drinke, have bestowed some of their time in carving the roots of Brionie, forming them to the shape of men and women: which falsifying practise hath confirmed the errour amongst the simple and unlearned people, who have taken them upon their report to be the true Mandrakes.

The female Mandrake is like unto the male, saving that the leaves hereof be of a more swart or darke greene colour: and the fruit is long like a peare, and the other like an apple.

¶ *The Place*.

Mandrake groweth in hot Regions, in woods and mountaines, as in mount Garganus in Apulia, and such like places; we have them onely planted in gardens, and are not elsewhere to be found in England.

¶ *The Time*.

They spring up with their leaves in March, and floure in the end of Aprill: the fruit is ripe in August.

¶ *The Names*.

Mandrake is called *Circæa*, of *Circe* the witch, who by art could procure love: for it hath beene thought that the Root hereof serveth to win love.

¶ *The Vertues*.

The wine wherein the root hath been boyled or infused provoketh sleepe and asswageth paine.

The smell of the Apples moveth to sleepe likewise; but the juice worketh more effectually if you take it in small quantitie.

Great and strange effects are supposed to bee in Mandrakes, to cause women to be fruitfull and beare children, if they shall but carry the same neere to their bodies. Some do from hence ground it, for that *Rahel* desired to have her sisters Mandrakes (as the text is translated) but if we look well into the circumstances which there we shall finde, we may rather deem it otherwise. Yong *Ruben* brought home amiable and sweet-smelling floures, (for so signifieth the Hebrew word, used *Cantic.* 7. 13. in the same sence) rather for their beauty and smell, than for their vertue. Now in the floures of Mandrake there is no such delectable or amiable smell as was in these amiable floures which *Ruben* brought home. Besides, we reade not that *Rahel* conceived hereupon, for *Leah Jacobs* wife had foure children before God granted that blessing of fruitfulnesse unto *Rahel*. And last of all, (which is my chiefest reason) *Jacob* was angry with *Rahel* when shee said, Give mee children or els I die; and demanded of her, whether he were in the stead of God or no, who had withheld from her the fruit of her body. And we know the Prophet *David* saith, Children & the fruit of the womb are the inheritance that commeth of the Lord, *Psal.* 127.

He that would know more hereof, may reade that chapter of Dr *Turners* booke concerning this matter, where he hath written largely and learnedly of this Simple.

---

(66)   CHAP. 52. *Of Henbane.*

¶ *The Description.*

1   THe common blacke Henbane hath great and soft stalkes, leaves very broad, soft, and woolly, somewhat jagged, especially those that grow neere to the ground, and those that grow upon the stalke, narrower, smaller, and sharper, the floures are bell-fashion, of a feint yellowish white, and browne within towards the bottome: when the floures are gone, there come hard knobby husks like small cups or boxes, wherein are small brown seeds.

¶ *The Place.*

Blacke Henbane grows almost every where by highways, in the borders of fields about dunghils and untoiled places: the white Henbane is not found but in the gardens of those that love physicall plants: the which groweth in my garden, and doth sow it selfe from yeare to yeare.

¶ *The Time.*

They spring out of the ground in May, bring forth their floures in August, and the seed is ripe in October.

¶ *The Vertues.*

Henbane causeth drowsinesse, and mitigateth all kinde of paine: it is good against hot & sharp distillations of the eyes and other parts.

The leaves stamped with the ointment *Populeon*, made of Poplar buds, asswageth the pain of the gout.

To wash the feet in the decoction of Henbane causeth sleepe; and also the often smelling to the floures.

The leaves, seed, and juice taken inwardly cause an unquiet sleep like unto the sleepe of drunkennesse, which continueth long, and is deadly to the party.

The seed of white Henbane is good against the cough.

The root boiled with vinegre, & the same holden hot in the mouth, easeth the pain of the teeth. The seed is used by Mountibank tooth-drawers which run about the country, to cause worms come forth of the teeth, by burning it in a chafing dish of coles, the party holding his mouth over the fume thereof: but some crafty companions to gain mony convey small lute-strings into the water, persuading the patient, that those small creepers came out of his mouth or other parts which he intended to ease.

---

(67) CHAP. 53. *Of yellow Henbane, or English Tabaco.*

¶ *The Description.*

YEllow Henbane groweth to the height of two cubits: the stalke is thicke, fat, and green of colour, ful of a spongeous pith, and is divided into sundry branches, set with smooth and even leaves, thicke and full of juice. The floures grow at the tops of the branches, orderly placed, of a pale yellow color, somthing lesser than those of the black Henbane. The cups wherein the floures do stand, are like, but lesser, tenderer, and without sharpe points, wherein is set the huske or cod somwhat round, full of very smal seed like the seed of marjerom. The root is small and threddy.

¶ *The Place.*

Yellow Henbane is sowne in gardens, where it doth prosper exceedingly, insomuch that it cannot be destroied where it hath once sown it self, & it is dispersed into most parts of London.

¶ *The Time.*

It floureth in the summer moneths, and oftentimes till Autumne be farre spent, in which time the seed commeth to perfection.

¶ *The Names.*

Yellow Henbane is called *Hyoscyamus luteus:* of some, *Nicotiana,* of *Nicot* a Frenchman that brought the seeds from the Indies, as also the seeds of the true Tabaco, whereof this hath bin taken for a kind; insomuch that *Lobel* hath called it *Dubius Hyoscyamus,* or doubtfull Henbane, as a plant participating of Henbane and Tabaco: and it is used of divers in stead of Tabaco, and called by the same name, for that it hath bin brought from Trinidada, a place so called in the Indies, as also from Virginia and other places, for Tabaco; and doubtlesse, taken in smoke it worketh the same kind of drunkennesse that the right Tabaco doth.

¶ *The Vertues.*

This herb availeth against all botches, and such like, beeing made into an unguent or salve as followeth: Take of the greene leaves three pounds and an halfe, stampe them very smal in a stone mortar; of oile Olive one quart: set them to boile in a brasse pan or such like, upon a gentle fire, continually stirring it untill the herbs seem blacke, and wil not boile or bubble any more: then shall you have an excellent green oile; which beeing strained from the feces or drosse, put the cleare and strained oile to the fire again, adding therto of wax half a pound, of rosen foure ounces, and of good turpentine two ounces: melt them all together, and keepe it in pots for your use, to cure all cuts or hurts in the head; wherewith I have gotten both crownes and credit.

It is used of some in stead of Tabaco, but to small purpose or profit, although it doth stupifie or dull the sences, and cause that kind of giddines that Tabaco doth, and likewise spitting, which any other herb of hot temperature will do, as Rosemary, Time, Winter-Savorie, sweet Marjerome, and such like: any of the which I like better to be taken in smoke, than this kind of doubtful Henbane.

⁽⁶⁸⁾ CHAP. 54. *Of Tabaco, or Henbane of Peru.*

¶ *The Kindes.*

THere be two sorts or kinds of Tabaco, one greater, the other lesser; the greater was brought into Europe out of the provinces of America, which we call the West Indies; the other from Trinidada, an Island neere unto the continent of the same Indies. Some have added a third sort, and others make the yellow Henbane a kind thereof.

¶ *The Description.*

1   TAbaco, or Henbane of Peru hath very great stalkes of the bignesse of a childes arme, growing in fertile and well dunged ground of seven or eight foot high, dividing it selfe into sundry branches of great length; whereon are placed in most comly order very faire long leaves, broad, smooth, and sharp pointed, soft, and of a light green colour, so fastned about the stalke, that they seeme to embrace and compasse it about. The floures grow at the top of the stalks, in shape like a bell-floure, somewhat long and cornered, hollow within, of a light carnation colour, tending to whitenesse toward the brims. The seed is contained in long sharpe pointed cods or seed-vessels like unto the seed of yellow Henbane, but somewhat smaller, and browner of colour. The root is great, thicke, and of a wooddy substance, with some threddy strings annexed thereunto.

2   Trinidada Tabaco hath a thicke tough and fibrous root, from which immediately rise up long broad leaves and smooth, of a greenish colour, lesse than those of Peru: among which rises up a stalk dividing it self at the ground into divers branches, wheron are set confusedly the like leaves but lesser. At the top of the stalks stand up long necked hollow floures of a pale purple tending to a blush colour: after which succeed the cods or seed-vessels, including many small seeds like unto the seed of Marjerom. The whole plant perisheth at the first approch of winter.

¶ *The Place.*

These were first brought into Europe out of America, which is called the West Indies, in which is the province or countrey of Peru:

but being now planted in the gardens of Europe it prospers very well, and comes from seed in one yeare to beare both floures and seed. The which I take to be better for the constitution of our bodies, than that which is brought from India; & that growing in India better for the people of the same country: notwithstanding it is not so thought of our Tabaconists; for according to the English proverb, Far fetcht & dear bought is best for Ladies.

¶ *The Time.*

Tabaco must be sowne in the most fruitfull ground that may be found, carelesly cast abroad in sowing, without raking it into the ground, or any such pain or industry taken as is requisit in the sowing of other seeds, as my self have found by proof, who have experimented every way to cause it quickly to grow: for I have committed some to the earth in the end of March, some in Aprill, and some in the beginning of May, because I durst not hasard all my seed at one time, lest some unkindely blast should happen after the sowing, which might be a great enemie thereunto.

† Hyoscyamus Peruvianus.
Tabaco, or Henbane of Peru.

¶ *The Names.*

The people of America call it *Petun.* Some, as *Lobel* and *Pena*, have given it these Latine names, *Sacra herba, Sancta herba*, and *Sanasancta Indorum.* Others, as *Dodonæus*, call it *Hyoscyamus Peruvianus*, or Henbane of Peru. *Nicolaus Monardus* names it *Tabacum.* That it is *Hyoscyami species*, or a kinde of Henbane, not only the forme being like to yellow Henbane, but the qualitie also doth declare; for it bringeth drowsinesse, troubleth the sences, and maketh a man as it were drunke by taking the fume only; as *Andrew Theuet* testifieth, and common experience sheweth: of some it is called *Nicotiana*, the which I refer to the yellow Henbane for distinctions sake.

¶ *The Vertues.*

Nicolaus Monardis saith, that the leaves hereof are a remedie for the paine of head called the Megram or Migram, that hath bin of long continuance.

It is a present remedie for the fits of the mother, it mitigateth the paine of the gout, if it be rosted in hot embers, and applied to the grieved part.

It is likewise a remedy for the tooth-ache, if the teeth and gumbs be rubbed with a linnen cloth dipped in the juice, and afterward a round ball of the leaves laid unto the place.

The weight of foure ounces of the juice hereof drunke procureth afterward a long and sound sleepe, as wee have learned of a friend by observation, who affirmed, That a strong countreyman of a middle age having a dropsie, took it, and being wakened out of his sleepe called for meat and drinke, and after that became perfectly cured.

Moreover, the same man reported, That he had cured many countreymen of agues, with the distilled water of the leaves drunke a little while before the fit.

Likewise there is an oile to be taken out of the leaves that healeth merri-galls, kibed heeles, and such like.

It is good against poyson, and taketh away the malignitie therof, if the juice be given to drink, or the wounds made by venomous beasts be washed therewith.

The dry leaves are used to be taken in a pipe set on fire and suckt into the stomacke, and thrust forth againe at the nosthrils, against the paines in the head, rheumes, aches in any part of the bodie, whereof soever the originall proceed, whether from France, Italy, Spaine, Indies, or from our familiar and best knowne diseases. Those leaves do palliate or ease for a time, but never perform any cure absolutely: for although they empty the body of humors, yet the cause of the griefe cannot be so taken away. But some have learned this principle, That repletion doth require evacuation; that is to say, That fulnesse craveth emptinesse; and by evacuation doe assure themselves of health. But this doth not take away so much with it this day, but the next bringeth with it more. As for example, a Well doth never yeeld such store of water as when it is most drawn and emptied. My selfe speake by proofe; who have cured of that infectious disease a great many, divers of which had covered or kept under the sickenesse by the helpe of Tabaco as they thought, yet in the end have bin constrained to have unto such an hard knot, a crabbed wedge, or else had utterly perished.

Some use to drink it (as it is termed) for wantonnesse, or rather custome, and cannot forbeare it, no not in the midst of their dinner; which kinde of taking is unwholsome and very dangerous: although to take it seldom, and that physically, is to be tolerated, and may do some good: but I commend the syrrup above this fume or smoky medicine.

It is taken of some physically in a pipe for that purpose once in a day at the most, and that in the morning fasting, against paines in the head, stomack, and griefe in the brest and lungs: against catarrhs and rheums, and such as have gotten cold and hoarsenesse.

Some have reported, That it doth little prevaile against an hot disease, and that it profiteth an hot complexion nothing at all. But experience hath not shewed as yet that it is injurious unto either.

They that have seene the proofe hereof, have credibly reported, That when the Moores and Indians have fainted either for want of food or rest, this hath bin a present remedie unto them, to supply the one, and to help them to the other.

The priests and Inchanters of the hot countries do take the fume thereof until they be drunke, that after they have lien for dead three or foure houres, they may tell the people what wonders, visions, or illusions they have seen, and so give them a prophetical direction or foretelling (if we may trust the Divell) of the successe of their businesse.

The juyce or distilled water of the first kind is very good against catarrhs, the dizzinesse of the head, and rheums that fall downe the eies, against the pain called the megram, if either you apply it unto the temples, or take one or two green leaves, or a dry leafe moistned in wine, and dried cunningly upon the embers, and laid thereto.

It cleeres the sight, and taketh away the webs and spots thereof, being annointed with the juyce bloud-warme.

The oile or juyce dropped into the eares is good against deafnesse; a cloth dipped in the same and layd upon the face, taketh away the lentils, rednesse, and spots thereof.

Many notable medicines are made hereof against the old and inveterat cough, against asthmaticall or pectorall griefes, all which if I should set downe at large, would require a peculiar volume.

It is also given unto such as are accustomed to swoune.

It is used in outward medicines, either the herbe boiled with oile, wax, rosin, and turpentine, as before is set downe in yellow Henbane, or the extraction thereof with salt, oile, balsam, the distilled water, and such like, against tumours, apostumes, old ulcers of hard curation, botches, scabbes, stinging with nettles, carbuncles, poisoned arrowes, and wounds made with gunnes or any other weapons.

It is excellent good in burnings and scaldings with fire, water, oile, lightning, or such like, boiled with hogges grease into the forme of an ointment, as I have often prooved, and found most true; adding a little of the juice of Thorne-Apple leaves, spreading it upon a cloth and so applying it.

I doe make hereof an excellent Balme to cure deep wounds and punctures made by some narrow sharpe pointed weapon. Which Balsame doth bring up the flesh from the bottome verie speedily, and also heale simple cuts in the flesh according to the first intention, that is, to glew or soder the lips of the wound together, not procuring matter or corruption to it, as is commonly seene in the healing of wounds. The Receit is this: Take Oile of Roses, Oile of S. Johns Wort, of either one pinte, the leaves of Tabaco stamped small in a stone mortar two pounds; boile them together to the consumption of the juice, straine it and put it to the fire againe, adding thereunto of Venice Turpentine two ounces, of Olibanum and Masticke of either halfe an ounce, in most fine and subtil pouder: the which you may at all times make an unguent or salve, by putting thereto wax and rosin to give unto it a stiffe body, which worketh exceeding well in malignant and virulent ulcers, as in wounds and punctures. I send this jewell unto you women of all sorts, especially such as cure and helpe the poore and impotent of your countrey without reward. But unto the beggarly rabble of witches, charmers, and such like couseners, that regard more to get money, than to helpe for charitie, I wish these few medicines far from their understanding, and from those deceivers, whom I wish to be ignorant herein. But courteous gentlewomen, I may not for the malice that I doe beare unto such, hide any thing from you of such importance: and therefore take one more that followeth, wherewith I have done many and good cures, although of small cost; but regard it not the lesse for that cause. Take the leaves of Tabaco two pounds, Hogs grease one pound, stampe the herbe small in a stone morter, putting thereto a small cup full of red or claret wine, stirre them well together, cover the morter from filth, and so let it rest untill morning; then put it to the fire and let it boile gently, continually stirring it untill the consumption of the wine: straine it and set it to the fire againe, putting thereto the juyce of the herbe one pound, of Venice turpentine foure ounces; boile them together to the consumption of the juice, then adde therto of the roots of round *Aristolochia* or Birthworth in most fine pouder two ounces, sufficient wax to give it a body; the which keep for thy wounded poore neighbor.

⁽⁷⁴⁾ ## Chap. 55. *Of Corne-Rose or wilde Poppy.*

¶ *The Description.*

1   THe stalks of red Poppy be blacke, tender, and brittle, somewhat hairy: the leaves are cut round about with deepe gashes like those of Succorie or wild Rocket. The flours grow forth at the tops of the stalks, being of a beautifull and gallant red colour, with blackish threds compassing about the middle part of the head, which being fully growne, is lesser than that of the garden Poppy: the seed is small and blacke.

Papauer ſylveſtre.
Wild Poppy.

¶ *The Place.*

They grow in earable lands, among wheat, spelt, rie, barley, oats, and other graine, and in the borders of fields.

¶ *The Time.*

The fields are garnished and overspred with these wilde Poppies in June and August.

¶ *The Names.*

† Wilde Poppy is called in Latine, *Papaver Rhœas,* because the floure thereof soon falls away: which name *Rhœas* may for the same cause be common not only to these,

but also to the others, if it be so called of the speedy falling of the floures.

¶ *The Vertues*.

Most men being led rather by false experiments than reason, commend the floures against the Pleurisie, giving to drinke as soon as the pain comes, either the distilled water, or syrrup made by often infusing the leaves. And yet many times it happens, that the paine ceaseth by that meanes, though hardly sometimes.

⁽⁷⁶⁾   CHAP. 56. *Of Winde-floures*.

¶ *The Kindes*.

THe stocke or kindred of the *Anemones* or Winde-floures, especially in their varieties of colours, are without number, or at the least not sufficiently knowne unto any one that hath written of plants. My selfe have in my garden twelve different sorts: and yet I do heare of divers more differing very notably from any of these: which I have briefely touched, though not figured, every new yeare bringing with it new and strange kindes; and every country his peculiar plants of this sort, which are sent unto us from far countries, in hope to receive from us such as our country yeeldeth.

¶ *The Description*.

1   THe first kinde of *Anemone* or Winde-floure hath small leaves very much snipt or jagged almost like unto Camomile, or Adonis floure: among which riseth up a stalke bare or naked almost unto the top; at which place is set two or three leaves like the other: and at the top of the stalke commeth forth a faire and beautifull floure compact of seven leaves, and sometimes eight, of a violet colour tending to purple. It is impossible to describe the colour in his full perfection, considering the variable mixtures. The root is tuberous or knobby, and very brittle.

2   The second kind of *Anemone* hath leaves like to the precedent, insomuch that it is hard to distinguish the one from the other but by the floures onely: for those of this plant are of a most bright and faire skarlet colour, and as double as the Marigold; and the other not so. The root is knobby and very brittle, as is the former.

3 The great *Anemone* hath double floures, usually called the *Anemone* of Chalcedon (which is a city in Bithynia) and great broad leaves deepely cut in the edges, not unlike to those of the field Crow-foot, of an overworne greene colour: amongst which riseth up a naked bare stalke almost unto the top, where there stand two or three leaves in shape like the others, but lesser; sometimes changed into reddish stripes, confusedly mixed here and there in the said leaves. On the top of the stalke standeth a most gallant floure very double, of a perfect red colour, the which is sometimes striped amongst the red with a little line or two of yellow in the middle; from which middle commeth forth many blackish thrums. The seed is not to be found that I could ever observe, but is carried away with the wind. The root is thicke and knobby.

Anemone tenuifolia flore coccineo.
The small leaved skarlet Anemone.

¶ *The Place.*

All the sorts of Anemones are stran-gers, and not found growing wilde in England; notwithstanding all and every sort of them do grow in my garden very plentifully.

¶ *The Time.*

They floure from the beginning of Januarie to the end of April, at what time the flours do fade, and the seed flieth away with the wind, if there be any seed at all; the which I could never as yet observe.

¶ *The Names.*

Anemone, or Wind-floure, is so called, for the floure doth never open it selfe but when the wind doth blow, as *Pliny* writeth: where-upon it is named of divers, *Herba venti*: in English, Wind-floure.

¶ *The Temperature.*

All the kinds of Anemones are sharp, biting the tongue, and of a binding facultie.

(82)   CHAP. 57. *Of water-Docke*.

¶ *The Description.*

1   THe great water-dock hath very long and great leaves, stiffe and hard, not unlike to the garden Patience, but much longer. The stalke riseth up to a great height, oftentimes to the height of five foot or more. The floure groweth at the top of the stalk in spoky tufts, brown of colour. The seed is contained in chaffie husks three square, of a shining pale colour. The root is very great, thick, brown without and yellowish within.

2   The smal water-Dock hath short narrow leaves set upon a stiffe stalke. The floures grow from the middle of the stalke upward in spoky rundles, set in spaces by certain distances round about the stalk, as are the floures of Horehound: which Docke is of all the kinds most common, and of least use, and takes no pleasure or delight in any one soile or dwelling place, but is found almost every where, as well upon the land as in waterie places, but especially in gardens among good and wholsome pot-herbs, being there better knowne, than welcome or desired: wherefore I intend not to spend farther time about his description.

3   The garden Patience hath very strong stalks furrowed or chamfered, of eight or nine foot high when it groweth in fertile ground, set about with great large leaves like to those of the water-Docke, having alongst the stalkes toward the top floures of a light purple colour declining to brownnesse. The seed is three square, contained in thin chaffie husks like those of the common Docke. The root is very great, browne without and yellow within, in colour and taste like the true Rubarb.

4   Bastard Rubarb hath great broad round leaves in shape like those of the garden Bur-docke. The stalke and seeds are so like unto the precedent that the one cannot be knowne from the other, saving that the seeds of this are somewhat lesse. The root is exceeding great and thicke, very like unto the Rha of Barbary, as well in proportion as colour and taste, and purgeth after the same manner, but must be taken in greater quantity, as witnesseth that famous learned physition now living, Mr Dr *Bright*, and others who have experimented the same.

5   This fifth kind of Dock [Bloudwort] is best knowne unto all of the stocke or kindred of Dockes: it hath long thin leaves sometimes red in every part thereof, and often striped here & there with lines and strakes of a darke red colour: among which rise up stiffe brittle stalkes of the same colour: on the top whereof come forth such floures and seed as the common wild Docke hath. The root is likewise red, or of a bloudy colour.

¶ *The Place.*

They grow for the most part in ditches and water-courses, very common thorow England. The two last save one do grow in gardens: my selfe and others in London and elsewhere have them growing for our use in physicke and Surgerie. The last is sown for a pot-herb in most gardens.

¶ *The Time.*

Most of the Docks doe rise up in the Spring of the yeare, and their seed is ripe in June and August.

¶ *The Names.*

The Monks Rubarb is called in Latine, *Rumex sativus*, and *Patientia*, or Patience, which word is borrowed of the French, who call this herb *Patience*: after whom the Dutchmen also name this pot herb Patientie: of some, *Rhabarbarum Monachorum*, or Monks Rubarb, because as it seemes some Monke or other hath used the root hereof in stead of Rubarb.

Bloudwort or bloudy Patience is called in Latine *Lapathum sanguineum*: of some, *Sanguis Draconis*, of the bloudy colour where-with the whole plant is possest: it is of pot-herbs the chiefe or prin-cipall, having the propertie of the bastard Rubarb, but of lesse force in his purging qualitie.

¶ *The Vertues.*

Monks Rubarb or Patience is an excellent wholsome pot-herb, for being put into the pottage in some reasonable quantitie, it helps the jaundice, and such like diseases proceeding of cold causes.

If you take the roots of Monks Rubarb and red Madder of each halfe a pound, Sena foure ounces, Anise seed and Licorice of each two ounces, Scabious and Agrimonie of each one handfull; slice the roots of the Rubarb, bruise the Anise seed and Licorice, breake the herbs with your hands and put them into a stone pot called a stean,

with foure gallons of strong ale, to steep or infuse the space of three
daies, and then drinke this liquor as your ordinary drink for three
weeks together at the least, though the longer you take it, so much
the better; providing in a readinesse another stean so prepared, that
you may have one under another, being alwaies carefull to keep a
good diet: it purifieth the bloud and makes yong wenches look faire
and cherry-like.

There have not bin any other faculties attributed to this plant,
either of the antient or later writers, but generally of all it hath bin
referred to the other Docks or Monks Rubarb: of which number I
assure my selfe this is the best, and doth approch neerest unto the
true Rubarb. Many reasons induce me so to thinke and say; first,
this hath the shape and proportion of Rubarb, the same color both
within and without, without any difference, they agree as well in
taste as smell; it coloureth the spittle of a yellow colour when it is
chewed, as Rubarb doth; and lastly, it purgeth after the same gentle
manner as the right Rubarb doth; only herein it differeth, that this
must be given in three times the quantitie of the other. Other
distinctions and differences I leave to the learned Physitions of our
London colledge, who are very well able to search this matter, as a
thing far above my reach, being no Graduat, but a Country Scholler,
as the whole frame of this historie doth well declare: but I hope my
good meaning will be well taken, considering I do my best: and I
doubt not but some of greater learning wil perfect that which I have
begun according to my small skill, especially the ice being broken to
him, and the wood rough-hewn to his hand. Notwithstanding I
thinke it good to say thus much more in my own defence, That
although there be many wants and defects in mee, that were requisite
to performe such a worke; yet may my long experience by chance
happen upon some one thing or other that may do the Learned good:
considering what a notable experiment I learned of one *John Benet*
a Surgeon of Maidstone in Kent, (a man as slenderly learned as my
selfe) which he practised upon a butchers boy of the said towne, as
himselfe reported unto me. His practise was this: Being desired to
cure the foresaid Lad of an ague which did grievously vex him, hee
promised him a medicine; and for want of one for the present (for a
shift, as himselfe confessed unto me) he tooke out of his garden three
or four leaves of this plant of Rubarb, which my selfe had among
other simples given him, which he stamped and strained with a

draught of ale, and gave it the lad in the morning to drinke: it wrought extreamely downeward and upward within one houre after, and never ceased until night: in the end, the strength of the boy overcame the force of the physick, it gave over working, and the Lad lost his Ague; since which time (as he saith) he hath cured with the same medicine many of the like maladie, having ever great regard to the quantitie, which was the cause of the violent working in the first cure. By reason of which accident, that thing hath bin revealed to posteritie, which heretofore was not so much as dreamed of. Whose blunt attempt may incourage some sharper Wit and greater Judgement in the faculties of plants, to seeke farther into their nature than any of the Antients have done; and none fitter than the learned Physitions of the Colledge of London, where are many singularly well learned and experienced in naturall things.

The roots sliced and boiled in the water of *Carduus benedictus*, to the consumption of the third part, adding thereto a little hony, and eight or nine spoonfulls of the decoction thereof drunke before the fit, cure the ague in two or three times so taking it at the most: unto robustious or strong bodies twelve spoonfuls may be given. This experiment was practised by a worshipfull Gentlewoman Mistresse *Anne Wylbraham* upon divers of her poore neighbours with good successe.

---

(89) CHAP. 58. *Of One-berry, or Herbe True-love,
and Moone-wort.*

¶ *The Description.*

1 HErbe Paris riseth up with one smal tender stalke two hands high; at the very top whereof come forth foure leaves directly set one against another in manner of a Burgundian Crosse or True-love knot: for which cause among the Antients it hath been called Herbe True-love. In the midst of the said leafe comes forth a starre-like floure of an herby or grassie colour; out of the middest whereof there ariseth up a blackish browne berry: the root is long and tender, creeping under the earth, and dispersing it selfe hither and thither.

2   The small Lunary springeth forth of the ground with one leafe like Adders-tongue, jagged or cut on both sides into five or six deepe cuts or notches, not much unlike the leaves of *Scolopendria*, or *Ceterach*, of a greene colour; whereupon doth grow a small naked stem of a finger long, bearing at the top many little seeds clustering together; which being gathered and laid in a platter or such like thing for the space of three weekes, there will fall from the same a fine dust or meale of a whitish colour, which is the seed if it bring forth any. The root is slender, and compact of many small threddy strings.

¶ *The Place.*

Herba Paris groweth plentifully in all these places following; that is to say, in Chalkney wood neere to wakes Coulne, seven miles from Colchester in Essex, and in the wood by Robinhoods well, neere to Nottingham; in the parsonage orchard at Radwinter in Essex, neere to Saffron Walden; in Blackburne at a place called Merton in Lancashire; in the Moore by Canterbury called the Clapper; in Dingley wood, six miles from Preston in Aundernesse; in Bocking parke by Braintree in Essex; at Hesset in Lancashire, and in Cotting wood in the North of England; as that excellent painefull and diligent Physition Mr Doctor *Turner* of late memorie doth record in his Herbal.

Lunaria or small Moone-wort groweth upon dry and barren mountaines and heaths. I have found it growing in these places following; that is to say, about Bathe in Somersetshire in many places, especially at a place called Carey, two miles from Bruton, in the next close unto the Churchyard; on Cockes Heath betweene Lowse and Linton, three miles from Maidstone in Kent: it groweth also in the ruines of an old bricke-kilne by Colchester, in the ground of Mr *George Sayer*, called Miles end: it groweth likewise upon the side of Blacke-heath, neere unto the stile that leadeth unto Eltham house, about an hundred paces from the stile: also in Lancashire neere unto a Wood called Fairest, by Latham: moreover, in Nottinghamshire by the Westwood at Gringley, and at Weston in the Ley field by the West side of the towne; and in the Bishops field at Yorke, neere unto Wakefield, in the close where Sir *George Savill* his house standeth, called the Heath Hall, by the relation of a learned Doctor in Physicke called Master *John Mershe* of Cambridge, and many other places.

¶ *The Time.*

Herba Paris floureth in Aprill, and the berry is ripe in the end of May.

Lunaria or small Moone wort is to be seene in the moneth of May.

¶ *The Vertues.*

The berries of Herbe Paris given by the space of twentie daies, are excellent good against poyson, or the pouder of the herbe drunke in like manner halfe a spoonefull at a time in the morning fasting.

The same is ministred with great successe unto such as are become peevish.

Small Moone-woort is singular to heale greene and fresh wounds. It hath beene used among the Alchymists and witches to doe wonders withall, who say, that it will loose lockes, and make them to fall from the feet of horses that grase where it doth grow, and hath beene called of them *Martagon*, whereas in truth they are all but drowsie dreames and illusions; but it is singular for wounds as aforesaid.

---

(91) CHAP. 59. *Of Lilly in the valley, or May Lilly.*

¶ *The Description.*

1   THe Convall Lilly, or Lilly of the Vally, hath many leaves like the smallest leaves of Water Plantaine; among which riseth up a naked stalke halfe a foot high, garnished with many white floures like little bels, with blunt and turned edges, of a strong savour, yet pleasant enough; which being past, there come small red berries, much like the berries of *Asparagus*, wherein the seed is contained. The root is small and slender, creeping far abroad in the ground.

2   The second kinde of May Lillies is like the former in every respect; and herein varieth or differeth, in that this kinde hath reddish floures, and is thought to have the sweeter smell.

¶ *The Place.*

1   The first groweth on Hampsted heath, foure miles from London, in great abundance: neere to Lee in Essex, and upon

Bushie heath, thirteene miles from London, and many other places.

2   The other kinde with the red floure is a stranger in England: howbeit I have the same growing in my garden.

¶ *The Time*.

They floure in May, and their fruit is ripe in September.

Lilium convallium.
Conuall Lillies.

¶ *The Names*.

The Latines have named it *Lilium Convallium*: in French, *Muguet*: yet there is likewise another herbe which they call *Muguet*, commonly named in English, Woodroof. It is called in English, Lilly of the Valley, or the Convall Lillie, and May Lillies, and in some places Liriconfancie.

¶ *The Vertues*.

The floures of the Valley Lillie distilled with wine, and drunke the quantitie of a spoonefull, restore speech unto those that have the dumb palsie and that are falne into the Apoplexie, and are good against the gout, and comfort the heart.

The water aforesaid doth strengthen the memory that is weakened and diminished; it helpeth also the inflammations of the eies, being dropped thereinto.

The floures of May Lillies put into a glasse, and set in a hill of ants, close stopped for the space of a moneth, and then taken out, therein you shall finde a liquor that appeaseth the paine and griefe of the gout, being outwardly applied; which is commended to be most excellent.

Chap. 60. *Of Sea Lavander.*

¶ *The Description.*

1 THere hath beene among writers from time to time great contention about this plant *Limonium*, no one Author agreeing with another: for some have called this herbe *Limonium*; some another herbe by this name; and some in remooving the rocke, have mired themselves in the mud, as *Matthiolus*, who described two kindes, but made no distinction of them, nor yet expressed which was the true *Limonium*; but as a man herein ignorant, he speakes not a word of them. Now then to leave controversies and cavilling, the true *Limonium* is that which hath faire leaves, like the Limon or Orenge tree, but of a darke greene colour, somewhat fatter, and a little crumpled: amongst which leaves riseth up an hard and brittle naked stalke of a foot high, divided at the top into sundry other small branches, which grow for the most part upon one side, full of little blewish floures, in shew like Lavander, with long red seed, and a thicke root like unto the small Docke.

Limonium.
Sea Lauander.

2 There is a kinde of *Limonium* like the first in each respect, but lesser, which groweth upon rockes and chalkie cliffes.

¶ *The Place.*

1 The first groweth in great plenty upon the walls of the fort against Gravesend: but abundantly on the bankes of the River below the same towne, as also below the Kings Store-house at Chattam: and fast by the Kings Ferrey going into the Isle of Shepey: in the salt marshes by Lee in Essex: in the Marsh by Harwich, and many other places.

2 The small kind I could never find in any other place but upon

the chalky cliffe going from the towne of Margate downe to the sea side, upon the left hand.

¶ *The Time.*

They floure in June and July.

¶ *The Names.*

It shall be needlesse to trouble you with any other Latine name than is exprest in their titles: The people neere the sea side where it growes do call it Marsh Lavander, and sea Lavander.

¶ *The Vertues.*

The seed beaten into pouder and drunk in Wine, helpeth the Collique.

---

(93) Chap. 61. *Of Serapia's Turbith, or sea Star-wort.*

¶ *The Description.*

1   T Ripolium hath long and large leaves somewhat hollow or furrowed, of a shining green colour declining to blewnesse, like the leaves of Woad: among which riseth up a stalke of two cubits high and more, which toward the top is divided into many small branches garnished with many floures like Camomill, yellow in the middle, set about or bordered with small blewish leaves like a pale, as in the floures of Camomill; which grow into a whitish rough downe that flieth away with the wind. The root is long and threddy.

¶ *The Place.*

These herbs grow plentifully alongst the English coasts in many places, as by the fort against Gravesend, in the Isle of Shepey in sundry places, in a marsh which is under the town wals of Harwich, in the marsh by Lee in Essex, in a marsh which is between the Isle of Shepey and Sandwich, especially where it ebbeth and floweth: being brought into gardens it flourisheth a long time, but there it waxeth huge, great, and ranke, and changeth the great roots into strings.

¶ *The Time.*

These herbs do floure in May and June.

¶ The Names.

It is reported by men of great fame and learning, That this plant was called *Tripolium* because it doth change the colour of his floures thrice in a day. This rumor we may beleeve as true, for that we see and perceive things of as great or greater wonder to proceed out of the earth. This herbe I planted in my garden, whither in his season I did repaire to finde out the truth hereof, but I could not espy any such variablenesse herein: yet thus much I may say, that as the heate of the sun doth change the colour of divers floures, so it fell out with this, which in the morning was very faire, but afterward of a pale or wan colour. Which proveth that to be but a fable which *Dioscorides* saith is reported by some, that in one day it changeth the colour of his floures thrice; that is to say, in the morning it is white, at noone purple, and in the evening crimson. But it is not untrue, that there may be found three colours of the floures in one day, by reason that the floures are not all perfected together, (as before I partly touched) but one after another by little and little. And there may easily be observed three colours in them, which is to be understood of them that are beginning to floure, that are perfectly floured, and those that are falling away. For they that are blowing and be not wide open and perfect are of a purplish colour, and those that are perfect and wide open of a whitish blew, and such as have fallen away have a white down: which changing hapneth unto sundry other plants. This herbe is called of *Serapio, Turbith*: women that dwell by the sea side call it in English, blew Daisies, or blew Camomill; & about Harwich it is called Hogs beans, for that the swine do greatly desire to feed thereon, as also for that the knobs about the roots doe somewhat resemble the garden bean.

(97)

C HAP. 62. *Of land Plantaine.*

¶ The Description.

1　A S the Greeks have called some kinds of herbs Serpents tongue, Dogs tongue, and Ox tongue; so have they termed a kinde of Plantain *Arnoglosson*, which is as if you should say Lambs tongue, well known to all, by reason of the great commoditie and plenty of it growing every where; and there-fore it is needlesse to spend time about them. The greatnes and fashion of the leaves hath been the cause of the varieties and diversities of their names.

Plantago incana.
Hoary Plantaine.

2 The second is like the first, and differeth in that, that this Plantaine hath greater but shorter spikes or knaps; and the leaves are of an hoary or overworne green colour: the stalks are likewise hoary and hairy.

¶ *The Vertues.*

The juice dropped in the eies cooles the heate and inflammation thereof. I find in antient writers many good-morrowes, which I thinke not meet to bring into your memorie againe; as, That three roots will cure one griefe, foure another disease, six hanged about the necke are good for another malady, &c. all which are but ridiculous toyes.

(103)

Chap. 63. *Of Golden Rod.*

¶ *The Description.*

1 Golden Rod hath long broad leaves somewhat hoary and sharpe pointed; among which rise up browne stalkes two foot high, dividing themselves toward the top into sundry branches, charged or loden with small yellow floures; which when they be ripe turn into downe which is carried away with the winde. The root is threddy and browne of colour.

¶ *The Vertues.*

It is extolled above all other herbes for the stopping of bloud in bleeding wounds; and hath in times past beene had in great estima-tion and regard than in these daies: for in my remembrance I have

known the dry herbe which came from beyond the sea sold in Buck-
lersbury in London for halfe a crowne an ounce. But since it was
found in Hampstead wood, even as it were at our townes end, no man
will give halfe a crowne for an hundred weight of it: which plainely
setteth forth our inconstancie and sudden mutabilitie, esteeming no
longer of any thing, how pretious soever it be, than whilest it is strange
and rare. This verifieth our English proverbe, Far fetcht and deare
bought is best for Ladies. Yet it may be more truely said of phan-
tasticall Physitions, who when they have found an approved medicine
and perfect remedy neere home against any disease; yet not content
therewith, they will seeke for a new farther off, and by that meanes
many times hurt more than they helpe. Thus much I have spoken
to bring these new fangled fellowes backe againe to esteeme better of
this admirable plant than they have done, which no doubt have the
same vertue now that then it had, although it growes so neere our
owne homes in never so great quantity.

(110)   CHAP. 64. *Of Neesing root or Neesewort.*

¶ *The Description.*

1   THe first kinde of white Hellebor hath leaves like unto
great Gentian, but much broader, and not unlike the
leaves of the great Plantaine, folded into pleits like a
garment plaited to be laid up in a chest: amongst these leaves riseth
up a stalke a cubit long, set towards the top full of little star-like
floures of an herby green colour tending to whitenes: which being
past, there come small husks containing the seed. The root is great
and thicke, with many small threds hanging thereat.

¶ *The Place.*

The white Hellebor groweth on the Alps and such like mountains
where Gentian growes. It was reported unto me by the Bishop of
Norwich, That white Hellebor groweth in a wood of his owne neere
to his house at Norwich. Some say likewise that it doth grow upon
the mountaines of Wales. I speake this upon report, yet I thinke it

may be true. Howbeit I dare assure you that they grow in my garden at London, where the first kinde floureth and seedeth very well.

¶ The Time.

The first floureth in June.

¶ The Names.

We of England call it white Hellebor, Neesewort, Lingwort, and the root Neesing pouder.

¶ The Vertues.

The root of white Hellebor is good against the falling sicknesse, phrensies, sciatica, dropsies, poison, and against all cold diseases that be of hard curation, and will not yeeld to any gentle medicine.

This strong medicine made of white Hellebor, ought not to bee given inwardly unto delicate bodies without great correction; but it may be more safely given unto countrey people which feed grosly, and have hard tough and strong bodies.

The pouder drawne up into the nose causeth sneesing, and purgeth the brain from grosse and slimie humors.

The root given to drinke in the weight of two pence, taketh away the fits of agues, killeth mice and rats, being made up with hony and floure of wheat.

---

(112)   ## CHAP. 65. *Of our Ladies Slipper.*

¶ The Description.

1   OUr Ladies Shoo or Slipper hath a thicke knobbed root, with certain markes or notes upon the same, such as the roots of Solomons Seale have, but much lesser, creeping within the upper crust of the earth; from which riseth up a stiffe and hairy stalke a foot high, set by certaine spaces with faire broad leaves, ribbed with the like sinues or nerves as those of the Plantain. At the top of the stalke groweth one single floure, seldome two, fashioned on the one side like an egge; on the other side it is open, empty, and hollow, and of the form of a shoo or slipper, whereof it tooke his

name; of a yellow colour on the outside, and of a shining deep yellow on the inside. The middle part is compassed about with foure leaves of a bright purple colour, often of a light red or obscure crimson, and sometimes yellow as in the middle part, which in shape is like an egge as aforesaid.

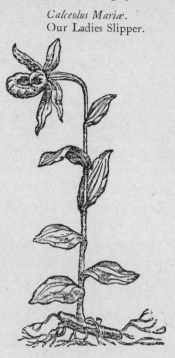

Calceolus Mariæ.
Our Ladies Slipper.

¶ *The Place.*

Ladies Slipper groweth upon the mountains of Germany, Hungary, and Poland. I have a plant thereof in my garden, which I received from Mr *Garret* Apothecarie, my very good friend.

¶ *The Nature and Vertues.*

Touching the faculties of our Ladies shoo we have nothing to write, it beeing not sufficiently known to the old writers, no nor to the new.

---

(115)

CHAP. 66. *Of Bell-floures.*

¶ *The Description.*

1 COventry-Bells have broad leaves rough and hairy, not unlike to those of the Golden Buglosse, of a swart greene colour: among which do rise up stiffe hairie stalkes the second yeare after the sowing of the seed: which stalkes divide themselves into sundry branches, whereupon grow many faire and pleasant bell-floures, long, hollow, and cut on the brim with five sleight gashes, ending in five corners toward night, when the floure shutteth it selfe up, as doe most of the Bell-floures: in the middle of the floures be three or foure whitish chives, as also much downie haire, such as is in the eares of a Dog, or such like beast. The whole floure is of a blew purple colour: which being past, there succeed great square or cornered seed-vessels, divided on the inside into divers

cels or chambers, wherein do lie scatteringly many small browne flat seeds. The root is long and great like a Parsenep, garnished with many threddy strings, which perisheth when it hath perfected his seed, which is in the second yeare after his sowing, and recovereth it selfe againe by the falling of the seed.

¶ The Place and Time.

They grow in woods, mountaines, and dark vallies, and under hedges among the bushes, especially about Coventry, where they grow very plentifully abroad in the fields, and are there called Coventry bells, and of some about London, Canterbury bells; but unproperly, for that there is another kinde of Bell-floure growing in Kent about Canterbury, which may more fitly be called Canterbury Bells, because they grow there more plentifully than in any other countrey. These pleasant Bell-floures wee have in our London gardens especially for the beauty of their floure, although they be kinds of Rampions, and the roots eaten as Rampions are.

They floure in June, July, and August; the seed waxeth ripe in the mean time; for these plants bring not forth their floures all at once, but when one floureth another seedeth.

¶ The Names.

Coventry bels are called in Latine *Viola mariana*: in English, *Mercuries* Violets, or Coventry Rapes, and of some, Mariets.

¶ The Nature and Vertues.

The root is not used in physicke, but only for a sallet root boiled and eaten, with oile, vineger, and pepper.

---

(123)   CHAP. 67. *Of white Sattin floure.*

¶ The Description.

1   B Olbonac or the Sattin floure hath hard and round stalks, dividing themselves into many other small branches, beset with leaves like Dames Violets or Queenes Gillofloures, somewhat broad, and snipt about the edges, and in fashion almost like

Sauce alone, or Jacke by the hedge, but that they are longer and sharper pointed. The stalks are charged or loden with many floures like the common stocke Gillofloure, of a purple colour: which being fallen, the seed comes forth, contained in a flat thin cod, with a sharp point or pricke at one end, in fashion of the Moon, but somewhat blackish. This cod is composed of three filmes or skins, whereof the two outmost are of an overworne ash colour, and the innermost or that in the middle, wheron the seed doth hang or cleave, is thinne and cleere shining, like a shred of white Sattin newly cut from the piece. The whole plant dieth the same yeare that it hath borne seed, and must be sown yearly. The root is compact of many tuberous parts like Key clogs, or like the great Asphodill.

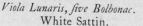

Viola Lunaris, five Bolbonac.
White Sattin.

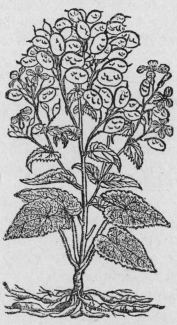

¶ *The Place.*

These Plants are set and sowne in gardens, notwithstanding the first hath bin found wild in the woods about Pinner and Harrow on the hill 12 miles from London, and in Essex likewise about Horn-church.

¶ *The Time.*

They floure in Aprill the next yeare after they be sowne.

¶ *The Names.*

We call this herbe in English, Penny floure, or Mony-floure, Silver Plate, Pricksong-wort; in Norfolke, Sattin, and white Sattin; and among our women it is called Honestie.

¶ *The Temperature and Vertues.*

The seed of Bulbonac is sharpe of taste, like in force to the seed of Treacle mustard: the roots likewise are somewhat of a biting qualitie, but not much: they are eaten with sallads as certaine other roots are.

A certain Helvetian Surgeon composed a most singular unguent for green wounds, of the leaves of Bolbonac and Sanicle stamped together, adding thereto oile and wax. The seed is greatly commended against the falling sicknesse.

CHAP. 68. *Of Willow-herbe, or Loose-strife.*

¶ *The Description.*

1   THe first kinde of Willow-herbe hath long and narrow leaves of a grayish greene colour, in shape like the Willow or Sallow leaves, standing three or foure one against another at severall distances round about the stalke; which toward the top divideth it selfe into many other branches, on the tops whereof grow tufts of faire yellow floures, consisting of five leaves apiece, without smell: which being past, there commeth forth seed like Coriander. The root is long and slender.

2   This being thought by some to be a bastard kinde, is (as I do esteeme it) of all the rest most goodly and stately plant, having leaves like the greatest Willow or Ozier. The branches come out of the ground in great numbers, growing to the height of six foot, garnished with brave floures of great beauty, consisting of foure leaves apiece, of an orient purple colour, having some threds in the middle of a yellow colour. The cod is long and full of downy matter, which flyeth away with the winde when the cod is opened.

3   The wilde Willow-Herbe hath fraile and very brittle stalkes, slender, commonly about the height of a cubit, and sometimes higher, whereupon do grow sharpe pointed leaves somewhat snipt about the edges, and set together by couples. There come forth at the first long slender cods, wherein is contained small seed, wrapped in a cottony or downy wooll, which is carried away with the winde when the seed is ripe: at the end of which commeth forth a small floure of a purplish colour; whereupon it was called *Filius ante Patrem*, be-cause the floure doth not appeare untill the cod be filled with his seed.

¶ *The Place.*

The first yellow *Lysimachia* groweth plentifully in moist Medowes, especially along the Medowes as you goe from Lambeth to Battersey neere London, and in many other places throughout England.

The second groweth in Yorkeshire in a place called the Hooke, neere unto a close called a Cow pasture, from whence I had these plants, which do grow in my Garden very goodly to behold, for the decking up of Houses and Gardens.

The third groweth hard by the Thames, as you goe from a place called the Divels Neckerchiefe to Redreffe, neere unto a stile that standeth in your way upon the Thames banke, among the plankes that do hold up the same banke. It groweth also in a ditch side not farre from the place of execution, called Saint Thomas Waterings.

¶ *The Names.*

Lysimachia, as *Dioscorides* and *Pliny* write, tooke his name of a speciall vertue that it hath in appeasing the strife and unrulinesse which falleth out among oxen at the plough, if it be put about their yokes: but it rather retaineth and keepeth the name *Lysimachia*, of King *Lysimachus* the Sonne of *Agathocles*, the first finder out of the nature and vertues of this herbe, as *Pliny* saith in his 25. book chap. 7. which retaineth the name of him unto this day.

¶ *The Vertues.*

The smoke of the burned herbe driveth away serpents, and killeth flies and gnats in a house; which *Pliny* speaketh of in his 23. booke, chap. 8. Snakes, saith he, craull away at the smell of Loos-strife. The same Author affirmeth in his 26. booke, last chap. that it dieth haire yellow, which is not very unlike to be done by reason the floures are yellow.

(130)   CHAP. 69. *Of Barren-woort.*

¶ *The Description.*

THis rare and strange plant was sent to me from the French Kings Herbarist *Robinus*, dwelling in Paris at the signe of the blacke head, in the streete called *Du bout du monde*, in English, The end of the world. This herbe I planted in my Garden, and in the beginning of May it came forth of the ground, with small, hard, and woody crooked stalkes: wherupon grow rough and sharpe pointed leaves, almost like *Alliaria*, that is to say, Sauce alone, or Jacke by the hedge. *Lobel* and *Dodon*, say, that the leaves are somewhat like Ivie; but in my judgement they are rather like *Alliaria*, somwhat snipt about the edges, and turning themselves flat upright, as a man turneth his hand upwards when hee receiveth money. Upon the same stalkes come forth small floures consisting of foure leaves, whose outsides are purple, the edges on the inner side red, the bottome yellow, & the middle part of a bright red colour, and the whole floure somewhat hollow. The root is small, and creepeth almost upon the uppermost face of the earth. It beareth his seed in very small cods which came not to ripenesse in my Garden, by reason that it was dried away with the extreme and unaccustomed heat of the Sun, which happened in the yeare 1590 since which time from yeare to yeare it bringeth seed to perfection. Further *Dioscorides* and *Pliny* do report, that it is without floure or seed.

¶ *The Place.*

† It groweth in the moist medowes of Italy about Bononia and Vincentia: it groweth in the Garden of my friend Mr *John Milion* in Old-street, and some other Gardens about towne.

---

(132)

Chap. 70. *Of Starre-wort.*

¶ *The Description.*

1   THe first kind of *Aster* or *Inguinalis* hath large broad leaves like *Verbascum Salvifolium* or the great *Conyza*; amongst which riseth up a stalke foure or five handfulls high, hard, rough, and hairy, beset with leaves like Rose Campions, of a darke greene colour. At the top of the said stalks come forth floures of a shining and glistering golden colour.

¶ *The Place.*

The kindes of Starwort grow upon mountaines and hilly places, and somtimes in woods & medowes lying by rivers sides.

The first kinds grow upon Hampsted heath foure miles from London, in Kent upon Southfleet Downes, and in many other such downy places.

‡ I could never yet find nor heare of any of these Star-floures to grow wilde in this kingdom, but have often seen the Italian Starwort growing in gardens. These kindes that our Author mentions to grow on Hampsted heath and in Kent, are no other than *Hieracia* or Hawkeweeds, which are much differing from these. ‡

¶ *The Names.*

This herb is called in Latine, *Aster Atticus, Bubonium,* and *Inguinalis*: in French, *Estrille,* and *Asper goutte menne*: in English, Starwort, and Sharewort.

After Atticus.
Starwort.

¶ *The Temperature.*

That with the blew or purple floure is thought to be that which is of *Virgil* called *Flos Amellus*: of which he maketh mention, *lib.* 4. of his Georgicks: in English thus:

> In Medes there is a floure *Amello* nam'd,
> By him that seeks it easie to be found,
> For that it seems by many branches fram'd
> Into a little wood: like gold the ground
> Thereof appeares; but leaves that it beset
> Shine in the colour of the Violet.

¶ *The Vertues.*

The leaves of *Aster* or *Inguinalis* stamped, and applied unto botches and bubones, which for the most part happen in *Inguine*, that is, the flanke or share, do mightily maturate them, whereof this herb *Aster* tooke the name *Inguinalis*.

The floures are good to be given unto children against the squinancie and falling sicknesse.

CHAP. 71. *Of Woad.*

¶ *The Description.*

1   G*Lastum* or garden Woad hath long leaves of a blewish green colour. The stalk growes two cubits high, set about with a great number of such leaves as come up first, but smaller, branching it selfe at the top into many little twigs,

whereupon do grow many small yellow floures: which being past, the seed comes forth like little blackish tongues. The root is white and single.

2   There is a wild kind of Woad very like unto the former in stalks, leaves, and fashion, saving that the stalke is tenderer, smaller, and browner, and the leaves and tongues narrower; otherwise there is no difference betwixt them.

¶ *The Place.*

The tame or garden Woad growes in fertile fields where it is sowne: the wilde kinde groweth where the tame hath bin sowne.

¶ *The Time.*

They floure from June to September.

¶ *The Names.*

Cæsar, *lib.* 5. of the French warres, saith, That all the Brittons do colour themselves with Woad, which giveth a blew colour: which thing also *Pliny*, *lib.* 22. *cap.* 1. doth testifie: In France they call it *Glastum*, which is like unto Plantaine, wherewith the Brittish wives and their daughters are colored all over, and go naked in some kinde of sacrifices. It is likewise called of divers *Guadum*: of the Italians, *Guado*, a word as it seemeth wrung out of the word *Glastum*: in English, Woad, and Wade.

¶ *The Vertues.*

The decoction of Woad drunken is good for wounds in bodies of a strong constitution, as of countrey people, and such as are accustomed to great labour and hard course fare.

It serveth well to dye and colour cloath, profitable to some few, and hurtfull to many.

Cʜᴀᴘ. 72. *Of Spurge.*

¶ *The Description.*

1   THe first kinde of Sea Spurge riseth forth of the sands, or baich of the sea, with sundry reddish stems or stalkes growing upon one single root, of a wooddy substance: and the stalkes are beset with small, fat, and narrow leaves like unto

the leaves of Flax. The floures are yellowish, and grow out of little dishes or Saucers like the common kinde of Spurge. After the floures come triangle seeds, as in the other Tithymales.

2 The second kinde (called *Helioscopius*, or *Solisequius*: and in English, according to his Greeke name, Sunne Spurge, or time Tithymale, of turning or keeping time with the Sunne) hath sundry reddish stalkes of a foot high: the leaves are like unto Purslane, not so great nor thicke, but snipt about the edges: the floures are yellowish, and growing in little platters.

Tithymalus Characias Monſpell.
Sweet wood Spurge.

¶ *The Place.*

The first kinde of Spurge groweth by the sea side upon the rowling Sand and Baich, as at Lee in Essex, at Lang-tree point right against Harwich, at Whitstable in Kent, and in many other places.

The second groweth in grounds that lie waste, and in barren earable soile, almost every where.

¶ *The Time.*

These plants floure from June to the end of July.

¶ *The Temperature.*

First the milke and sap is in speciall use, then the fruit and leaves, but the root is of least strength. The strongest kinde of Tithymale, and of greatest force is that of the sea.

Some write by report of others, that it enflameth exceedingly, but my selfe speak by experience; for walking along the sea coast at Lee in Essex, with a Gentleman called Mr *Rich*, dwelling in the same towne, I tooke but one drop of it into my mouth; which neverthelesse did so inflame and swell in my throte that I hardly escaped with my life. And in like case was the Gentleman, which caused us to take our horses, and poste for our lives unto the next farme house to drinke some milke to quench the extremitie of our heat, which then ceased.

¶ *The Vertues.*

The juyce mixed with hony, causeth haire to fall from that place which is anointed therewith, if it be done in the Sun.

The juyce or milke is good to stop hollow teeth, being put into them warily, so that you touch neither the gums, nor any of the other teeth in the mouth with the said medicine.

It killeth fish, being mixed with any thing that they will eat.

These herbes by mine advise would not be received into the body, considering that there be so many other good and wholesome potions to be made with other herbes, that may be taken without perill.

---

(151) CHAP. 73. *Of Navelwoort, or Penniwoort of the Wall.*

¶ *The Description.*

1   THe great Navelwoort hath round and thicke leaves, somewhat bluntly indented about the edges, and somewhat hollow in the midst on the upper part, having a short tender stemme fastened to the middest of the leafe, on the lower side underneath the stalke, whereon the floures do grow, is small and hollow, an handfull high and more, beset with many small floures of an overworne incarnate colour. The root is small like an olive, of a white colour.

2   The second kinde of Wall Penniwort or Navelwoort hath broad thicke leaves somewhat deepely indented about the edges: spred upon the ground in manner of a tuft, set about the tender stalke; among which riseth up a tender stalke whereon doe grow the like leaves. The floures stand on the top consisting of five small leaves of a whitish colour, with redde spots in them. ‡ This by some is called *Sedum Serratum.* ‡

3   There is a kinde of Navelwoort that groweth in watery places, which is called of the husbandman Sheeps bane, because it killeth sheepe that do eat thereof: it is not much unlike the precedent, but the round edges of the leaves are not so even as the other; and this creepeth upon the ground, and the other upon the stone walls.

¶ *The Place*.

The first kind of Penniwoort groweth plentifully in Northampton upon every stone wall about the towne, at Bristow, Bathe, Wells, and most places of the West countrie upon stone walls. It groweth upon Westminster Abbey, over the doore that leadeth from *Chaucers* tombe to the old palace. ‡ In this last place it is not now to be found. ‡

'The second and third grow upon the Alpes neere Piedmont, and Bavier, and upon the mountaines of Germany: I found the third growing upon Bieston Castle in Cheshire.

‡ The third growes upon the Bogges upon Hampstead Heath, and many such rotten grounds in other places. ‡

¶ *The Time*.

They are greene and flourish especially in Winter: They floure also in the beginning of Summer.

¶ *The Names*.

Navelwoort is called of some, *Hortus Veneris*, or Venus garden, and *Terræ umbilicus*, or the Navel of the earth: in English, Penniwoort, Wall-Penniwoort, Ladies Navell, Hipwoort and Kidneywoort.

Water Penniwoort is called in English, Sheepe-killing Pennigrasse.

¶ *The Vertues*.

The ignorant Apothecaries doe use the Water Pennywort in stead of this of the wall, which they cannot doe without great error, and much danger to the patient: for husbandmen know well, that it is noisome unto Sheepe, and other cattell that feed thereon, and for the most part bringeth death unto them, much more to men by a stronger reason.

(154)

CHAP. 74. *Of Sampier*.

¶ *The Description*.

1 ROcke Sampier hath many fat and thicke leaves somwhat like those of the lesser Purslane, of a spicie taste, with a certain saltnesse; amongst which rises up a stalk divided into many smal spraies or sprigs, on the top whereof grow spoky tufts

of white floures, like the tufts of Fennell or Dill; after that comes the seed, like the seed of Fenell, but greater: the root is thicke and knobby, beeing of smell delightfull and pleasant.

Crithmum ſpinoſum.
Thorny Sampier.

2 The second Sampier, called *Pastinaca marina*, or sea Parsnep, hath long fat leaves very much jagged or cut even to the middle rib, sharp or prickely pointed, which are set upon large fat jointed stalks; on the top wherof do grow tufts of whitish or else reddish floures. The seed is wrapped in thorny husks: the root is thicke and long, not unlike to the Parsenep, very good and wholsome to be eaten.

§ *The Place.*

Rocke Sampier growes on the rocky clifts at Dover, Winchelsey, by Rie, about Southampton, the Isle of Wight, and most rocks about the West and North parts of England.

The second groweth neere the sea upon the sands and Baych betweene Whitstable and the Isle of Tenet, by Sandwich, and by the sea neere West-chester.

§ *The Vertues.*

The leaves kept in pickle, and eaten in sallads with oile and vineger, is a pleasant sauce for meat.

---

(155)

CHAP. 75. *Of Glasse Saltwort.*

§ *The Description.*

1 GLassewort hath many grosse thicke and round stalks a foot high, full of fat and thicke sprigs, set with many knots or joints, without any leaves at all, of a reddish greene colour: the whole plant resembles a branch of Corall: the root is very small and single.

¶ *The Place.*

These plants are to be found in salt marshes almost everie where.

¶ *The Time.*

They floure and flourish in the Summer moneths.

¶ *The Names.*

Stones are beaten to pouder and mixed with ashes, which beeing melted together, become the matter whereof glasse is made. Which while it is made red hot in the furnace, and is melted, becomming liquid and fit to worke upon, doth yeeld as it were a fat floting aloft; which when it is cold waxeth as hard as a stone, yet is it brittle and quickly broken. This is commonly called *Axungiavitri*: in English, Sandever: in French, *Suin de Voirre*: in Italian, *Fior de Cristallo, i.* Floure of Crystal. The herb is also called of divers, *Cali articulatum,* or jointed Glassewort: in English, Crab-grasse, and Frog-grasse.

¶ *The Vertues.*

A great quantitie taken is mischievous and deadly: the smel and smoke also of this herb being burnt drives away serpents.

---

(158) CHAP. 76. *Of S. Johns Wort.*

¶ *The Description.*

SAint Johns wort hath brownish stalks beset with many small and narrow leaves, which if you behold betwixt your eies and the light, do appeare as it were bored or thrust thorow in an infinite number of places with pinnes points. The branches divide themselves into sundry smal twigs, at the top whereof grow many yellow floures, which with the leaves bruised do yeeld a reddish juice of the colour of bloud. The seed is contained in little sharp pointed huskes blacke of colour, and smelling like Rosin. The root is long, yellow, and of a wooddy substance.

¶ *The Place.*

They grow very plentifully in pastures in every countrie.

¶ *The Time.*

They floure and flourish for the most part in July and August.

¶ *The Names.*

S. Johns wort is called in Latine *Hypericum*: in shops, *Perforata*: of divers, *Fuga dæmonum*: in French *Mille Pertuys*: in English, S. Johns wort, or S. Johns grasse.

¶ *The Vertues.*

The leaves, floures, and seeds stamped, and put into a glasse with oile olive, and set in the hot sun for certain weeks together, and then

Hypericum tomentofum Lobelij. Lobels woolly S. Johns wort.

strained from those herbs, and the like quantitie of new put in and sunned in like manner, doth make an oile of the colour of bloud, which is a most pretious remedie for deep wounds and those that are thorow the body, for the sinues that are prickt, or any wound made with a venomed weapon. I am accustomed to make a compound oile hereof, the making of which you shall receive at my hands, because I know that in the world there is not a better, no not the naturall Balsam it selfe; for I dare undertake to cure any such wound as absolutely in each respect, if not sooner and better, as any man shall or may with naturall Balsam.

Take white wine two pintes, oile olive foure pounds, oile of Turpentine two pounds, the leaves, floures, and seeds of S. Johns wort of each two great handfulls gently bruised; put them all together into a great double glasse, and set it in the Sun eight or ten daies; then boile them in the same glasse *per Balneum Mariæ*, that is, in a kettle of water, with some straw in the bottome, wherein the glasse must stand to boile: which done, strain the liquor from the herbs, and do as you did before, putting in the like quantitie of herbs, floures, and seeds, but not any more wine. Thus have you a great secret for the purposes aforesaid.

(164) ## CHAP. 77. *Of Calves snout, or Snapdragon.*

¶ *The Description.*

1   THe purple Snapdragon hath great and brittle stalks, which divideth it selfe into many fragile branches, where-upon do grow long leaves sharpe pointed, very greene, like unto those of wilde flax, but much greater, set by couples one opposite against another. The floures grow at the top of the stalkes, of a purple colour, fashioned like a frogs mouth, or rather a dragons mouth, from whence the women have taken the name Snapdragon. The seed is blacke, contained in round huskes fashioned like a calves snout, (whereupon some have called it Calves snout) or in mine opinion it is more like unto the bones of a sheeps head that hath beene long in the water, or the flesh consumed cleane away.

Antirrhinum luteum.
Yellow Snapdragon.

2   The second agreeth with the pre-cedent in every part, except in the colour of the floures, for this plant bringeth forth white floures, and the other purple, wherein consists the difference.

3   The yellow Snapdragon hath a long thicke wooddy root, with certain strings fastned thereto; from which riseth up a brittle stalke of two cubits and a halfe high, divided from the bottome to the top into divers branches, whereupon do grow

long greene leaves like those of the former, but greater and longer. The floures grow at the top of the maine branches, of a pleasant yellow colour, in shape like unto the precedent.

¶ *The Place*.

They grow in most gardens.

¶ *The Time*.

That which hath continued the whole Winter doth floure in May, and the rest of Summer afterwards; and that which is planted later, and in the end of Summer, floureth in the Spring of the following yeare: they do hardly endure the injurie of our cold Winter.

¶ *The Names*.

Snapdragon is called in English, Calves snout, Snapdragon, and Lyons snap: in French, *Teste de chien*, and *Teste de Veau*.

¶ *The Vertues*.

They report (saith *Dioscorides*) that the herbe being hanged about one preserveth a man from being bewitched, and that it maketh a may gracious in the sight of people.

---

(146)

CHAP. 78. *Of Garden flaxe*.

¶ *The Description*.

FLax riseth up with slender and round stalks. The leaves thereof bee long, narrow, and sharpe pointed: on the tops of the sprigs are faire blew floures, after which spring up little round knobs or buttons, in which is contained the seed, in forme somewhat long, smooth, glib or slipperie, of a darke colour. The roots be small and threddy.

¶ *The Place*.

It prospereth best in a fat and fruitfull soile, in moist and not dry places; for it requireth, as *Columella* saith, a very fat ground, and somewhat moist. Some, saith *Palladius*, do sow it thicke in a leane ground, and by that meanes the flaxe groweth fine. *Pliny* saith that it is to be sowne in gravelly places, especially in furrowes: and that it burneth the ground, and maketh it worser: which thing also *Virgil* testifieth in his Georgickes. In English thus:

> Flaxe and Otes sowne consume
> The moisture of a fertile field:
> The same worketh Poppy, whose
> Juyce a deadly sleepe doth yeeld.

¶ *The Time.*

Flaxe is sowne in the spring, it floureth in June and July. After it is cut downe (as *Pliny*, *lib*. 19. *cap*. 1. saith) the stalks are put into the water, subject to the heat of the Sun, & some weight laid on them to be steeped therein; the loosenes of the rinde is a signe when it is well steeped: then is it taken up and dried in the Sun, and after used as most huswives can tell better than my selfe.

¶ *The Vertues.*

The oile which is pressed out of the seed, is profitable for many purposes in Physicke and Surgerie; and is used of painters, picture makers, and other artificers.

The seeds stamped with the roots of wild Cucumbers, draweth forth splinters, thornes, broken bones, or any other thing fixed in any part of the body.

(169)   ## CHAP. 79. *Of Milkewort.*

¶ *The Description.*

1   THere have been many plants neerely resembling *Polygala*, and yet not the same indeed, which doth verifie the Latine saying, *Nullum simile est idem*. This neere resemblance doth rather hinder those that have spent much time in the knowledge of Simples, than increase their knowledge: and this also hath been an occasion that many have imagined a sundrie *Polygala* unto themselves, and so of other plants. Of which number this whereof I speake is one, obtaining this name of the best writers and herbarists

of our time, describing it thus: It hath many thicke spreading branches creeping on the ground, bearing leaves like those of *Herniaria*, standing in rowes like the sea Milkwort; among which grow smal whorles or crownets of white floures, the root being exceeding small and threddy.

2 The second kinde of *Polygala* is a small herbe with pliant slender stemmes, of a wooddy substance, an handfull long, creeping by the ground: the leaves be small and narrow like to Lintels, or little Hyssop. The floures grow at the top, of a blew colour, fashioned like a little bird, with wings, taile, and body easie to be discerned by them that do observe the same: which being past, there succeed small pouches like those of *Bursa pastoris*, but lesser. The root is small and wooddy.

Polygala repens.
Creeping Milkwort.

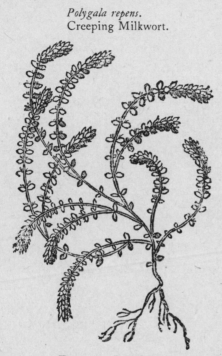

3 This third kinde of *Polygala* or Milkwort, hath leaves and stalkes like the last before mentioned, and differeth from it only herein, that this kinde hath smaller branches, and the leaves are not so thicke thrust together, and the floures are like the other, but that they be of a red or purple colour.

4 The fourth kinde is like the last spoken of in every respect, but that it hath white floures, otherwise it is very like.

5 Purple Milkewort differeth from the others in the colour of the floures, it bringeth forth moe branches than the precedent, and the floures are of a purple colour, wherin especially consists the difference.

6 The sixt Milkwort is like unto the rest in each respect, saving that the floures are of an overworne ilfavored colour, which maketh it to differ from all the other of his kinde.

¶ *The Place.*

These plants or Milke-worts grow commonly in every wood or fertil pasture wheresoever I have travelled.

¶ *The Time.*

They floure from May to August.

¶ *The Names.*

Milkwort is called by *Dodonæus, Flos Ambarvalis*, because it doth especially floure in the Crosse or Gang weeke, or Rogation weeke: of which floures the maidens which use in the countries to walke the Procession do make themselves garlands and Nosegaies: in English wee may call it Crosse-floure, or Procession floure, Gang-floure, Rogation-floure, and Milkwort, of their vertues in procuring milke in the brests of nurses. *Hieronymus Tragus* as also *Dioscorides* call it *Polygalon.* ‡ *Gesner* calls this *Crucis flos*; and in his Epistles he nameth it *Amarella:* it is vulgarly knowne in Cheapeside to the herbe women by the name of hedge Hyssop; for they take it for *Gratiola* or hedge Hyssop, and sell it to such as are ignorant for the same.   ‡

¶ *The Vertues.*

Galen, Dioscorides, and *Theophrastus* doe account these for Milke-woorts, and that they may without errour be used for those purposes whereunto *Glaux* serveth.

(173)   Cʜᴀᴘ. 80. *Of wilde Time.*

¶ *The Description.*

1 BOth *Dioscorides* and *Pliny* make two kindes of *Serpillum*, that is, of creeping or wilde Time; whereof the first is our common creeping Time, which is so well knowne, that it needeth no description; yet this ye shall understand, that it beareth floures of a purple colour, as every body knoweth. Of which kinde I found another sort, with floures as white as snow, and have planted it in my garden, where it becommeth an herbe of great beauty.

2 This wilde Time that bringeth forth white floures differeth not from the other, but onely in the colour of the floures, whence it may be called *Serpillum vulgare flore albo.* White floured Wilde Time.

6   Wilde Time of Candy is like unto the other wild Times, saving that his leaves are narrower and longer, and more in number at each joynt. The smell is more aromaticall than any of the others, wherein is the difference.

¶ *The Place.*

The first groweth upon barren hills and untoiled places: the second groweth in Gardens. The white kinde I found at South fleet in Kent.

Serpillum Creticum.
Wilde Time of Candy.

¶ *The Time.*

They floure from May to the end of Summer.

¶ *The Names.*

Wild Time is called in Latine, *Serpillum, à serpendo,* of creeping: in English, wilde Time, Puliall mountaine, Pella Mountaine, running Time, creeping Time, Mother of Time.

Ælianus in his ninth booke of his sundry Histories seemeth to number wilde Time among the floures. *Dionysius Junior* (saith he) comming into the city Locris in Italy, possessed most of the houses of the city, and did strew them with roses, wilde Time, and other such kindes of floures. Yet *Virgil* in the second Eclog of his Bucolicks doth most manifestly testifie, that wilde Time is an herbe, in these words:

Thestilis for mowers tyr'd with parching heate,
    Garlicke, wilde Time, strong smelling herbes doth beate.

Out of which place it may be gathered, that common wilde time is the true and right *Serpillum,* or wilde Time.

¶ *The Vertues.*

It helpeth against the bitings of any venomous beast, either taken in drinke, or outwardly applied.

(177)

CHAP. 81. *Of Hyssope.*

¶ *The Description.*

1   **D**ioscorides that gave so many rules for the knowledge of simples, hath left Hyssope altogether without description, as being a plant so well knowne that it needed none: whose example I follow not onely in this plant, but in many others which be common, to avoid tediousnesse to the Reader.

¶ *The Place.*

All kindes of Hyssope do grow in my Garden, and in some others also.

¶ *The Time.*

They floure from June to the end of August.

¶ *The Names.*

Hyssope is called in Latine, *Hyssopus*: the which name is likewise retained among the Germans, Brabanders, Frenchmen, Italians, and Spaniards.

¶ *The Vertues.*

A decoction of Hyssope made with figges, water, honey, and rue, and drunken, helpeth the old cough.

---

(179)

CHAP. 82. *Of Lavander Spike.*

¶ *The Description.*

1   **L**avander Spike hath many stiffe branches of a wooddy substance, growing up in the manner of a shrub, set with many long hoarie leaves, by couples for the most part, of a strong smell, and yet pleasant enough to such as do love strong savors. The floures grow at the top of the branches, spike fashion, of a blew colour. The root is hard and wooddie.

2   The second differeth not from the precedent, but in the colour

of the floures: For this plant bringeth milke white floures; and the other blew, wherein especially consisteth the difference.

¶ *The Time.*

They floure and flourish in June and July.

¶ *The Names.*

Lavander Spike is called in Latine *Lavendula*, and *Spica*: in Spanish, *Spigo*, and *Languda*. The first is the male, and the second the female. It is thought of some to bee that sweet herbe *Casia*, whereof *Virgil* maketh mention in the second Eclog of his Bucolicks:

Lavendula minor, five Spica.
Lauander Spike.

And then shee'l Spike and such sweet
      hearbs infold
And paint the Jacinth with the Mari-
      gold.

And likewise in the fourth of his Georgickes, where he intreateth of chusing of seats and places for Bees, and for the ordering thereof, he saith thus:

About them let fresh Lavander and
      store
Of wilde Time with strong Savorie to
      floure.

¶ *The Vertues.*

The distilled water of Lavander smelt unto, or the temples and forehead bathed therewith, is a refreshing to them that have the Catalepsy, a light migram, and to them that have the falling sicknesse, and that use to swoune much. But when there is abundance of humours it is not then to be used safely, neither is the composition to be taken which is made of distilled wine: in which such kinds of herbes, floures, or seeds, and certain spices are infused or steeped, though most men do rashly and at adventure give them without making any difference at al. For by using such hot things that fill and stuffe the head, both the disease is made greater, and the sick man also brought into daunger. Thus much by way of admonition, because that every where some unlearned Physitians and divers rash & over-bold Apothecaries, and other foolish women, do by and by give such compositions, and others of the like kind, not only to those that have the Apoplexy; but also to those that are taken, or have the Catuche or Catalepsis with a Fever; to whom they can give nothing worse, seeing those things do very much hurt, and oftentimes bring death it selfe.

The floures of Lavander picked from the knaps, I meane the blew part and not the husk, mixed with Cinnamon, Nutmegs, & Cloves, made into pouder, and given to drinke in the distilled water thereof, doth helpe the panting and passion of the heart, prevaileth against giddinesse, turning, or swimming of the braine, and members subject to the palsie.

Conserve made of the floures with sugar, profiteth much against the diseases aforesaid, if the quantitie of a beane be taken thereof in the morning fasting.

It profiteth them much that have the palsie, if they be washed with the distilled water of the floures, or anointed with the oile made of the floures, and oile olive, in such maner as oile of Roses is, which shall be expressed in the treatise of Roses.

---

(181)

CHAP. 83. *Of Fleawort.*

❡ *The Description.*

1   P *Syllium,* or the common Fleawort, hath many round and tender branches, set full of long and narrow leaves some-what hairy. The tops of the stalks are garnished with sundrie round chaffie knops beset with small yellow floures: which beeing ripe containe many little shining seeds, in proportion, colour, and bignesse like unto fleas.

2   The second kinde of *Psyllium* Fleawort hath long and tough branches, of a woody substance like the precedent, but longer and harder, with leaves resembling the former, but much longer and narrower. The chaffie tuft which containeth the seed is like the other, but more like the eare of *Phalaris,* which is the eare of *Alpisti,* the Canary seed which is meat for birds that come from the Islands of

Canarie. The root hereof lasteth all the winter, and likewise keepes his greene leaves; whereof it tooke this addition of *Sempervirens*.

¶ *The Place.*

These plants are not growing in our fields of England, as they do in France and Spaine, yet I have them growing in my garden.

¶ *The Time.*

They floure in June and July.

¶ *The Names.*

Fleawort is called in English, Fleawort; not because it killeth fleas, but because the seeds are like fleas.

¶ *The Vertues.*

The seed of Fleawort boiled in water or infused, and the decoction or infusion drunke, cooleth the heate of the inward parts, and quencheth drowth and thirst.

The seed stamped, and boiled in water to the form of a plaister, and applied, takes away all swellings of the joints, especially if you boile the same with vineger and oile of roses, and apply it as aforesaid.

Some hold, That the herb strewed in the chamber where any fleas be, will drive them away; for which cause it tooke the name Fleawort: but I thinke it is rather because the seed doth resemble a flea so much, that it is hard to discern the one from the other.

¶ *The Danger.*

Too much Fleawort seed taken inwardly is hurtfull to mans nature: so that I wish you not to follow the minde of *Galen* and *Dioscorides* in this point, being a medicine rather bringing a malady, than taking away the griefe: remembring the old proverb, A man may buy gold too deare, and the hony is too deare that is lickt from thorns.

(182)   CHAP. 84. *Of Clove Gillofloures*.

¶ *The Kindes*.

THere are at this day under the name of *Cariophyllus* comprehended divers and sundry sorts of plants, of such various colours, and also severall shapes, that a great and large volume would not suffice to write of every one at large in particular; considering how infinite they are, and how every yeare every clymate and country bringeth forth new sorts, such as have not heretofore been written of; some whereof are called Carnations, others Clove Gillofloures, some Sops in wine, some Pagiants, or Pagion color, Horse-flesh, blunket, purple, white, double and single Gillofloures, as also a Gillofloure with yellow flours: the which a worshipful Merchant of London M^r. *Nicholas Lete* procured from Poland, and gave me thereof for my garden, which before that time was never seen nor heard of in these countries. Likewise there be sundry sorts of Pinks comprehended under the same title, which shall be described in a severall chapter. There be under the name of Gillofloures also those floures which we call Sweet-Johns and Sweet-Williams. And first of the great Carnation and Clove Gillofloure.

Cariophyllus multiplex.
The double Cloue Gillofloure.

¶ *The Description*.

1   THe great Carnation Gillo-floure hath a thick round wooddy root, from which riseth up many strong joynted stalks set with long green leaves by couples: on the top of the stalks do grow very fair floures of an excellent sweet smell, and pleasant Carnation colour, whereof it tooke his name.

2   The Clove Gillofloure differeth not from the Carnation but in greatnesse as well of the flowres as leaves. The floure is exceeding

well knowne, as also the Pinkes and other Gillofloures; wherefore I will not stand long upon the description.

¶ *The Place.*

These Gillofloures, especially the Carnations, are kept in pots from the extremitie of our cold Winters. The Clove Gillofloure endureth better the cold, and therefore is planted in gardens.

¶ *The Time.*

They flourish and floure most part of the Summer.

¶ *The Names.*

The Clove Gillofloure is called of the later Herbarists *Caryophylleus Flos*, of the smell of cloves wherewith it is possessed.

Johannes Ruellius saith, That the Gillofloure was unknowne to the old writers: whose judgement is very good, especially because this herb is not like to that of *Vetonica*, or *Cantabrica*. It is marvell, saith he, that such a famous floure, so pleasant & sweet, should lie hid, and not be made known by the old writers: which may be thought not inferior to the rose in beautie, smell, and varietie.

¶ *The Vertues.*

The conserve made of the floures of the Clove Gillofloure and sugar, is exceeding cordiall, and wonderfully above measure doth comfort the heart, being eaten now and then.

---

(183) CHAP. 85. *Of Pinks, or wilde Gillofloures.*

¶ *The Description.*

1 THe double purple Pinke hath manie grassie leaves set upon small joynted stalkes by couples, one opposite against another, whereupon doe grow pleasant double purple floures, of a most fragrant smell, not inferior to the Clove Gillofloure: the root is smal & woody.

There be divers other sorts of Pinks, whereof to write particularly were to small purpose, considering they are all well known to the most, if not to all.

¶ *The Place.*

These kindes of Pinkes do grow for the most part in gardens, and likewise many other sorts, the which were over long to write of particulary. Those that be wilde do grow upon mountaines, stony rockes, and desert places.

¶ *The Vertues.*

These are not used in Physicke, but esteemed for their use in Garlands and Nosegaies.

---

(184) CHAP. 86. *Of Sweet Saint Johns and Sweet Williams.*

¶ *The Description.*

1 SWeet Johns have round stalkes as have the Gillofloures, (whereof they are a kinde) a cubit high, whereupon doe grow long leaves broader than those of the Gillofloure, of a greene grassie colour: the floures grow at the top of the stalkes, very like unto Pinkes, of a perfect white colour.

Armeria rubra latifolia.
Broad leaued Sweet-William.

2 We have in our London Gardens a kinde hereof bearing most fine and pleasant white floures, spotted very confusedly with reddish spots, which setteth forth the beautie thereof; and hath bin taken of some (but not rightly) to be the plant called of the later Writers *Superba Austriaca*, or the Pride of Austria. ‡ It is now commonly in most places called London-Pride. ‡

3 The great Sweet-William hath round joynted stalkes thicke and fat, somewhat reddish about the lower joynts, a cubit high, with long broad and ribbed leaves like as those of the Plantaine, of a greene grassie colour.

The floures at the top of the stalkes are very like to the small Pinkes, many joyned together in one tuft or spoky umbell, of a deepe red colour: the root is thicke and wooddy.

¶ *The Place.*

These plants are kept and maintained in gardens more for to please the eye, than either the nose or belly.

¶ *The Temperature and Vertues.*

These plants are not used either in meat or medicine, but esteemed for their beauty to decke up gardens, the bosomes of the beautifull, garlands and crownes for pleasure.

---

(167) ## CHAP. 87. *Of Thrift, or our Ladies Cushion.*

¶ *The Description.*

1 THrift is also a kinde of Gillofloure, by *Dodonæus* reckoned among grasses, which brings forth leaves in great tufts, thicke thrust together, smaller slenderer and shorter than grasse: among which rise up small tender stalkes of a spanne high, naked and without leaves; on the tops whereof stand little floures in a spokie tuft, of a white colour tending to purple. The root is long and threddy.

2 The other kind of Thrift, found upon the mountaines neer unto the Levant or Mediterranean sea, differeth not from the precedent in leaves, stalkes or floures, but yet is altogether greater, and the leaves are broader.

¶ *The Place.*

1 The first is found in the most salt marshes in England, as also in Gardens, for the bordering up of beds and bankes, for the which it serveth very fitly. The other is a stranger in these Northerne Regions.

¶ *The Time.*

They floure from May, till Summer be farre spent.

¶ *The Names.*

Thrift is called in Latine, *Gramen Polyanthemum*, of the multitude of the floures: of some, *Gramen marinum*: of *Lobel*, *Caryophyllus Marinus*: in English, Thrift, Sea-grasse, and our Ladies Cushion.

¶ *The Temperature and Vertues.*

Their use in Physicke as yet is not knowne, neither doth any seeke into the Nature thereof, but esteeme them only for their beautie and pleasure.

---

(189)

CHAP. 88. *Of Sneesewoort.*

¶ *The Description.*

1 THe small Sneese-woort hath many round and brittle branches, beset with long & narrow leaves, hackt about the edges like a saw; at the tops of the stalks do grow smal single floures like the wild field Daisie. The root is tender and full of strings, creeping far abroad in the earth, and in short time occupieth very much ground: the whole plant is sharp, biting the tongue and mouth like Pellitorie of Spaine, for which cause some have called it wild Pellitorie. The smel of this plant procureth sneesing, whereof it tooke the name *Sternutamentoria*, that is, the herbe which procureth sneesing, or Neesewoort.

2 Double floured Sneeswoort, or *Ptarmica*, is like unto the former in leaves, stalks, and roots, so that unlesse you behold the floure, you cannot discerne the one from the other, and it is exceeding white, and double like unto double Fetherfew. This plant is of great beautie, and if it be cut downe in the time of his flouring there will come within a moneth after a supplie or crop of floures fairer than the rest.

3 There is also another kind hereof, of exceeding great beauty, having long leaves somewhat narrow like those of Olive tree: the stalks are of a cubit high, on the top whereof grow very beautifull floures of the bignesse of a small single Marygold, consisting of fifteen or sixteen large leaves, of a bright shining red colour tending

to purple; set about a ball of thrummy substance, such as is in the middle of the Daisie, in manner of a pale; which floures stand in scalie knops like those of Knapweed or Matfellon. The root is straight, and thrusteth deepe into the ground.

¶ *The Place.*

The first kind of Sneesewort growes wild in dry and barren pastures in many places, and in the three great fields next adjoyning to a village neer London called Kentish towne, and in sundry fields in Kent about Southfleet.

† The rest grow only in gardens.

¶ *The Vertues.*

The juice mixed with vineger and holden in the mouth, easeth much the pain of the tooth-ach.

The herb chewed and held in the mouth, bringeth mightily from the braine slimie flegme like Pellitorie of Spain; and therefore from time to time it hath bin taken for a wild kinde thereof.

---

(185)

CHAP. 89. *Of Pimpernell.*

¶ *The Description.*

1 PImpernell is like unto Chickweed; the stalkes are foure square, trailing here and there upon the ground, whereupon do grow broad leaves, and sharpe pointed, set together by couples: from the bosomes whereof come forth slender tendrels, whereupon doe grow small purple floures tending to rednesse: which being past there succeed fine round bullets, like unto the seed of Coriander, wherein is contained small dusty seed. The root consisteth of slender strings.

2 The female Pimpernell differeth not from the male in any one point, but in the colour of the floures; for like as the former hath reddish floures, this plant bringeth forth floures of a most perfect blew colour; wherein is the difference.

‡ 3 Of this there is another variety set forth by *Clusius* by the name of *Anagallis tenuifolio Monelli,* because he received the figure

and History thereof from *John Monell* of Tourney in France; it differs thus from the last mentioned, the leaves are longer and narrower, somewhat like those of *Gratiola*, and they now and then grow three at a joynt, and out of the bosomes of the leaves come commonly as many little foot-stalkes as there are leaves, which carry floures of a blew colour with the middle purplish, and these are somewhat larger than them of the former, otherwise like. ‡

4   The yellow Pimpernell hath many weake and feeble branches trailing upon the ground, beset with leaves one against another like the great Chickweed, not unlike to *Nummularia*, or Moneywoort; betweene which and the stalkes, come forth two single and small tender foot-stalkes, each bearing at their top one yellow floure and no more. The root is small and threddy.

‡ *Anagallis tenuifolia.*
Narrow leaued Pimpernell.

¶ *The Place.*

They grow in plowed fields neere path waies, in Gardens and Vineyards almost every where. The yellow Pimpernell growes in the woods betweene Highgate and Hampstead, and in many other woods.

¶ *The Time.*

They floure in Summer, and especially in the moneth of August, at what time the husbandmen having occasion to go unto their harvest worke, will first behold the floures of Pimpernell, whereby they know the weather that shall follow the next day after; as for example, if the floures be shut close up, it betokeneth raine and foule weather; contrariwise, if they be spread abroad, faire weather.

¶ *The Temperature.*

Both the sorts of Pimpernell are of a drying faculty without biting, and somewhat hot, with a certaine drawing quality, insomuch that it doth draw forth splinters and things fixed in the flesh, as *Galen* writeth.

¶ *The Vertues.*

Dioscorides writes, That they are of power to mitigate paine, to cure inflammations and hot swellings, to draw out of the body and flesh thornes, splinters, or shivers of wood, and to helpe the Kings Evill.

The juyce purgeth the head by gargarising or washing the throat therewith; it cures the tooth-ach being snift up into the nosethrils, especially into the contrary nosethrill.

It helpeth those that be dim sighted: the juyce mixed with hony cleanses the ulcers of the eye called in Latine *Argema*.

Moreover he affirmeth, That it is good against the stinging of Vipers, and other venomous beasts.

---

(199) ## CHAP. 90. *Of Herbe Two-pence.*

¶ *The Description.*

I HErbe Two-pence hath a smal and tender root, spreding and dispersing it selfe far within the ground, from which rise up many little, tender, flexible stalks trailing upon the ground, set by couples at certaine spaces, with smooth greene leaves somewhat round, whereof it tooke his name: from the bosome of which leaves shoot forth small tender foot-stalks, whereon do grow little yellow floures, like those of Cinkefoile or Tormentill.

¶ *The Place.*

It groweth neere unto ditches and streames, and other waterie places, and is somtimes found in moist woods: I found it upon the banke of the river of Thames, right against the Queenes palace of White-hall; and almost in every countrey where I have travelled.

¶ *The Time.*

It floureth from May till Summer be well spent.

¶ *The Names.*

Herb Two-pence is called in Latine *Nummularia* and *Centum-morbia*: and of divers *Serpentaria*. It is reported, that if serpents be hurt or wounded, they do heale them-selves with this herb, wherupon came the name *Serpentaria*: it is thought to be called *Centummorbia*, of the wonderfull effect which it hath in curing diseases; and it is called *Nummularia* of the forme of money, whereunto the leaves are like: in English, Money-woort, Herbe Two-pence, and Two-penny grasse.

Nummularia.
Herbe Two-pence.

¶ *The Vertues.*

The floures and leaves stamped and laid upon wounds and ulcers do cure them: but it worketh most effectually being stamped and boiled in oile olive, with some rosin, wax, and turpentine added thereto.

Boiled with wine and hony it cureth the wounds of the inward parts, and ulcers of the lungs; & in a word, there is not a better wound herb, no not Tabaco it selfe, nor any other whatsoever.

The herb boiled in wine, with a little hony or mead, prevaileth much against the cough in children, called the Chin-cough.

---

(200)   Chap. 91. *Of Bugle or middle Comfrey.*

¶ *The Description.*

1   BUgula spreadeth and creepeth along the ground like Monywort: the leaves be long, fat, and oleous, and of a browne colour for the most part. The floures grow about the stalks in rundles, compassing the stalke, leaving between every rundle bare or naked spaces, and are of a faire blew colour, and often

white. I found many plants of it in a moist ground upon black-Heath neere London, fast by a village called Charleton; but the leaves were green, and not brown at all like the other.

¶ *The Place.*

Bugula groweth almost in every wood and copse, and such like shadowie and moist places, and is much planted in gardens: the other varieties are seldome to be met withall.

¶ *The Time.*

Bugula floureth in April and May.

¶ *The Names.*

Bugle is reckoned among the Consounds or wound-herbs; and it is called of some, *Consolida media.*

¶ *The Vertues.*

Ruellius writeth that they commonly say in France, how hee needs neither Physition nor Surgeon, that hath Bugle and Sanicle.

---

(201)   CHAP. 92. *Of Selfe-heale.*

¶ *The Description.*

I   PRunell or Brunell hath square hairie stalks of a foot high, beset with long hairy and sharp pointed leaves, and at the top of the stalkes grow floures thicke set together like an eare or spiky knap, of a brown colour, mixed with blew floures and sometimes white; of which kinde I found some plants in Essex neere Heningham castle. The root is small and very threddy.

¶ *The Place.*

Prunell or Brunel groweth very commonly in all our fields throughout England.

¶ *The Time.*

These plants floure for the most part all Summer long.

¶ *The Names.*

Brunell is called in English, Prunel, Carpenters herb, Selfe-heale, Hook-heale, and Sicklewort.

¶ *The Vertues.*

The decoction of Prunell made with wine and water, doth joine together and make whole and sound all wounds both inward and outward, even as Bugle doth.

Prunel bruised with oile of roses and vineger, and laid to the fore-part of the head, swageth and helpeth the pain and aking thereof.

To be short, it serveth for the same that Bugle doth, and in the world there are not two better wound herbs, as hath bin often proved.

(203)

Chap. 93. *Of little Daisies.*

¶ *The Description.*

1   THe Daisie bringeth forth many leaves from a threddy root, smooth, fat, long, and somwhat round withall, very sleightly indented about the edges, for the most part lying upon the ground: among which rise up the floures, everie one with his owne slender stem, almost like those of Camomill, but lesser, of a perfect white colour, and very double.

2   The double red Daisie is like unto the precedent in everie respect, saving in the color of the floures; for this plant bringeth forth floures of a red colour; and the other white as aforesaid.

‡ 3   Furthermore, There is another pretty Daisie which differs from the first described onely in the floure, which at the sides thereof puts forth many footstalks, carrying also little double flours, being commonly of a red colour; so that each stalke carrieth as it were an old one and the brood thereof; whence they have fitly termed it the childing Daisie. ‡

¶ *The Place.*

The double Daisies are planted in gardens: the others grow wilde everywhere.

¶ *The Time.*

The Daisies do floure most part of the Summer.

The Names.

The Daisie is called of some, *Herba Margarita*, or Margarites herb: in French, *Marguerites*: In English, Daisies, and Bruisewort.

¶ *The Vertues.*

The Daisies do mitigate all kinde of paines, but especially in the joints, and gout, if they be stamped with new butter unsalted, and

Bellis minor prolifera.
Childing Daisie.

applied upon the pained place: but they worke more effectually if Mallowes be added thereto.

The juice of the leaves and roots snift up into the nosthrils, purgeth the head mightily, and helpeth the megrim.

The same given to little dogs with milke, keepeth them from growing great.

The leaves stamped take away bruises and swellings proceeding of some stroke, if they be stamped and laid thereon; whereupon it was called in old time Bruisewort.

The juice put into the eies cleareth them, and taketh away the watering of them.

The decoction of the field Daisie (which is the best for physicks use) made in water and drunke, is good against agues.

(204)

Chap. 94. *Of Mouse-eare*.

¶ *The Description.*

1 THe great Mouse-eare hath great and large leaves, thicke, and full of substance: the stalkes and leaves bee hoary and white, with a silken mossinesse in handling like silke, pleasant and faire in view: it bears three or foure quadrangle stalkes somewhat knotty, a foot long: the roots are hard, wooddy, and full of strings; the floures come forth at the top of the stalk, like unto the small Dandelion, of a bright yellow colour.

2 The second kinde of *Pylosella* is that which we call *Auricula muris*, or Mous-eare, being a very common herbe, but few more worthy of consideration because of his good effect, and yet not re-membred of the old writers. It is called *Pylosella*, of the rough hairy and whitish substance growing upon the leaves, which are somewhat long like the little Daisie, but that they have a small hollownesse in them resembling the eare of a mouse: upon which consideration some have called it *Myosotis*.

¶ *The Place.*

They grow upon sandy banks and untoiled places that lie open to the aire.

¶ *The Time.*

They floure in May and June.

¶ *The Vertues.*

The decoction of *Pylosella* drunke doth cure and heale all wounds, both inward and outward.

The leaves dried and made into pouder, doe profit much in healing of wounds, beeing strewed thereupon.

The decoction of the juice is of such excellencie, that if steele-edged tooles red hot be drenched, and cooled therein oftentimes, it maketh them so hard, that they will cut stone or iron, bee they never so hard, without turning the edge or waxing dull.

CHAP. 95. *Of Cotton-weed or Cud-weed.*

¶ *The Description.*

1 ENglish Cudweed hath sundry slender and upright stalks divided into many branches, and groweth as high as common Wormwood, whose colour and shape it much resembleth. The leaves shoot from the bottome of the turfe full of haires, among which do grow small pale coloured floures like those of the small *Coniza* or Flea-bane. The whole plant is of a bitter taste.

Filago sive Herba impia.
Herbe impious, or wicked Cudweed.

8 There is a kinde of Cotton-weed, being of greater beautie than the rest, that hath strait and upright stalkes 3 foot high or more, covered with a most soft and fine wooll, and in such plentifull manner, that a man may with his hands take it from the stalke in great quantitie: which stalke is beset with many small long and narrow leaves, greene upon the inner side, and hoary on the other side, fashioned somewhat like the leaves of Rosemary, but greater. The floures do grow at the top of the stalkes in bundles or tufts, consisting of many small floures of a white colour, and very double, compact, or as it were consisting of little silver scales thrust close together, which doe make the same very double. When the floure hath long flourished, and is waxen old, then comes there in the middest of the floure a certaine browne yellow thrumme, such as is in the middest of the Daisie: which floure being gathered when it is young, may be kept in such manner as it was gathered (I meane in such freshnesse and well liking) by the space of a whole yeare after, in your chest or elsewhere: wherefore our English women have called it Live-long, or Live for ever, which name doth aptly answer his effects.

9 This plant hath three or foure small grayish cottony or woolly

stalkes, growing strait from the root, and commonly divided into many little branches: the leaves be long, narrow whitish, soft and woolly, like the other of his kinde: the floures be round like buttons, growing very many together at the top of the stalkes, but nothing so yellow as Mouse-eare, which turne into downe, and are carried away with the winde.

10   The tenth is like unto the last before mentioned, in stalkes, leaves, and floures, but much larger, and for the most part those floures which appeare first are the lowest, and basest, and they are overtopt by other floures which come on younger branches, and grow higher, as children seeking to overgrow or overtop their parents, (as many wicked children do) for which cause it hath beene called *Herba impia*, that is, the wicked Herbe, or Herbe Impious.

¶ *The Vertues.*

The fume or smoke of the herbe dried, and taken with a funnell, being burned therein, and received in such manner as we use to take the fume of Tabaco, that is, with a crooked pipe made for the same purpose by the Potter, prevaileth against the cough of the lungs, the great ache or paine of the head, and cleanseth the breast and inward parts.

---

(206)   Chap. 96. *Of Golden Moth-wort, or Cudweed.*

¶ *The Description.*

Golden Mothwort bringeth forth slender stalkes somewhat hard and wooddy, divided in divers small branches; where-upon doe grow leaves somewhat rough, and of a white colour very much jagged like Southernwood. The floures stand on the tops of the stalkes, joyned together in tufts, of a yellow colour glittering like gold, in forme resembling the scaly floures of Tansie, or the middle button of the floures of Camomill; which being gathered before they be ripe or withered, remaine beautifull long time after, as my selfe did see in the hands of Mr *Wade*, one of the Clerks of her Majesties counsell, which were sent him among other things from Padua in Italy. For which cause of long lasting, the images and carved gods were wont to weare garlands thereof: where-upon some have called it Gods floure. For which purpose *Ptolomy* King of Ægypt did most diligently observe them, as *Pliny* writeth.

¶ *The Place.*

It growes in most untilled places of Italy and Spaine, in medowes where the soile is barren, and about the bankes of rivers; it is a stranger in England.

¶ *The Vertues.*

The branches and leaves laid amongst cloathes keepeth them from mothes, whereupon it hath beene called of some Moth-weed, or Moth-wort.

---

(210)   CHAP. 97. *Of Fetherfew.*

¶ *The Description.*

1   FEverfew bringeth forth many little round stalkes, divided into certaine branches. The leaves are tender, diversly torne and jagged, and nickt on the edges like the first and nethermost leaves of Coriander, but greater. The floures stand on the tops of the branches, with a small pale of white leaves, set round about a yellow ball or button, like the wild field Daisie. The root is hard and tough: the whole plant is of a light whitish greene colour, of a strong smell, and bitter taste.

¶ *The Place.*

The common single Feverfew groweth in hedges, gardens, and about old wals, it joyeth to grow among rubbish. There is oftentimes found when it is digged up a little cole under the strings of the root, and never without it, whereof *Cardane* in his booke of Subtilties setteth down divers vaine and trifling things.

¶ *The Vertues.*

Feverfew dried and made into pouder, and two drams of it taken with hony or sweet wine, purgeth by siege melancholy and flegme; wherefore it is very good for them that are giddie in the head, or which have the turning called *Vertigo*, that is, a swimming and turning in the head. Also it is good for such as be melancholike, sad, pensive, and without speech.

⁽²¹⁶⁾ ## CHAP. 98. *Of Eye-bright.*

¶ *The Description.*

Euphrasia or Eye-bright is a small low herbe not above two handfulls high, full of branches, covered with little blackish leaves dented or snipt about the edges like a Saw. The floures are small and white, sprinkled and poudered on the inner side, with yellow and purple speckes mixed therewith. The root is small and hairie.

¶ *The Place.*

This plant groweth in dry medowes, in greene and grassie waies and pastures standing against the Sun.

¶ *The Time.*

Eye-bright beginneth to floure in August, and continueth unto September, and must bee gathered while it floureth for physicks use.

¶ *The Names.*

It is commonly called *Euphrasia.*

¶ *The Vertues.*

It is very much commended for the eies. Being taken it selfe alone, or any way else, it preserves the sight, and being feeble & lost it restores the same: it is given most fitly being beaten into pouder; oftentimes a like quantitie of Fennell seed is added thereto, and a little mace, to the which is put so much sugar as the weight of them all commeth to.

Eye-bright stamped and laid upon the eyes, or the juice thereof mixed with white Wine, and dropped into the eyes, or the distilled water, taketh away the darknesse and dimnesse of the eyes, and cleareth the sight.

Three parts of the pouder of Eye-bright, and one part of maces mixed therewith, taketh away all hurts from the eyes, comforteth the memorie, and cleareth the sight, if halfe a spoonefull be taken every morning fasting with a cup of white wine.

(218)

Chap. 99. *Of wilde Marjerome.*

¶ *The Description.*

1 **B**Astard Marjerome of Candy hath many threddy roots; from which rise up divers weake and feeble branches trailing upon the ground, set with faire greene leaves, not unlike those of Penny Royall, but broader and shorter: at the top of those branches stand scalie or chaffie eares of a purple colour. The whole plant is of a most pleasant sweet smell. The root endured in my garden and the leaves also greene all this Winter long, 1597. although it hath beene said that it doth perish at the first frost, as sweet Marjerome doth.

Origanum Creticum.
Wilde Marjerome of Candy.

2 English wilde Marjerome is exceedingly well knowne to all, to have long, stiffe, and hard stalkes of two cubits high, set with leaves like those of sweet Marjerome, but broader and greater, of a russet greene colour, on the top of the branches stand tufts of purple floures, composed of many small ones set together very closely umbell fashion.

¶ *The Names.*

Bastard Marjerome is called in shops, *Origanum Hispanicum*, Spanish Organy.

¶ *The Vertues.*

Organy given in wine is a remedy against the bitings, and stingings of venomous beasts, and cureth them that have drunke *Opium*, or the juyce of blacke Poppy, or hemlockes, especially if it be given with wine and raisons of the sunne.

It is profitably used in a looch, or a medicine to be licked, against the old cough and the stuffing of the lungs.

The juyce mixed with a little milke, being poured into the eares, mitigateth the paines thereof.

The same mixed with the oile of *Ireos*, or the roots of the white Florentine floure-de-luce, and drawne up into the nosthrils, draweth downe water and flegme: the herbe strowed upon the ground driveth away serpents.

These plants are easie to be taken in potions, and therefore to good purpose they may be used and ministred unto such as cannot brooke their meate, and to such as have a sowre squamish and watery stomacke, as also against the swouning of the heart.

---

(221) CHAP. 100. *Of Pennie Royall, or pudding grasse.*

¶ *The Description.*

PUlegium regium vulgatum is so exceedingly well knowne to all our English Nation, that it needeth no description, being our common Pennie Royall.

¶ *The Place.*

The common Penny Royall groweth naturally wild in moist and overflown places, as in the Common neere London called Miles end, about the holes and ponds thereof in sundry places, from whence poore women bring plenty to sell in London markets; and it groweth in sundry other Commons neere London likewise.

¶ *The Time.*

They floure from the beginning of June to the end of August.

¶ *The Vertues.*

If you have when you are at the sea Penny Royall in great quantitie dry, and cast it into corrupt water, it helpeth it much, neither will it hurt them that drinke thereof.

A Garland of Pennie Royall made and worne about the head is of great force against the swimming in the head, and the paines and giddinesse thereof.

Chap. 101. *Of Nep or Cat-Mint.*

¶ *The Description.*

1 CAt-Mint or Nep growes high, it brings forth stalks above a cubit long, covered, chamfered, and full of branches: the leaves are broad, nickt in the edges like those of Bawm or Hore-hound, but longer. The floures are of a whitish colour, they partly compasse about the uppermost sprigs, and partly grow on the very top, set in manner of an eare or catkin: the root is diversly parted, and endureth a long time: the whole herb together with the leaves & stalks are soft, and covered with a white down, but lesser than Horse-mint: it is of a sharp smel, and pierceth into the head: it hath a hot taste with a certain bitternesse.

¶ *The Place.*

The first groweth about the borders of gardens and fields, neere to rough banks, ditches, and common wayes: it is delighted with moist and watery places, and is brought into gardens.

¶ *The Time.*

The Cat-mints flourish by and by after the Spring: they floure in July and August.

¶ *The Names.*

The later Herbarists doe call it *Herba Cattaria*, & *Herba Catti*, because cats are very much delighted herewith; for the smell of it is so pleasant unto them, that they rub themselves upon it, & wallow or tumble in it, and also feed on the branches and leaves very greedily. It is named of the Apothecaries *Nepeta* (but *Nepeta* properly so called is a Calamint, having the smell of Penny-Royall).

¶ *The Vertues.*

It is a present helpe for them that be bursten inwardly by means of some fall received from an high place, and that are very much bruised, if the juice be given with wine or meade.

(227) CHAP. 102. *Of Horse-Mint or Water-Mint.*

❡ *The Description.*

1 WAter Mint is a kinde of wilde Mint like to garden Mint: the leaves thereof are round, the stalkes cornered, both the leaves and stalkes are of a darke red colour: the roots creep far abroad, but every part is greater, and the herb it selfe is of a stronger smell: the floures in the tops of the branches are gathered together into a round eare, of a purple colour.

❡ *The Place.*

They grow in moist and waterie places, as in medowes neere unto ditches that have water in them, and by rivers.

❡ *The Time.*

They floure when the other Mints do, and revive in the Spring.

❡ *The Vertues.*

It is commended to have the like vertues that the garden Mint hath, & also to be good against the stinging of bees and wasps, if the place be rubbed therewith.

The savor or smell of the water Mint rejoyceth the heart of man, for which cause they use to strew it in chambers and places of recreation, pleasure, and repose, and where feasts and banquets are made.

There is no use hereof in physick whilest we have with us the garden Mint, which is sweeter and more agreeing to mans nature.

---

(229) CHAP. 103. *Of Bawme.*

❡ *The Description.*

1 APiastrum, or *Melissa,* is our common best knowne Balme or Bawme, having many square stalkes and blackish leaves like to *Ballote,* or blacke Horehound, but larger, of a pleasant smell, drawing neere in smell and savour unto a Citron: the floures are of a Carnation colour; the root of a wooddy substance.

¶ *The Place.*

Bawme is much sowen and set in Gardens, and oftentimes it groweth of it selfe in Woods and mountaines, and other wilde places: it is profitably planted in Gardens, as *Pliny* writeth, *lib.* 21. *cap.* 12. about places where Bees are kept, because they are delighted with this herbe above others, whereupon it hath beene called *Apiastrum*: for, saith he, when they are straied away, they doe finde their way home againe by it, as *Virgil* writeth in his Georgicks:

Melissa Fuchsij flore albo.
Baſtard Bawme with white floures.

──Here liquors cast in fitting sort,
Of bruised Bawme and more base
　Honywort.

All these I have in my garden from yeare to yeare.

¶ *The Vertues.*

Bawme drunke in wine is good against the bitings of venomous beasts, comforts the heart, and driveth away all melancholy and sadnesse.

The hives of Bees being rubbed with the leaves of Bawme, causeth the Bees to keep together, and causeth others to come unto them.

The later age, together with the Arabians and Mauritanians, affirme Balme to be singular good for the heart, and to be a remedy against the infirmities thereof; for *Avicen* in his booke written of the infirmities of the heart, teacheth that Bawme makes the heart merry and joyfull, and strengtheneth the vitall spirits.

Dioscorides writeth, That the leaves drunke with wine, or applied outwardly, are good against the stingings of venomous beasts, and the biting of mad dogs: also it helpeth the tooth-ache, the mouth being washed with the decoction, and is likewise good for those that cannot take breath unlesse they hold their neckes upright.

Smiths Bawme or Carpenters Bawme is most singular to heale up greene wounds that are cut with yron; it cureth the rupture in short time. *Dioscorides* and *Pliny* have attributed like vertues unto this kinde of Bawme, which they call Iron-wort. The leaves (say they) being applied, close up wounds without any perill of inflammation. *Pliny* saith that it is of so great vertue, that though it be but tied to his sword that hath given the wound, it stancheth the bloud.

(235)   Chap. 104. *Of Archangell or dead Nettle.*

¶ *The Description.*

1 WHite Archangell hath foure square stalkes a cubit high, leaning this way and that way, by reason of the great weight of his ponderous leaves, which are in shape like unto those of Nettles, nicked round about the edges, yet not stinging at all, but soft and as it were downy: the floures compasse the stalkes round about at certaine distances.

† 1 *Lamium album.*
White Archangell.

2 Yellow Archangell hath square stalks rising from a threddy root, set with leaves by couples very much cut or hackt about the edges, and sharp pointed, the uppermost whereof are oftentimes of a faire purple colour: the flours grow among the said leaves, of a gold yellow colour, fashioned like those of the white Archangell, but greater, and wider gaping open.

3 Red Archangell, being called *Urtica non mordax*, or dead Nettle, hath many leaves spred upon the ground; among which rise up stalkes hollow and square, whereupon grow rough leaves of an overworne colour, among which come forth purple floures set about in round wharles or rundles. The root is small, and perisheth at the first approch of winter.

¶ *The Place.*

These plants are found under hedges, old walls, common waies, among rubbish, in the borders of fields, and in earable grounds, oftentimes in gardens ill husbanded.

That with the yellow floure groweth not so common as the others. I have found it under the hedge on the left hand as you go from the village of Hampsted neer London to the Church, & in the wood therby, as also in many other copses about Lee in Essex, neer Watford & Bushy in Middlesex, and in the woods belonging to the Lord Cobham in Kent.

¶ *The Time.*

They floure for the most part all Summer long, but chiefely in the beginning of May.

¶ *The Names.*

Archangell is called in English, Archangell, blinde Nettle, and dead Nettle.

¶ *The Vertues.*

The floures are baked with sugar as Roses are, which is called Sugar roset: as also the distilled water of them, which is used to make the heart merry, to make a good colour in the face, and to refresh the vitall spirits.

---

(237)   CHAP. 105. *Of stinging Nettle.*

¶ *The Description.*

1   THe stalks of the first be now and then halfe a yard high, round and hollow within: the leaves are broad, sharp pointed, cut round about like a saw, rough on both sides, and covered with a stinging down, which with a light touch only causeth a great burning, and raiseth hard knots in the skin like blisters, somtimes making it red.

2   The second Nettle being our common Nettle is like to the former in leaves and stalks, but yet now and then higher and more full of branches; it is also covered with a downe that stingeth and burneth as well as the other.

¶ *The Place.*

Nettles grow in untilled places, & the first in thicke woods, and is a stranger in England, notwithstanding it groweth in my garden.

The second is more common, and groweth of it selfe neere hedges, bushes, brambles, and old walls almost every where.

¶ *The Time.*

They all flourish in Summer: the second suffereth the winters cold: the seed is ripe & may be gathered in July and August.

¶ *The Names.*

It is called in Latine, *Urtica, ab urendo,* of his burning and stinging qualitie; whereupon *Macer* saith,

> Neither without desert his name he seemes to git,
> As that which quickly burnes the fingers touching it.

¶ *The Temperature.*

Nettle is of temperature dry, a little hot, scarse in the first degree: it is of thin and subtil parts; for it doth not therefore burne and sting by reason it is extreme hot, but because the downe of it is stiffe and hard, piercing like fine little prickles or stings, and entring into the skin: for if it be withered or boiled it stingeth not at all, by reason that the stiffenesse of the down is fallen away.

¶ *The Vertues.*

Nicander affirmeth, that it is a remedie against the venomous qualitie of Hemlocke, Mushroms, and Quicksilver.

And *Apollodorus* saith that it is a counterpoison for Henbane, Serpents, and Scorpions.

Pliny saith, the same Author writeth, that the oile of it takes away the sting that the Nettle it selfe maketh.

CHAP. 106. *Of Betony.*

¶ *The Description.*

1   BEtony groweth up with long leaves and broad, of a darke greene colour, slightly indented about the edges like a saw. The stalke is slender, foure square, somewhat rough, a foot high more or lesse. It beareth eared floures, of a purplish colour, and sometimes reddish; after the floures, commeth in place long cornered seed. The root consisteth of many strings.

2   Betony with white floures is like the precedent in each respect, saving that the flours of this plant are white, and of greater beautie, and the others purple or red as aforesaid.

¶ *The Place.*

Betony loves shadowie woods, hedge-rowes, and copses, the borders of pastures, and such like places.

Betony with white floures is seldome seene. I found it in a wood by a Village called Hampstead, neere unto a Worshipfull Gentlemans house, one of the Clerkes of the Queenes counsell called M^r. *Wade*, from whence I brought plants for my Garden, where they flourish as in their naturall place of growing.

¶ *The Vertues.*

Betony is good for them that be subject to the falling sickenesse, and for those also that have ill heads upon a cold cause.

It maketh a man to have a good stomacke and appetite to his meate.

It is also good for ruptures, cramps, and convulsions: it is a remedy against the biting of mad dogs and venomous serpents, being drunk, and also applied to the hurts, and is most singular against poyson.

It is commended against the paine of the Sciatica, or ache of the huckle bone.

There is a conserve made of the floures and sugar good for many things, and especially for the head-ache.

(246)

Chap. 107. *Of Vervaine.*

¶ *The Description.*

1 THe stalke of upright Vervaine riseth from the root single, cornered, a foot high, seldome above a cubit, and afterwards divided into many branches. The leaves are long, greater than those of the Oke, but with bigger cuts and deeper: the floures along the sprigs are little, blew, or white, orderly placed: the root is long, with strings growing on it.

2 Creeping Vervaine sendeth forth stalkes like unto the former, now and then a cubit long, cornered, more slender, for the most part lying upon the ground. The leaves are like the former, but with deeper cuts, and more in number. The floures at the tops of the sprigs are blew, and purple withall, very small as those of the last described, and placed after the same manner and order. The root groweth straight downe, being slender and long, as is also the root of the former.

2 Verbena sacra.
Holy Veruaine.

¶ *The Place.*

Both of them grow in untilled places neere unto hedges, high-waies, and commonly by ditches almost every where. ‡ I have not seene the second, and doubt it is not to be found wilde in England. ‡

¶ *The Time.*

The Vervaines floure in July and August.

¶ *The Names.*

Vervaine is called in Latine, *Verbena*, and *Sacra herba*: *Verbenæ* are any manner of herbes that were taken from the Altar, or from some holy place, which because the Consull or Pretor did cut up, they were likewise called *Sagmina*, which oftentimes are mentioned

in *Livy* to be grassie herbes cut up in the Capitoll. In English, Juno's
teares, Mercuries moist bloud, Holy-herbe; and of some, Pigeons
grasse, or Columbine, because pigeons are delighted to be amongst
it, as also to eat thereof, as *Apuleius* writeth.

¶ *The Vertues.*

It is reported to be of singular force against the Tertian and
Quartaine Fevers: but you must observe mother *Bombies* rules, to
take just so many knots or sprigs, and no more, lest it fall out so that
it do you no good, if you catch no harme by it. Many odde old wives
fables are written of Vervaine tending to witchchraft and sorcery,
which you may reade elsewhere, for I am not willing to trouble your
eares with reporting such trifles, as honest eares abhorre to heare.

Most of the later Physitions do give the juice or decoction hereof
to them that have the plague: but these men are deceived, not only
in that they looke for some truth from the father of falshood and
leasings, but also because in stead of a good and sure remedy they
minister no remedy at all; for it is reported, that the Divell did
reveale it as a secret and divine medicine.

(247) CHAP. 108. *Of Scabious.*

¶ *The Description.*

1 THe first kinde of Scabious being the most common and
best knowne, hath leaves long and broad, of a grayish,
hoary, and hairy colour, spred abroad upon the ground,
among which rise up round and rough stems, beset with hairy jagged
leaves, in fashion like great Valerian, which we call Setwall. At the
top of the stalkes grow blew floures in thicke tufts or buttons. The
root is white and single.

2 Sheeps Scabious hath small and tender branches trailing upon
the ground, whereupon doe grow small leaves very finely jagged or
minced even almost to the middle ribbe, of an overworne colour.
The floures grow at the top of a blewish colour, consisting of much
thrummie matter, hard thrust together like a button: the root is
small, and creepeth in the ground.

¶ *The Place*.

These kindes of Scabious do grow in pastures, medowes, corn fields, and barren sandy grounds almost every where.

The strange sorts do grow in my garden, yet are they strangers in England.

¶ *The Time*.

They floure and flourish in the Summer moneths.

¶ *The Vertues*.

Scabious scoureth the chest and lungs; it is good against an old cough, shortnesse of breath, paine in the sides, and such like infirmities of the chest.

The later Herbarists do also affirm, that it is a remedy against the bitings of Serpents and stingings of venomous beasts, being outwardly applied or inwardly taken.

---

(248)

Chap. 109. *Of Divels bit*.

¶ *The Description*.

Divels bit hath small upright round stalkes of a cubite high, beset with long leaves somwhat broad, very little or nothing snipt about the edges, somwhat hairie and even. The floures also are of a dark purple colour, fashioned like the floures of Scabious: the seeds are smal and downy, which being ripe are carried away with the winde. The root is blacke, thick, hard and short, with many threddie strings fastned thereto. The great part of the root seemeth to be bitten away: old fantasticke charmers report, that the divel did bite it for envie, because it is an herbe that hath so many good vertues, and is so beneficial to mankinde.

¶ *The Place*.

Divels bit groweth in dry medows and woods, & about waies sides.

¶ *The Time.*

It floureth in August, and is hard to be knowne from Scabious, saving when it floureth.

Morſus Diaboli.
Diuels bit.

¶ *The Names.*

It is commonly called *Morsus Diaboli,* or Divels bit, of the root (as it seems) that is bitten off: for the superstitious people hold opinion, that the divell for envy that he beareth to mankinde, bit it off, because it would be otherwise good for many uses.

¶ *The Vertues.*

There is no better thing against old swellings of the Almonds, and upper parts of the throat that be hardly ripened.

It clenseth away slimie flegme that sticketh in the jawes, it digesteth and consumeth it: and it quickely taketh away the swellings in those parts, if the decoction thereof bee often held in the mouth and gargarized, especially if a little quantitie of *Mel Rosarum,* or honie of Roses be put into it.

---

(251) CHAP. 110. *Of the Blew-Bottle or Corne-Floure.*

¶ *The Description.*

1 THe great Blew-Bottle hath long leaves smooth, soft, downy, and sharp pointed: among the leaves rise up crooked and pretty thicke branches, chamfered, furrowed, and garnished with such leaves as are next the ground: on the tops wherof stand faire blew flours tending to purple, consisting of divers little flours, set in a scaly huske or knap like those of Knapweed: the seed is rough or bearded at one end, smooth at the other and shining: the root is tough and long lasting (contrary to the rest of the Corne-

floures) and groweth yearly into new shoots whereby it greatly encreaseth.

2   The common Corn-floure hath leaves spred upon the ground,
of a whitish green colour, somwhat hackt or cut in the edges like
those of corne Scabious: among which riseth up a stalke divided into
divers small branches, whereon do grow long leaves of an overworne
green colour, with few cuts or none at all. The floures grow at the
top of the stalks, of a blew colour, consisting of many smal floures set
in a scaly or chaffie head like those of the Knapweeds: the seed is
smooth, bright shining, and wrapped in a woolly or flocky matter.
The root is small and single, and perisheth when it hath perfected his
seed.

3   This Bottle is like to the last described in each respect, saving
in the colour of the floures, which are purple, wherein consisteth the
difference.

4   The fourth Bottle is also like the precedent, not differing in
any point but in the floures; for as the last before mentioned are of a
purple colour, contrariwise these are milke white, which sets forth the
difference.

¶ *The Place.*

The first groweth in my garden, and in the gardens of Herbarists,
but not wilde that I know of. The others grow in corn fields among
Wheat, Rie, Barley, and other graine: it is sowne in gardens, and by
cunning looking to doth oft times become of other colours, and some
also double, as hath beene touched in their severall descriptions.

¶ *The Time.*

They bring forth their floures from the beginning of May to the
end of Harvest.

¶ *The Names.*

The old Herbarists call it *Cyanus flos*, of the blew colour which it
naturally hath: in Italian, *Baptisecula*, as though it should be called
Blaptisecula, because it hindereth and annoyeth the Reapers, by
dulling and turning the edges of their sicles in reaping of corne: in
English it is called Blew-Bottle, Blew-Blow, Corne-floure, and hurt-
Sicle.

¶ *The Temperature and Vertues.*

The faculties of these floures are not yet sufficiently known. Sith there is no use of them in physicke, we will leave the rest that might be said to a further consideration: notwithstanding some have thought the common Blew-Bottle to be of temperature something cold, and therefore good against the inflammation of the eyes, as some thinke.

(252)   CHAP. 111. *Of Goats Beard, or Go to bed at noone.*

¶ *The Description.*

1   GOats-beard, or Go to bed at noone hath hollow stalks, smooth, and of a whitish green colour, whereupon do grow long leaves crested downe the middle with a swelling rib, sharp pointed, yeelding a milkie juice when it is broken, in shape like those of Garlick: from the bosome of which leaves thrust forth smal tender stalks, set with the like leaves, but lesser: the floures grow at the top of the stalks, consisting of a number of purple leaves, dasht over as it were with a little yellow dust, set about with nine or ten sharp pointed green leaves: the whole floure resembles a Star when it is spred abroad; for it shutteth it selfe at twelve of the clock, and sheweth not his face open untill the next daies Sunne doth make it floure anew, whereupon it was called Go to bed at noone: when these floures be come to their full maturitie and ripenesse, they grow into a downy Blowball like those of Dandelion, which is carried away with the winde.

Tragopogon luteum.
Yellow Goats-beard.

2   The yellow Goats beard hath the like leaves, stalks, root, seed, and downie blow-balls that the other hath, and also yeeldeth the like quantitie of milke, insomuch that if the pilling while it is greene be pulled from the stalks, the milky juice followeth: but when it hath there remained

a little while it waxeth yellow. The floures hercof are of a gold yellow colour, and have not such long green leaves to garnish it withall, wherein consisteth the difference.

¶ *The Place.*

The first growes not wild in England that I could ever see or heare of, except in Lancashire on the banks of the river Chalder, neere to my Lady *Heskiths* house, two miles from Whawley: it is sown in gardens for the beauty of the floures almost every where. The other growes plentifully in most of the fields about London, and in divers other places.

¶ *The Time.*

They floure and flourish from the beginning of June to the end of August.

¶ *The Names.*

Goats-beard is called in English, Josephs floure, Star of Jerusalem, Noon tide, and Go to bed at noone.

¶ *The Vertues.*

The roots of Goats-beard boiled in wine and drunk, asswageth the pain and pricking stitches of the sides.

The same boiled in water untill they be tender, and buttered as parsneps and carrots, are a most pleasant and wholesome meate, in delicate taste far surpassing either Parsenep or Carrot: which meat procures appetite, and strengthneth those that have been sicke of a long lingring disease.

(254)

Chap. 112. *Of Marigolds.*

¶ *The Description.*

1   THe greatest double Marigold hath many large, fat, broad leaves, springing immediatly from a fibrous or threddy root; the upper sides of the leaves are of a deepe greene, and the lower side of a more light and shining greene: among which

rise up stalkes somewhat hairie, and also somewhat joynted, and full of a spungeous pith. The floures in the top are beautifull, round, very large and double, something sweet, with a certaine strong smell, of a light saffron colour, or like pure gold: from the which follow a number of long crooked seeds, especially the outmost, or those that stand about the edges of the floure; which being sowne commonly bring forth single floures, whereas contrariwise those seeds in the middle are lesser, and for the most part bring forth such floures as that was from whence it was taken.

Calendula major polyanthos.
The great double Marigold.

2 This fruitfull or much bearing Marigold is likewise called of the vulgar sort of women, Jacke-an-apes on horse backe: it hath leaves, stalkes, and roots like the common sort of Marigold, differing in the shape of his floures, for this plant doth bring forth at the top of the stalke one floure like the other Marigolds; from the which start forth sundry other small floures, yellow likewise, and of the same fashion as the first, which if I be not deceived commeth to passe *per accidens*, or by chance, as Nature oftentimes liketh to play with other floures, or as children are borne with two thumbes on one hand, and such like, which living to be men, do get children like unto others; even so is the seed of this Marigold, which if it be sowen, it brings forth not one floure in a thousand like the plant from whence it was taken.

¶ The Time.

The Marigold floureth from Aprill or May even untill Winter, and in Winter also, if it bee warme.

¶ The Names.

The Marigold is called *Calendula*: it is to be seene in floure in the Calends almost of every moneth: it is also called *Chrysanthemum*, of his golden colour.

Columella in his tenth booke of Gardens hath these words;

> Stock-Gillofloures exceeding white,
> And Marigolds most yellow bright.

¶ *The Vertues.*

The floures and leaves of Marigolds being distilled, and the water dropped into red and watery eies, ceaseth the inflammation, and taketh away the paine.

Conserve made of the floures and sugar taken in the morning fasting, cureth the trembling of the heart.

The yellow leaves of the floures are dried and kept throughout Dutchland against Winter, to put into broths, in Physicall potions, and for divers other purposes, in such quantity, that in some Grocers or Spice-sellers houses are to be found barrels filled with them, and retailed by the penny more or lesse, insomuch that no broths are well made without dried Marigolds.

(258)

Chap. 113. *Of African Marigold.*

¶ *The Description.*

1 THe common Africane, or as they vulgarly terme it French Marigold, hath small weake and tender branches trailing upon the ground, reeling and leaning this way and that way, beset with leaves consisting of many particular leaves, indented about the edges, which being held up against the sunne, or to the light, are seene to be full of holes like a sieve, even as those of Saint Johns woort: the floures stand at the top of the springy branches forth of long cups or husks, consisting of eight or ten small leaves, yellow underneath, on the upper side of a deeper yellow tending to the colour of a darke crimson velvet, as also soft in handling: but to describe the colour in words, it is not possible, but this way; lay upon paper with a pensill a yellow colour called Masticot, which being dry, lay the same over with a little saffron steeped in water or wine, which setteth forth most lively the colour. The whole plant is of a most ranke and unwholesome smell, and perisheth at the first frost.

¶ *The Nature and Vertues.*

The unpleasant smel, especially of that common sort with single floures doth shew that it is of a poisonsome and cooling qualitie; and also the same is manifested by divers experiments: for I remember, saith *Dodonæus,* that I did see a boy whose lippes and mouth when hee began to chew the floures did swell extreamely; as it hath often happened unto them, that playing or piping with quils or kexes of Hemlockes, do hold them a while betweene their lippes: likewise he saith, we gave to a cat the floures with their cups, tempered with fresh cheese, shee forthwith mightily swelled, and a little while after died: also mice that have eaten of the seed thereof have been found dead. All which things doe declare that this herbe is of a venomous and poysonsome facultie; and that they are not to be hearkened unto, that suppose this herb to be a harmlesse plant: so to conclude, these plants are most venomous and full of poison, and therefore not to be touched or smelled unto, much lesse used in meat or medicine.

(259) ## Chap. 114. *Of the Floure of the Sun, or the Marigold of Peru.*

¶ *The Description.*

1   THe Indian Sun, or the golden floure of Peru, is a plant of such stature and talnesse, that in one summer, beeing sowne of a seed in Aprill, it hath risen up to the height of fourteene foot in my garden, where one floure was in weight three pound and two ounces, & crosse overthwart the floure by measure sixteen inches broad. The stalks are upright & straight, of the big-nesse of a strong mans arme, beset with large leaves even to the top, like unto the great Clot bur: at the top of the stalk commeth forth for the most part one floure, yet many times there spring out sucking buds which come to no perfection: this great floure is in shape like to the Camomil floure, beset round about with a pale or border of goodly yellow leaves, in shape like the leaves of the floures of white Lillies: the middle part whereof is made as it were of unshorn velvet, or some curious cloath wrought with the needle: which brave worke,

if you do thorowly view and marke well, it seemeth to be an in-
numerable sort of small floures, resembling the nose or nosle of a
candlestick broken from the foot thereof; from which small nosle
sweats forth excellent fine and cleare turpentine, in sight, substance,
savor, and tast. The whole plant in like manner being broken
smelleth of turpentine: when the plant groweth to maturitie the
floures fall away, in place whereof appeareth the seed, black and
large, much like the seed of Gourds, set as though a cunning work-
man had of purpose placed them in very
good order, much like the hony-combs of
Bees.

Flos Solis maior.
The greater sun-floure.

¶ *The Place.*

These plants grow of themselves without setting or sowing, in Peru, and in
divers other provinces of America, from
whence the seeds have beene brought into
these parts of Europ. There hath bin seen
in Spain and other hot regions a plant
sowne and nourished up from seed, to
attaine to the height of 24 foot in one yeare.

¶ *The Time.*

The seed must be set or sowne in the
beginning of April, if the weather be temperat, in the most fertill ground that may
be, and where the Sun hath most power the
whole day.

¶ *The Names.*

The flour of the Sun is called in Latine *Flos Solis*, for that some
have reported it to turn with the Sun, which I could never observe,
although I have indeavored to finde out the truth of it: but I rather
thinke it was so called because it resembles the radiant beams of the
Sunne, whereupon some have called it *Corona Solis*, and *Sol Indianus*,
the Indian Sunne-floure: others, *Chrysanthemum Peruvianum*, or the
Golden floure of Peru: in English, the floure of the Sun, or the Sun-
floure.

¶ *The Vertues.*

There hath not any thing bin set down either of the antient or later writers, concerning the vertues of these plants, notwithstanding we have found by triall, that the buds before they be floured boiled and eaten with butter, vineger, and pepper, after the manner of Artichokes, are exceeding pleasant meat.

(260) ## Chap. 115. *Of Jerusalem Artichoke.*

ONe may wel by the English name of this plant perceive, that those that vulgarly give names to plants, have little either judgement or knowledge of them: for this plant hath no similitude in leafe, stalke, root, or manner of growing, with an Artichoke, but only a little likenesse of taste in the dressed root; neither came it from Jerusalem, or out of Asia, but out of America: whence *Fabius Columna* one of the first setters of it forth, fitly names it *Aster Peruvianus tuberosus*, and *Flos Solis Farnesianus*, because it so much resembles the *Flos Solis*, and for that he first observed it growing in the garden of Cardinal *Farnesius*, who had procured roots thereof from the West Indies. Also our countryman Mr *Parkinson* hath exactly delivered the historie of this by the name of *Battatas de Canada*, Englishing it Potatoes of Canada: now al these that have written and mentioned it bring it from America, but from far different places, as from Peru, Brasill, and Canada: but this is not much materiall, seeing it now growes so well and plentifully in so many places of England. I will therefore deliver you the historie as I have received it from my oft mentioned friend Mr *Goodyer*, who, as you may see by the date, tooke it presently upon the first arrivall into England.

¶ *The Description.*

THis wonderfull encreasing plant hath growing up from one root, one, somtimes two, three, or more round greene rough hairy straked stalks, commonly about twelve foot high, somtimes sixteene foot or higher, as big as a childes arme, full of white spongeous pith within. The leaves grow all alongst the stalkes out of order, of a light greene colour, rough, sharpe pointed, about 8 inches broad, and ten or eleven inches long, deeply notched or indented about the edges, very like the leaves of the common *Flos solis Peruanus*, but nothing crumpled, and not so broad: the stalks divide themselves into many long branches even from the roots to their very tops, bearing leaves smaller and smaller toward the tops, making the herbe appear like a little tree, narrower and slenderer toward the top, in fashion of a steeple or pyramide. The floures with us grow onely at the tops of the stalks and branches, like those of the said *Flos solis*, but no bigger than our common single Marigold, consisting of twelve or thirteen straked sharpe pointed bright yellow bordering leaves, growing forth of a scaly small hairy head, with a small yellow thrummy matter within. These floures by reason of their late flouring, which is commonly two or three weekes after Michaelmasse, never bring their seed to perfection; and it maketh shew of abundance of smal heads neere the tops of the stalkes and branches, forth of the bosoms of the leaves, which never open and floure with us, by reason they are destroyed with the frosts, which otherwise it seemeth would be a goodly spectacle.

Flos solis Pyramidalis.
Ierufalem Artichoke.

¶ *The Place.*

Where this plant groweth naturally I know not. In *An.* 1617 I received two small roots thereof from Mᵣ *Franqueuill* of London, no bigger than hens egges; the one I planted, and the other I gave to a friend: myne brought me a pecke of roots, wherewith I stored Hampshire.

¶ *The Vertues.*

These roots are dressed divers wayes, some boile them in water, and after stew them with sacke and butter, adding a little ginger. Others bake them in pies, putting Marrow, Dates, Ginger, Raisons of the sun, Sacke, &c. Others some other way as they are led by their skill in Cookerie. But in my judgement, which way soever they be drest and eaten, they are a meat more fit for swine, than men. 17 Octob. 1621. *John Goodyer.* ‡

Chap. 116. *Of Leopards bane.*

¶ *The Description.*

1 OF this plant *Doronicum*, there be sundry kindes. *Dodonæus* unproperly calleth it *Aconitum Pardalianches*, which hath hapned through the negligence of *Dioscorides* and *Theophrastus*, who in describing *Doronicum*, have not onely omitted the floures thereof, but have committed that negligence in many and divers other plants, leaving out in many plants which they have described, the speciall accidents; which hath not a little troubled the study and determination of the best Herbarists of late yeares, not knowing certainly what to determine and set downe in so ambiguous a matter, some taking it one way, and some another, and some esteeming it to be *Aconitum*. But for the better understanding hereof, know that this word *Aconitum*, as it is a name attributed to divers plants, so it is to be considered, that all plants called by this name are malignant and venomous, as with the juyce and root whereof such as hunted after wilde and noysome beasts, were woont to embrue and dip their arrowes, the sooner and more surely to dispatch and slay the beast in chase. But for the proofe of the goodnesse of this *Doronicum*, and the rest of his kinde, know also, That *Lobel* writeth of one called *John de Vroëde*, who ate very many of the roots at sundry times, and found them very pleasant in tast, and very comfortable. But to leave controversies, circumstances, and objections which here might be brought in and alledged, assure your selves that this plant *Doronicum minus Officinarum* (whose roots *Pena* reporteth he found plentifully growing upon the Pede-mountaine hills and certaine high places in France) hath many leaves spred upon the ground, somwhat like Plantaine: among which rise up many tender hairy stalks some handfull and an halfe high, bearing at the top certaine single yellow floures, which when they fade change into downe, and are carried away with the wind. The roots are thick and many, very crookedly crossing and tangling one within another, resembling a Scorpion, and in some yeares do grow in our English gardens into infinite numbers.

¶ *The Time.*

They floure in the months of June and July.

¶ *The Nature and Vertues.*

I have sufficiently spoken of that for which I have warrant to write, both touching their natures and vertues; for the matter hath continued so ambiguous and so doubtfull, yea, and so full of controversies, that I dare not commit that to the world which I have read: these few lines therefore shall suffice for this present; the rest which might be said I refer to the great and learned Doctors, and to your owne consideration.

These herbes are mixed with compound medicines that mitigate the paine of the eies, and by reason of his cold quality, being fresh and greene, it helpeth the inflammation or fiery heate of the eyes.

It is reported and affirmed, that it killeth Panthers, Swine, Wolves, and all kinds of wilde beasts, being giving them with flesh, *Theophrastus* saith, That it killeth Cattell, Sheep, Oxen, and all fourefooted beasts, within the compasse of one day. Yet hee writeth further, That the root being drunke is a remedy against the stinging of Scorpions; which sheweth, that this herbe or the root thereof is not deadly to man, but to divers beasts only: which thing also is found out by triall and manifest experience; for *Conrade Gesner* (a man in our time singularly learned, and a most diligent searcher of many things) in a certaine Epistle written two *Adolphus Occo*, sheweth, That he himselfe hath oftentimes inwardly taken the root hereof greene, dry, whole, preserved with hony, and also beaten to pouder; and that even the very same day in which he wrote these things, he had drunke with warme water two drams of the roots made into fine pouder, neither felt he any hurt thereby: and that he oftentimes also had given the same to his sicke Patients, both by it selfe, and also mixed with other things, and that very luckily. Moreover, the Apothecaries in stead of *Doronicum* doe use (though amisse) the roots thereof without any manifest danger.

That this *Aconite* killeth dogs, it is very certaine, and found out by triall: which thing *Matthiolus* could hardly beleeve, but that at length he found it out to be true by a manifest example, as he confesseth in his Commentaries.

CHAP. 117. *Of Mullein.*

❡ *The Description.*

1 THe male Mullein or Higtaper hath broad leaves, very soft, whitish and downy; in the midst of which riseth up a stalk, straight, single, and the same also whitish all over, with a hoary down, and covered with the like leaves, but lesser and

Tapfus barbatus flore albo.
White floured Mullein.

lesser even to the top; among which taperwise are set a multitude of yellow floures consisting of five leaves apiece: in the places wherof come up little round vessels, in which is contained very small seed. The root is long, a finger thicke, blacke without, and full of strings.

2 The female Mullein hath likewise many white woolly leaves, set upon an hoary cottony upright stalke of the height of foure or five cubits: the top of the stalke resembleth a torch decked with infinite white floures, which is the speciall marke to know it from the male kinde, being like in every other respect.

❡ *The Place.*

These plants grow of themselves neere the borders of pastures, plowed fields, or causies & dry sandy ditch banks, and in other untilled places. They grow in great plenty neere unto a lyme-kiln upon the end of Blacke heath next to London, as also about the Queenes house at Eltham neere to Dartford in Kent; in the highwayes about Highgate neere London, and in most countries of England that are of a sandy soile.

❡ *The Time.*

They are found with their floure from July to September, and bring forth their seed the second yeare after it is sowne.

¶ *The Names.*

Mullein is called in shops, *Tapsus Barbatus*: of divers, *Candela Regia*, *Candelaria*, and *Lanaria*: in French, *Bouillon*: in English, Mullein, or rather Woollen, Higtaper, Torches, Longwort, and Bullocks Longwort; and of some, Hares beard.

¶ *The Vertues.*

The country people, especially the husbandmen in Kent, do give their cattel the leaves to drink against the cough of the lungs, being an excellent approved medicine for the same, wherupon they call it Bullocks Lungwort.

The report goeth (saith *Pliny*) that figs do not putrifie at all that are wrapped in the leaves of Mullein.

---

(273)

Chap. 118. *Of Cowslips.*

¶ *The Description.*

1   THose herbs which at this day are called Primroses, Cowslips, and Oxlips, are reckoned among the kindes of Mulleins; notwithstanding for distinctions sake I have marshalled them in a chapter, comming in the rereward as next neighbors to the Mulleins, for that the Antients have named them *Verbasculi*, that is to say, small Mulleins. The first, which is called in English the field Cowslip, is as common as the rest, therefore I shal not need to spend much time about the description.

2   The second is likewise well knowne by the name of Oxlip, and differeth not from the other save that the floures are not so thicke thrust together, and they are fairer, and not so many in number, and do not smell so pleasant as the other: of which kind we have one lately come into our gardens, whose floures are curled and wrinkled after a most strange maner, which our women have named Jack-anapes on horsebacke.

3   Double Paigle, called of *Pena*, *Primula hortensis Anglica omnium maxima*, & *serotina floribus plenis*; that is, The greatest

English garden Cowslip with double yellow floures, is so commonly knowne that it needeth no description.

4   The fourth is likewise known by the name of double Cowslips, having but one floure within another, which maketh the same once double, where the other is many times double, called by *Pena*,

Primula veris maior.   Primula veris minor.
Field Cowflips.   Field Primrofe.

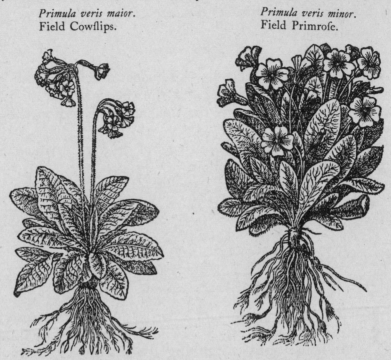

Geminata, for the likenesse of the floures, which are brought forth as things against nature, or twinnes.

5   The fifth being the common whitish yellow field Primrose, needeth no description.

6   The sixth, which is our garden double Primrose, of all the rest is of greatest beauty, the description whereof I refer unto your owne consideration.

7   The seventh is also very well known, being a Primrose with greenish floures somwhat welted about the edges.

¶ *The Place.*

Cowslips and Primroses joy in moist and dankish places, but not altogether covered with water: they are found in woods and the borders of fields.

¶ *The Time.*

They flourish from Aprill to the end of May, and some one or other of them do floure all Winterlong.

¶ *The Names.*

They are commonly called *Primula veris*, because they are the first among those plants that doe floure in the Spring, or because they floure with the first.

Primula veris flore rubro.
Red Bird-eyne.

The greater sort, called for the most part Oxlips or Paigles, are named of divers *Herba S. Petri*: in English, Oxlip, and Paigle.

¶ *The Vertues.*

A practitioner of London who was famous for curing the phrensie, after he had performed his cure by the due observation of physick, accustomed every yeare in the moneth of May to dyet his Patients after this manner: Take the leaves and floures of Primrose, boile them a little in fountaine water, and in some rose and Betony waters, adding thereto sugar, pepper, salt, and butter, which being strained, he gave them to drinke thereof first and last.

The roots of Primrose stamped and strained, and the juice sniffed into the nose with a quill or such like, purgeth the brain, and qualifieth the pain of the megrim.

An unguent made with the juice of Cowslips and oile of Linseed, cureth all scaldings or burnings with fire, water, or otherwise.

(275) Chap. 119. *Of Beares eares, or mountaine Cowslips.*

¶ *The Kindes.*

THere be divers sorts of Mountaine Cowslips, or Beares-eares, differing especially in the colour of their floures, notwithstanding it may appeare to the curious, that there is great difference in the roots also, considering some of them have knobbed roots, and others threddy: notwithstanding there is no difference in the roots at all.

¶ *The Description.*

AUricula Ursi was called of *Matthiolus, Pena,* and other Herbarists, *Sanicula Alpina,* by reason of his singular faculty in healing of wounds, both inward and outward. They doe all call it *Paralytica,* because of his vertues in curing the palsies, cramps, and convulsions, and is numbred among the kindes of Cowslips, whereof no doubt they are kindes as others are which do hereafter follow under the same title, although there be some difference in the colour of the floures. This beautifull and brave plant hath thicke, greene, and fat leaves, somewhat finely snipt about the edges, not altogether unlike those of Cowslips, but smoother, greener, and nothing rough or crumpled: among which riseth up a slender round stem a handfull high, bearing a tuft of floures at the top, of a faire yellow colour, not much unlike to the floures of Oxe-lips, but more open and consisting of one only leafe like Cotiledon: the root is very threddy, and like unto the Oxe-lip.

¶ *The Place.*

They grow naturally upon the Alpish and Helvetian mountaines: most of them do grow in our London Gardens.

¶ *The Time.*

These herbes do floure in Aprill and May.

¶ *The Names.*

Either the antient writers knew not these plants, or else the names of them were not by them or their successors diligently committed unto posterity. *Matthiolus* and other later writers have given names according to the similitude, or of the shape that they beare unto other plants, according to the likenesse of the qualities and operations: you may call it in English, Beares-eare: they that dwell about the Alpes doe call it by reason of the effects thereof; for the root is amongst them in great request for the strengthning of the head, that when they are on the tops of places that are high, giddinesse and the swimming of the braine may not afflict them: it is there called the Rocke-Rose, for that it groweth upon the rockes, and resembleth the brave colour of the rose.

¶ *The Vertues.*

Those that hunt in the Alps and high mountaines after Goats and bucks, do as highly esteeme hereof as of *Doronicum*, by reason of the singular effects that it hath, but (as I said before) one especially, even in that it preventeth the losse of their best joynts (I meane their neckes) if they take the roots hereof before they ascend the rocks or other high places.

---

(277)   CHAP. 120. *Of Fox-Gloves.*

¶ *The Description.*

1   FOx-glove with the purple floure is most common; the leaves whereof are long, nicked in the edges, of a light greene, in manner like those of Mullein, but lesser, and not so downy: the stalke is straight, from the middle whereof to the top stand the floures, set in a course one by another upon one side of the stalke, hanging downwards with the bottome upward, in forme long, like almost to finger stalkes, whereof it tooke his name *Digitalis*, of a red purple colour, with certaine white spots dasht within the floure; after which come up round heads, in which lies the seed somewhat browne, and as small as that of Time. The roots are many slender strings.

2   The Fox-Glove with white floures differs not from the precedent but in the colour of the floures; for as the other were purple, these contrariwise are of a milke-white colour.

3   We have in our Gardens another sort hereof, which bringeth

Digitalis purpurea.
Purple Fox-gloues.

forth most pleasant yellow floures, and somewhat lesser than the common kinde, wherein they differ.

¶ *The Place.*

Fox-glove groweth in barren sandy grounds, and under hedges almost every where.

¶ *The Time.*

They floure and flourish in June and July.

¶ *The Names.*

Fox-gloves some call in French, *Gantes nostre dame.*

¶ *The Temperature.*

The Fox-gloves in that they are bitter, are hot and dry, with a certaine kinde of clensing qualitie joyned therewith; yet are they of no use, neither have they any place amongst medicines, according to the Antients.

---

(278)   CHAP. 121. *Of Baccharis out of* Dioscorides.

¶ *The Description.*

1   ABout this plant *Baccharis* there hath beene great contention amongst the new Writers; *Matthiolus* and *Dodonæus* have mistaken this plant, for *Coniza major,* *Virgil* and *Athæneus* have confounded *Baccharis,* and *Azarum* together: but following the antient Writers, it hath many blackish rough leaves, somwhat bigger than the leaves of Primrose: amongst which riseth up a stalke two cubits high, bearing at the top little chaffie or scalie floures in small bunches, of a darke yellowish or purple colour, which turne into downe, and are carried away with the winde, like unto the kindes of Thistles: the root is thicke, grosse,

and fat, spreading about in the earth, full of strings: the fragrant smell that the root of this plant yeeldeth, may well be compared unto the savour of Cinnamon, *Helenium*, or *Enula Campana*, being a plant knowne unto very many or most sort of people, I meane in most parts of England.

¶ *The Place.*

Baccharis delighteth to grow in rough and craggy places, and in a leane soile where no moisture is: it groweth very plentifully about Montpellier in France, and divers places in the West parts of England.

¶ *The Time.*

It springeth up in April, it floureth in June, and perfecteth his seed in August.

¶ *The Names.*

The learned Herbarists of Montpellier have called this plant *Baccharis*. In English it may be called the Cinamom root, or Plowmans Spiknard: *Virgil* in his seventh Ecloge of his Bucolicks maketh mention of *Baccharis*, and doth not onely shew that it is a Garland plant, but also such a one as prevaileth against inchantments, saying,

> With Plowmans Nard my forehead girt,
> Lest evill tongue thy Poët hurt.

Baccharis is likewise an ointment in *Athenæus*, in his 15. booke, which may take his name of the sweet herbe *Baccharis*: for as *Pliny* writeth, *Aristophanes* of old, being an antient comical Poët witnesseth, that ointments were wont to bee made of the root thereof: to bee briefe, *Cratevas*, his *Asarum* is the same that *Dioscorides* his *Baccharis* is. ‡ This plant here described is the *Coniza major* of *Matthiolus*, *Tragus*, and others. ‡

¶ *The Vertues.*

Baccharis is a singular remedy to heale inflammations, and the smell thereof provoketh sleepe.

When it is boiled in wine, it is given with great profit against the biting of Scorpions, or any venomous beast, being implaistered and applied thereto.

CHAP. 122. *Of Dittany.*

❧ *The Description.*

I DIttanie of Crete now called Candie (as *Dioscorides* saith) is a hot and sharpe hearbe, much like unto Penni-Royall, saving that his leaves be greater and somewhat hoary, covered over with a soft downe or white woollie cotton: at the top of the branches grow small spikie eares or scaly aglets, hanging by little small stemmes, resembling the spiky tufts of Marjerome, of a white colour: amongst which scales there do come forth small floures like the flouring of Wheat, of a red purple colour; which being past, the knop is found full of small seed, contrary to the saying of *Dioscorides*, who saith, it neither beareth floure nor seed, but my selfe have seene it beare both in my Garden: the whole plant perished in the next Winter following.

❧ *The Place.*

The first Dittany commeth from Crete, an Island which we call Candie, where it growes naturally: I have seene it in my garden, where it hath floured and borne seed; but it perished by reason of the injury of our extraordinary cold Winter that then happened: nevertheless *Dioscorides* writeth against all truth, that it neither beareth floures nor seed.

❧ *The Vertues.*

The juyce taken with wine is a remedy against the stinging of serpents.

The same is thought to be of so strong an operation, that with the very smell also it drives away venomous beasts, and doth astonish them.

It is reported likewise that the wilde Goats or Deere in Candy when they be wounded with arrowes, do shake them out by eating of this plant, and heale their wounds.

It prevaileth much against all wounds, and especially those made with invenomed weapons, arrowes shot out of guns, or such like, and is very profitable for Chirurgians that use the sea and land wars, to carry with them and have in readinesse: it draweth forth also splinters of wood, bones, or such like.

Chap. 123. *Of Borage.*

¶ *The Description.*

1 BOrage hath broad leaves, rough, lying flat upon the ground, of a blacke or swart green colour: among which riseth up a stalke two cubits high, divided into divers branches, whereupon do grow gallant blew floures, composed of five leaves apiece; out of the middle of which grow forth blacke threds joined in the top, and pointed like a broch or pyramide: the root is threddy.

2 Borage with white floures is like unto the precedent, but differeth in the floures, for those of this plant are white, and other of a perfect blew colour, wherein is the difference.

¶ *The Place.*

These grow in my garden and in others also.

¶ *The Time.*

Borage floures and flourishes most part of all Summer, and till Autumne be far spent.

¶ *The Names.*

Borage is called in shops *Borago*: *Pliny* calleth it *Euphrosinum*, because it makes a man merry and joyfull: which thing also the old verse concerning Borage doth testifie:

Ego Borago gaudia semper ago.
I Borage bring alwaies courage.

¶ *The Vertues.*

Those of our time do use the floures in sallads, to exhilerate and make the minde glad. There be also many things made of them, used for the comfort of the heart, to drive away sorrow, & increase the joy of the minde.

The leaves and floures of Borrage put into wine make men and women glad and merry, driving away all sadnesse, dulnesse, and melancholy, as *Dioscorides* and *Pliny* affirme.

Syrrup made of the floures of Borrage comforteth the heart, purgeth melancholy, and quieteth the phrenticke or lunaticke person.

The floures of Borrage made up with sugar, do all the aforesaid with greater force and effect.

Syrrup made of the juice of Borrage with sugar, adding thereto pouder of the bone of a Stags heart, is good against swouning, the cardiacke passion of the heart, against melancholy and the falling sicknesse.

The root is not used in medicine: the leaves eaten raw ingender good bloud, especially in those that have bin lately sicke.

---

(284)　CHAP. 124. *Of Alkanet or wilde Buglosse.*

¶ *The Description.*

THese herbes comprehended under the name of *Anchusa*, were so called of the Greeke word that is, to colour or paint any thing: Whereupon those plants were called *Anchusa*, of that flourishing and bright red colour which is in the root, even as red as pure and cleare bloud.

1　The first kinde of Alkanet hath many leaves like *Echium* or small Buglosse, covered over with a pricky hoarinesse, having commonly but one stalke, which is round, rough, and a cubit high. The cups of the floures are of a sky colour tending to purple, not unlike the floures of *Echium*: the seed is small, somwhat long, and of a pale colour: the root is a finger thicke, the pith or inner part thereof is of a wooddy substance, dying the hands or whatsoever toucheth the same, of a bloudy colour, or of the colour of Sanders.

2　The second kinde of *Anchusa* or Alkanet is of greater beauty and estimation than the first, the branches are lesse and more bushy in the top; it hath also greater plenty of leaves, and those more woolly or hairy: the stalk groweth to the height of two cubits: at the top grow floures of a yellow colour, far different from the other: the root is more shining, of an excellent delicate purple colour, and more ful of juice than the first.

¶ *The Place.*

These plants do grow in the fields of Narbone, and about Montpellier, and many other parts of France: I found these plants growing in the Isle of Thanet neere unto the sea, betwixt the house sometime belonging to Sir *Henry Crispe*, and Margate; where I found some in their naturall ripenes, yet scarcely any that were come to that beautiful color of Alkanet: but such as is sold for very good in our Apothecaries shops I found there in great plenty.

‡ I doubt whether our Author found any of these in the place here set down, for I have sought it but failed of finding; yet if he found any it was only the first described, for I thinke the other three are strangers. ‡

¶ *The Time.*

The Alkanets floure and flourish in the Summer moneths: the roots doe yeeld their bloudy juyce in harvest time, as *Dioscorides* writeth.

¶ *The Vertues.*

Divers of the later Physitions do boile with the root of Alkanet and wine, sweet butter, such as hath in it no salt at all, untill such time as it becommeth red, which they call red butter, and give it not only to those that have falne from some high place, but also report it to be good to drive forth the measels and small pox, if it be drunke in the beginning with hot beere.

The roots of these are used to color sirrups, waters, gellies, & such like infections as Turnsole is.

John of *Ardern* hath set down a composition called *Sanguis Veneris*, which is most singular in deep punctures or wounds made with thrusts, as follows: take of oile olive a pint, the root of Alkanet two ounces, earth worms purged, in number twenty, boile them together & keep it to the use aforesaid.

The Gentlewomen of France do paint their faces with these roots, as it is said.

(290)   Chap. 125. *Of Colts-foot, or Horse-foot.*

¶ *The Description*

1   **T**Ussilago or Fole-foot hath many white and long creeping
roots, somewhat fat; from which rise up naked stalkes (in
the beginning of March and Aprill) about a spanne long,
bearing at the top yellow floures, which change into downe and are

Tuſsilago florens.
Colts-foot in floure

Tuſsilaginis folia.
The leaues of Colts-foot.

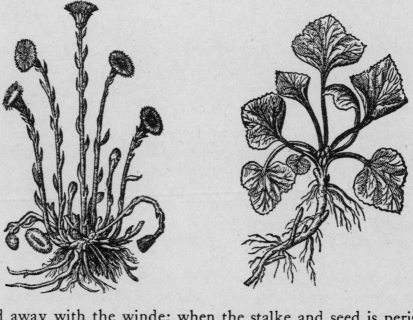

caried away with the winde: when the stalke and seed is perished,
there appeare springing of out the earth many broad leaves, greene
above, and next the ground of a white hoarie or grayish colour,
fashioned like an Horse foot; for which cause it was called Fole-
foot, and Horse-hoofe: seldome or never shall you find leaves and
floures at once, but the flours are past before the leaves come out of
the ground; as may appeare by the first picture, which setteth forth
the naked stalkes and floures; and by the second, which pourtraiteth
the leaves only.

¶ *The Place.*

This groweth of it selfe neere unto Springs, and on the brinkes of brookes and rivers, in wet furrowes, by ditches sides, and in other moist and watery places neere unto the sea, almost everywhere.

¶ *The Time.*

The floures which quickly fade, are to be seene in the end of March, and about the Calends of Aprill, which speedily wither together with the stems: after them grow forth the leaves, which remaine greene all Summer long: and hereupon it came that Colts-foot was thought to be without floures; which thing also *Pliny* hath mentioned in his six and twentieth booke, *cap.* 6.

¶ *The Names.*

Fole-foot is called in English, Folefoot, Colts-foot, Horse-hoofe, and Bull-foot.

¶ *The Vertues.*

A decoction made of the greene leaves and roots, or else a syrrup thereof, is good for the cough that proceedeth of a thin rheume.

The green leaves of Fole-foot pound with hony, do cure and heale inflammations.

The fume of the dried leaves taken through a funnell or tunnell, burned upon coles, effectually helpeth those that are troubled with the shortnesse of breath, and fetch their winde thicke and often.

Being taken in manner as they take Tobaco, it mightily prevaileth against the diseases aforesaid.

---

(295)   CHAP. 126. *Of Frogge-bit.*

¶ *The Description.*

THere floteth or swimmeth upon the upper parts of the water a small plant, which we usually call Frog-bit, having little round leaves, thicke and full of juyce, very like to the leaves of wall Peniwort: the floures grow upon long stems among the leaves, of a white colour, with a certain yellow thrum in the middle consisting of three leaves: in stead of roots it hath slender strings, which grow out of a short and small head, as it were, from whence the leaves spring, in the bottom of the water: from which head also come forth slopewise certain strings, by which growing forth it multiplieth it selfe.

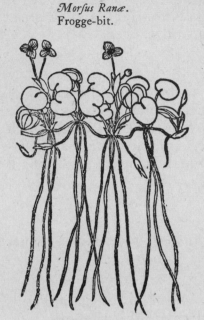

Morſus Ranæ.
Frogge-bit.

¶ *The Place.*

It is found swimming or floting almost in every ditch, pond, poole, or standing water, in all the ditches about Saint George his fields, and in the ditches by the Thames side neere to Lambeth Marsh, where any that is disposed may see it.

¶ *The Time.*

It flourisheth and floureth most part of all the yeare.

¶ *The Names.*

It is called of some *Ranæ morsus*, and *Morsus Ranæ*, and *Nymphæaparua.*

¶ *The Temperature and Vertues.*

It is thought to be a kinde of Pond-weed (or rather of Water Lillie) and to have the same faculties that belong unto it.

---

(298) Chap. 127. *Of Water Saligot, water Caltrops, or water Nuts.*

¶ *The Description.*

1   WAter Caltrops have long slender stalks growing up and rising from the bottom of the water, and mounting above the same: the root is long, having here & there under the water certaine tassels full of small strings or threddy haires: the stem towards the top of the water is very great in respect

of that which is lower; the leaves are large and somewhat round, not unlike those of the Poplar or Elme tree leaves, a little crevised or notched about the edges: amongst or under the leaves grow the fruit, which is triangled, hard, sharp pointed and prickly, in shape like those hurtfull engins in the wars, cast in the passage of the enemy to annoy the feet of their horses, called Caltrops, whereof this tooke it's name: within these heads or Nuts is contained a white kernell in taste almost like the Chesnut, which is reported to bee eaten green, and being dried and ground to serve in stead of bread.

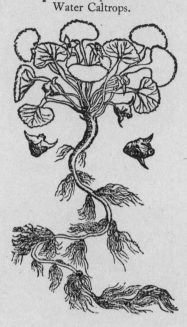

1   *Tribulus aquaticus.*
Water Caltrops.

¶ The Place.

Cordus saith that it groweth in Germanie in myrie lakes, and in city ditches that have mud in them: in Brabanc and other places of the Low countries it is found oftentimes in standing waters and springs. *Mathiolus* writeth, that it growes not only in lakes of sweet water, but also in certain ditches by the sea neere unto Venice.

CHAP. 128. *Of Ducks meat.*

¶ The Description.

DUcks meat is as it were a certain green mosse, with very little round leaves of the bignes of Lentils: out of the midst whereof on the nether side grow downe very fine threds like haires, which are to them in stead of roots: it hath neither stalke, floure, nor fruit.

¶ The Place.

It is found in ponds, lakes, city ditches, & other standing waters every where.

Lens paluſtris.
Duck's meat.

¶ *The Time.*

The time of Ducks meat is known to all.

¶ *The Names.*

Duckes meat is called Ducks herb, because Ducks do feed thereon; whereupon also it is called Ducks meat: some term it after the Greek, water Lentils.

¶ *The Vertues.*

Ducks meat mingled with fine wheaten floure, and applied, prevaileth much against hot Swellings.

(302)

CHAP. 129. *Of Water Crow-foot.*

¶ *The Description.*

WAter Crow-foot hath slender branches trailing far abroad, whereupon grow leaves under the water, most finely cut and jagged like those of Cammomill: those above the water are somwhat round, indented about the edges, in forme not unlike the smal tender leaves of the Mallow, but lesser: among which doe grow the floures, small, and white of colour, made of fine little leaves, with some yellownesse in the middle like the floures of the Strawberry, and of a sweet smell: after which there come round rough and prickly knaps like those of the field Crowfoot. The roots be very small hairy strings.

¶ *The Place.*

Water Crowfoot growes by ditches and shallow springs, and in other moist and plashy places.

¶ *The Time.*

It floureth in Aprill and May, and somtimes in June.

¶ *The Names.*

Water Crow-foot is called in Latine *Ranunculus aquatilis*, and *Polyanthemum aquatile*: in English, water Crow-foot, and white water

Ranunculus aquatilis.
Water Crow-foot.

Crow-foot. Most Apothecaries and Herbarists doe erroniously name it *Hepatica aquatica*, and *Hepatica alba*; and with greater error they mix it in medicines in stead of *Hepatica alba* or grasse of Parnassus. ‡ I know none that commit this great error here mentioned, neither have I knowne either the one or the other ever used or appointed in medicine with us in England; though *Dodonæus* (from whom our Author had this and most else) blame his countrymen for this mistake and error.

---

(304)   CHAP. 130. *Of Cuckow pint, or wake-Robin.*

¶ *The Description.*

1   *A Rum* or Cockow pint hath great, large, smooth, shining, sharpe pointed leaves, bespotted here and there with blackish spots, mixed with some blewnesse: among which riseth up a stalke nine inches long, bespeckled in many places with

certaine purple spots. It beareth also a certaine long hose or hood, in proportion like the eare of an hare: in the middle of which hood commeth forth a pestle or clapper of a darke murry or pale purple colour: which being past, there succeedeth in place thereof a bunch or cluster of berries in manner of a bunch of grapes, greene at the first, but after they be ripe of a yellowish red like corall, and full of juyce, wherein lie hid one or two little hard seeds. The root is tuberous, of the bignesse of a large Olive, white and succulent, with some threddy additaments annexed thereto.

¶ The Place.

Cockow pint groweth in woods neere unto ditches under hedges, every where in shadowie places.

¶ The Time.

The leaves appeare presently after Winter: the pestell sheweth it selfe out of his huske or sheath in June, whilest the leaves are in withering: and when they are gone, the bunch or cluster of berries becommeth ripe, which is in July and August.

¶ The Names.

In English, Cuckow pint, and Cuckow pintle, wake-Robin, Priests pintle, Aron, Calfes foot, and Rampe; and of some Starchwort.

¶ The Vertues.

Beares after they have lien in their dens forty daies without any manner of sustenance, but what they get with licking and sucking their owne feet, doe as soone as they come forth eat the herbe Cuckow-pint, through the windie nature thereof the hungry gut is opened and made fit againe to receive sustenance: for by abstaining from food so long a time, the gut is shrunke or drawne so close together, that in a manner it is quite shut up, as *Aristotle*, *Ælianus*, *Plutarch*, *Pliny*, and others do write.

The most pure and white starch is made of the roots of Cuckow-pint; but most hurtfull to the hands of the Laundresse that hath the handling of it, for it choppeth, blistereth, and maketh the hands rough and rugged, and withall smarting.

(310)

Chap. 131. *Of Sow-bread*.

¶ *The Description.*

1 THe first being the common kinde of Sow-bread, called in shops *Panis porcinus*, and *Arthanita*, hath many greene and round leaves like unto Asarabacca, saving that the upper part of the leaves are mixed here and there confusedly with white spots, and under the leaves next the ground of a purple colour: among which rise up little stemmes like unto the stalkes of violets, bearing at the top small purple floures, which turne themselves backward (being full blowne) like a Turks cap, or Tulepan, of a small sent or savour, or none at all: which being past, there succeed little round knops or heads which containe slender browne seeds: these knops are wrapped after a few daies in the small stalkes, as thred

‡ *Cyclamen Vernum.* Spring Sow-bread.

about a bottome, where it remaineth so defended from the injurie of Winter close upon the ground, covered also with the greene leaves aforesaid, by which meanes it is kept from the frost, even from the time of his seeding, which is in September, untill June: at which time the leaves doe fade away, the stalkes & seed remaining bare and naked, whereby it injoyeth the Sun (whereof it was long deprived) the sooner to bring them unto maturitie.

¶ *The Place.*

Sow-bread groweth plentifully about Artoies and Vermandois in France, and in the Forest of Arden, and in Brabant.

It is reported unto mee by men of good credit, that *Cyclamen* or Sow-bread groweth upon the mountaines of Wales; on the hils of Lincolnshire, and in Somerset shire by the house of a gentleman called M^r. *Hales*; upon a Fox-borough also not far from M^r. *Bam-fields*, neer to a town called Hardington. The first two kindes grow in my garden, where they prosper well. ‡ I cannot learne that this growes wilde in England. ‡

¶ *The Vertues.*

Being beaten and made up into trochisches, or little flat cakes, it is reported to be a good amorous medicine to make one in love, if it be inwardly taken.

---

(311)

CHAP. 132. *Of Birthwoorts.*

¶ *The Description.*

1   LOng Birthwoort hath many small long slender stalkes creeping upon the ground, tangling one with another very intricately, beset with round leaves not much unlike Sow-bread or Ivie, but larger, of a light or overworne green colour,

Piſtolochia Cretica, ſive Virginiana. Virginian Snake-root.

and of a grievous or lothsome smell and savour: among which come forth long hollow floures, not much unlike the flours of Aron, but without any pestell or clapper in the same; of a darke purple colour: after which follow small fruit like unto little peares, containing triangled seeds of a blackish colour. The root is long, thicke, of the colour of box, of a strong savour and bitter taste.

‡ 6 *Clusius* figures and describes another smal *Pistolochia*, by the name of *Pistolochia Cretica*, to which I thought good to adde the Epithit *Virginiana* also, for that the much admired Snakeweed of Virginia seems no otherwise to differ from it than an inhabitant of Candy from one of the Virginians, which none I think wil say to differ in *specie*.

¶ *The Place.*

Pliny sheweth, That the Birthworts grow in fat and Champian places: The fields of Spaine are full of these Birthworts: they are also found in Italy and Narbone or Languedoc a country of France They grow all in my garden.

¶ *The Time.*

They floure in May, June, and July.

¶ *The Vertues.*

Dioscorides writeth, That a dram weight of long Birthwort drunke with wine and so applied, is good against serpents and deadly things.

The round *Aristolochia* doth beautifie, clense, and fasten the teeth, if they be often fretted or rubbed with the pouder thereof.

‡ The root of the Virginian *Pistolochia*, which is of a strong and aromatick sent, is a singular and much used antidote against the bite of the Rattle-snake, or rather Adder or Viper, whose bite is very deadly; and therefore by the providence of the Creator hee hath upon his taile a skinny dry substance parted into cels, which contain some loose hard dry bodies that rattle in them (as if one should put little stones or pease into a stiffe and very dry bladder) that so he may by this noise give warning of his approch, the better to be avoided: but if any be bitten, they know nor stand in need of no better antidote than this root, which they chew and apply to the wound, & also swallow some of it downe, by which means they quickly overcome the malignitie of this poisonous bite, which otherwise in a very short time would prove deadly. ‡

(312)

CHAP. 133. *Of Violets.*

¶ *The Kindes.*

THere might be described many kindes of floures under this name of Violets, if their differences should be more curiously looked into than is necessarie: for we might joine hereunto the stock Gillofloures, Wall-floures, Dames Gillofloures, Marian violets, & likewise some of the bulbed floures, because some of them by *Theophrastus* are termed Violets. But this was not our charge, holding it sufficient to distinguish and divide them as neere as may be in kindred and neighbourhood; addressing my selfe unto the Violets called the blacke or purple violets, or March Violets of the garden, which have a great prerogative above others, not only because the mind conceiveth a certain pleasure and recreation by smelling and handling those most odoriferous floures, but also for that very many by these violets receive ornament and comely grace; for there be made of them garlands for the head, nosegaies and poesies, which are delightfull to looke on and pleasant to smel to, speaking nothing of their appropriat vertues; yea gardens themselves receive by these the greatest ornament of all, chiefest beauty, and most excellent grace, and the recreation of the minde which is taken hereby cannot be but very good and honest; for they admonish and stirre up a man to that which is comely and honest; for floures through their beauty, variety of colour, and exquisit forme, do bring to a liberall and gentle manly minde, the remembrance of honestie, comlinesse, and all kindes of vertues: for it would be an unseemly and filthy thing (as a certain wise man saith) for him that doth looke upon and handle faire and beautiful things, to have his mind not faire, but filthy and deformed.

¶ *The Description.*

1 THe blacke or purple Violet doth forthwith bring from the root many leaves, broad, sleightly indented in the edges, rounder than the leaves of Ivy; among the midst wherof spring up fine slender stems, and upon every one a beautifull flour sweetly smelling, of a blew darkish purple, consisting of five

little leaves, the lowest whereof is the greatest: after them do appeare little hanging cups or knaps, which when they be ripe do open and divide themselves into three parts. The seed is smal, long, and somwhat round withall: the root consisteth of many threddy strings.

2   The white garden Violet hath many milke white floures, in forme and figure like the precedent; the colour of whose floures especially setteth forth the difference.

3   The double garden Violet hath leaves, creeping branches, and roots like the garden single Violet; differing in that, that this Violet bringeth forth most beautifull sweet double floures, and the other single.

4   The white double Violet like-wise agrees with the other of his kinde, differing onely in the colour; for as the last described bringeth double blew or purple floures, contrariwise this plant beareth double white floures, which maketh the difference.

Viola flore albo.
The white garden Violet.

¶ The Place.

The Violet groweth in gardens almost every where: the others which are strangers have beene touched in their descriptions.

¶ The Time.

The floures for the most part appeare in March, at the farthest in Aprill.

¶ The Names.

The Violet is called in Greeke, *Ion*: in Latine, *Nigra viola* or blacke Violet, of the blackish purple colour of the floures. The Apothecaries keepe the Latine name *Viola*, but they call it *Herba Violaria*, and *Mater Violarum*: in Spanish, *Violeta*: in English, Violet. *Nicander* in his Geoponicks beleeveth (as *Hermolaus* sheweth) that the Grecians did call it *Ion*, because certain Nymphs of Iönia gave that floure first to *Jupiter*. Others say it was called *Ion* because when *Jupiter* had turned the young damosell *Iö*, whom he tenderly loved, into a Cow, the earth brought forth this floure for her food; which being made for her sake, received the name from her: and thereupon it is thought that the Latines also called it *Viola*, as though they should say *Vitula*, by blotting out the letter *t*.

¶ *The Vertues*.

The floures are good for all inflammations, especially of the sides and lungs; they take away the hoarsenesse of the chest, the ruggednesse of the winde-pipe and jawes, and take away thirst.

There is likewise made of Violets and sugar certaine plates called Sugar violet, Violet tables, or Plate, which is most pleasant and wholesome, especially it comforteth the heart and the other inward parts.

---

(314)   ## CHAP. 134. *Of Ground-Ivy, or Ale-hoofe*.

¶ *The Description*.

1   GRound Ivy is a low or base herbe; it creepeth and spreads upon the ground hither and thither all about, with many stalkes of an uncertaine length, slender, and like those of the Vine, something cornered, and sometimes reddish: whereupon grow leaves something broad and round, wrinckled, hairy, nicked in the edges, for the most part two out of everie joint: amongst which come forth the floures gaping like little hoods, not unlike to those of Germander, of a purplish blew colour: the roots are very threddy: the whole plant is of a strong smell and bitter taste.

¶ *The Place*.

It is found as well in tilled as in untilled places, but most commonly in obscure and darke places, upon banks under hedges, and by the sides of houses.

¶ *The Time*.

It remaineth greene not onely in Summer, but also in Winter at any time of the yeare: it floureth from Aprill till Summer be far spent.

¶ *The Names*.

In English, Ground-Ivy, Ale-hoofe, Gill go by ground, Tune-hoof, and Cats-foot.

¶ *The Vertues.*

Ground-Ivy is commended against the humming noyse and ring-ing sound of the eares, being put into them, and for them that are hard of hearing.

Ground-Ivy, Celandine, and Daisies, of each a like quantitie, stamped and strained, and a little sugar and rose water put thereto, and dropped with a feather into the eies, taketh away all manner of inflammation, spots, webs, itch, smarting, or any griefe whatsoever in the eyes, yea although the sight were nigh hand gone: it is proved to be the best medicine in the world.

The herbes stamped as aforesaid, and mixed with a little ale and honey, and strained, take away the pinne and web, or any griefe out of the eyes of horse or cow, or any other beast, being squirted into the same with a syringe, or I might have said the liquor injected into the eies with a syringe. But I list not to be over eloquent among Gentlewomen, to whom especially my Workes are most necessarie.

The women of our Northerne parts, especially about Wales and Cheshire, do turne the herbe Ale-hoof into their Ale; but the reason thereof I know not: notwithstanding without all controversie it is most singular against the griefes aforesaid; being tunned up in ale and drunke, it also purgeth the head from rheumaticke humors flowing from the braine.

---

(315)

Chap. 135. *Of Ivy.*

¶ *The Description.*

1 THe greater Ivie climbeth on trees, old buildings, and walls: the stalkes thereof are wooddy, and now and then so great as it seemes to become a tree; from which it sendeth a multitude of little boughes or branches every way, whereby as it were with armes it creepeth and wandereth far about: it also bringeth forth continually fine little roots, by which it fastneth it selfe and cleaveth wonderfull hard upon trees, and upon the smooth-est stone walls: the leaves are smooth, shining especially on the upper

Hedera corymbofa.
Clymbing or berried Ivie.

side, cornered with sharpe pointed corners. The floures are very small and mossie; after which succeed bundles of black berries, every one having a small sharpe pointall.

¶ *The Time.*

Ivie flourisheth in Autumne: the berries are ripe after the Winter Solstice.

¶ *The Vertues.*

The leaves laid in steepe in water for a day and a nights space, helpe sore and smarting waterish eies, if they be bathed and washed with the water wherein they have beene infused.

(316)

CHAP. 136. *Of rough Binde-weed.*

¶ *The Description.*

1   ALthough we have great plenty of the roots of this Binde-weed of Peru, which we usually call *Zarza*, or *Sarsa parilla*, wherewith divers griefes and maladies are cured, and that these roots are very well knowne to all; yet such hath beene the carelesnesse and small providence of such as have travelled into the Indies, that hitherto not any have given us instruction sufficient, either concerning the leaves, floures, or fruit: onely *Monardus* saith, that it hath long roots deepe thrust into the ground: which is as much as if a great learned man should tell the simple, that our common carrion Crow were of a blacke colour. For who is so blinde that seeth the root it selfe, but can easily affirme the root to be very long? Notwithstanding, there is in the reports of such as say they have seene the plant it selfe growing, some contradiction or contrarietie: some report that it is a kind of Bindweed, and especially one of these rough

Bind-weeds: others, as one M^r. *White* an excellent painter, who carried very many people into Virginia (or after some Norembega) there to inhabit, at which time he did see thereof great plenty, as he himselfe reported unto me, with this bare description; It is (saith he) the root of a small shrubby tree, or hedge tree, such as are those of our country called Haw-thorns, having leaves resembling those of Ivy, but the floures or fruit he remembreth not. ‡ It is most certaine, that *Sarsa parilla* is the root of the Americane *Smilax aspera*, both by consent of most Writers, and by the rela-tion of such as have seene it growing there. ‡

Smilax aspera.
Common rough Bindeweed.

2 The common rough Bind-weed hath many branches set full of little sharpe prickles, with certaine clasping tendrels, wherewith it taketh hold upon hedges, shrubs, and whatsoever standeth next unto it, winding and clasping it selfe about from the bottome to the top; where-on are placed at every joint one leafe like that of Ivie, without corners, sharpe pointed, lesser and harder than those of smooth Binde-weed, oftentimes marked with little white spots, and garded or bordered about the edges with crooked prickles. The floures grow at the top of crooked stalks of a white colour, and sweet of smell. After commeth the fruit like those of the wilde Vine, greene at the first, and red when they be ripe, and of a biting taste; wherein is contained a blackish seed in shape like that of hempe. The root is long, somewhat hard, and parted into very many branches.

¶ *The Place.*

Zarza Parilla, or the prickly Binde-weed of America, groweth in Peru a province of America, in Virginia, and in divers other places both in the East and West Indies.

The others grow in rough and untilled places, about the edges and borders of fields, on mountaines and vallies, in Italy, Languedoc in France, Spaine, and Germany.

¶ *The Time*.

They floure and flourish in the Spring: their fruit is ripe in Autumne, or a little before.

¶ *The Names*.

Divers affirme that the root (brought out of Peru a Province in America) which the later Herbarists do call *Zarza*, is the root of this Bindeweed. *Garcias Lopius Lusitanus* granteth it to be like thereunto, but yet he doth not affirme that it is the same. Plants are oftentimes found to be like one another, which notwithstanding are proved not to be the same by some little difference; the divers constitutions of the weather and of the soile maketh the difference.

Zarza parilla of Peru is a strange plant, and is brought unto us from the Countries of the new world called America; and such things as are brought from thence, although they also seeme and are like to those that grow in Europe, notwithstanding they do often differ in vertue and operation: for the diversitie of the soile and of the weather doth not only breed an alteration in the forme but doth most of all prevaile in making the vertues and qualities greater or lesser. Such things as grow in hot places be of more force, and greater smell; and in cold, of lesser. Some things that are deadly and pernitious, being removed wax milde, and are made wholesome: so in like manner, although *Zarza parilla* of Peru be like to rough Bind-weed, or to Spanish *Zarza parilla*, notwithstanding by reason of the temperature of the weather, and also through the nature of the soile, it is of a great deale more force than that which groweth either in Spaine or in Africke.

The roots of *Zarza parilla* of Peru, which are brought alone without the plant, be long and slender, like to the lesser roots of common liquorice, very many oftentimes hanging from one head, in which roots the middle string is hardest. They have little taste, and so small a smell that it is not to be perceived. These are reported to grow in Honduras a province of Peru. They had their name of the like-nesse of rough Binde-weed, which among the inhabitants it keepeth; signifying in Spanish, a rough or prickly vine, as *Garcias Lopius* witnesseth.

¶ *The Vertues*.

The roots are a remedie against long continuall paine of the joynts and head, and against cold diseases. They are good for all manner of infirmities wherein there is hope of cure by sweating, so that there be no ague joyned.

The cure is perfected in few daies, if the disease be not old or great; but if it be, it requireth a longer time of cure. The roots here meant are as I take it those of *Zarza parilla*.

---

(319) CHAP. 137. *Of Scammonie, or purging Bindweed.*

¶ *The Description.*

1 SCammonie of Syria hath many stalkes rising from one root, which are long, slender, and like the clasping tendrels of the vine, by which it climeth and taketh hold of such things as are next unto it. The leaves be broad, sharpe pointed like those of the smooth or hedge Bind-weed: among which come forth very faire white floures tending to a blush colour, bell-fashion. The root is long, thicke, and white within: out of which is gathered a juyce that being hardned, is greatly used in Physicke: for which consideration, there is not any plant growing upon the earth, the knowledge whereof more concerneth a Physition, both for his shape and properties, than this Scammonie, which *Pena* calleth *Lactaria scansoriaque volvula*, that is, milky and climbing Windweed, whereof it is a kinde; although for distinction sake I have placed them as two severall kinds. And although this herbe be suspected, and halfe condemned of some learned men, yet there is not any other herbe to be found, whereof so small a quantity will do so much good: neither could those which have carped at it, and reproved this herbe, finde any simple in respect of his vertues to be put in his roome: and hereof ensueth great blame to all practitioners, who have not endevoured to be better acquainted with this herbe, chiefely to avoid the deceit of the crafty Drug-seller and Medicine-maker of this confected Scammony, brought us from farre places, rather to be called I feare infected Scammony, or poysoned Scammony, than confected. But he that will know more concerning the making, difference, choise and use of Scammony, let him read *Pena* in his chapter of Scammonie, in the place formerly cited, where he shall

finde many excellent secrets worthy the noting of those which would know how to use such rare and excellent medicines.

2   Scammony of Valentia (whereof I have plenty in my Garden) is also a kinde of Bindweed, growing naturally by the sea side upon the gravelly shore, by the mouth of the river Rhodanus, at the waters called *Aquas Marianas*, where the Apothecaries of Montpellier gather of it great plentie, who have attempted to harden the milkie juyce thereof, to use it in stead of Scammony of Antioch. This plant

Scammonium Syriacum
Syrian Scammonie.

bringeth forth many slender branches, which will climbe and very well run upon a pole; as being supported therewith, and mounteth to the height of five or six cubits, climbing and ramping like the first kinde of Scammony. The leaves are greene, smooth, plaine, and sharpe pointed, which being broken do yeeld abundance of milke: the floures are white, small, and starre-fashion: the roots white and many, shooting forth sundry other roots, whereby it mightily increaseth.

¶ *The Place.*

It doth grow in hot regions, in a fat soile, as in Misia, Syria, and other like countries of Asia; it is likewise found in the Island of Candia as *Bellon.* witnesseth; from whence I had some seeds, of which seed I received two plants that prospered exceeding well; the one whereof I bestowed upon a learned Apothecary of Colchester, which continueth to this day, bearing both floures and ripe seed. But an ignorant weeder of my garden plucked mine up, and cast it away in my absence, in stead of a weed: by which mischance I am not able to write hereof so absolutely as I determined: it likewise groweth neere unto the sea side about Tripolis in Syria, where the inhabitants doe call it *Meudheudi.*

¶ *The Time.*

It floured in my Garden about S. *James* tide, as I remember, for when I went to Bristow Faire I left it in floure; but at my returne it was destroied as aforesaid.

¶ *The Vertues.*

The quantitie of Scammonie or of *Diagridium* it selfe, to be taken at one time, as *Mesue* writeth, is from five grains to ten or twelve: it may be kept as the same Author sheweth, foure yeres: *Pliny* judgeth it to be little worth after 2 yeares: it is to be used, saith he, when it is two yeres old, and it is not good before, nor after. The mixing or otherwise the use therof, more than is set down, I think it not expedient to set forth in the Physicall vertues of Scammony, upon the receipt whereof many times death insueth: my reasons are divers, for that the same is very daungerous, either if too great a quantitie thereof be taken, or if it be given without correction; or taken at the hands of some runnagat physick-monger, quack salver, old women-leaches, and such like abusers of phisick, and deceivers of people. The use of Scammony I commit to the learned, unto whom it especially and onely belongeth, who can very carefully and curiously use the same.

(323)

Chap. 138. *Of the manured Vine.*

¶ *The Description.*

THe trunke or body of the Vine is great and thicke, very hard, covered with many barks, which are full of cliffes or chinks; from which grow forth branches as it were armes, many wayes spreading; out of which come forth jointed shoots or springs; and from the bosom of those joints, leaves and clasping tendrels, and likewise bunches or clusters full of grapes: the leaves be broad, something round, five cornered, and somewhat indented about the edges: amongst which come forth many clasping tendrels, that take hold of such props or staies as stand next unto it. The grapes differ both in colour and greatnesse, and also in many other things, which to distinguish severally were impossible, considering the infinite sorts or kinds, and also those which are transplanted from one region or clymat to another, do likewise alter both from the forme and taste they had before: wherefore it shall be sufficient to set forth the figure of the manured grape, and speak somwhat of the rest.

There be some Vines that bring forth grapes of a whitish or reddish yellow colour; others of a deep red, both in the outward skin, juice, and pulpe within.

There be others whose grapes are of a blew colour, or something red, yet is the juice like those of the former. These grapes doe yeeld forth a white wine before they are put into the presse, and a reddish

Vitis Vinifera
The manured vine.

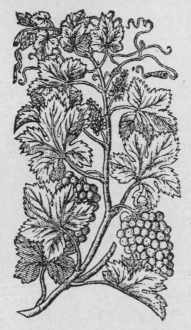

or paller wine when they are trodden with the husks, & so left to macerate or ferment, with which if they remain too long, they yeeld forth a wine of a higher colour.

There be others which make a black and obscure red wine, whereof some bring bigger clusters, and consist of greater grapes, others of lesser; some grow more clustered or closer together, others looser; some have but one stone, others more; some make a more austere or harsh wine, others a more sweet: of some the old wine is best, of divers the first yeres wine is most excellent: some bring forth fruit foure square, of which kindes we have great plenty.

¶ *The Time.*

Columella saith Vines must be pruned before the yong branches spring forth. *Palladius* writeth, in Februarie: if they be pruned later they lose their nourishment with weeping.

¶ *Of Grapes.*

GRapes have the preheminence among the Autumne fruits, and nourish more than they all, but yet not so much as figges; and they have in them little ill juice, especially when they bee thorow ripe.

Grapes may be kept the whole yeare, being ordered after the same manner that *Joachimus Camerarius* reporteth. You shall take, saith hee, the meale of mustard seed, and strew in the bottome of any earthen pot well leaded; whereupon you shall lay the fairest bunches of the ripest grapes, the which you shall cover with more of the fore-said meale, and lay upon it another sort of Grapes, so doing untill the pot be full: then shall you fill up the pot to the brimme with a kind of sweet wine called Must. The pot being very close covered shall be set into some cellar or other cold place: the grapes you may take forth at your pleasure, washing them with faire water from the pouder.

¶ Of Wine.

TO speake of wine the juice of Grapes, which being newly pressed forth is called *Mustum* or new wine; after the dregs and drosse are setled, and it appeareth pure and cleer, it is called in English, Wine, and that not unproperly. For certain other juices, as of Apples, Pomegranats, Peares, Medlars, Services, or such other-wise made (for examples sake) of Barley and Graine, be not at all simply called wine, but with the name of the thing added whereof they do consist. Hereupon is the wine which is pressed forth of the Pomegranate berries named *Rhoites*, or wine of Pomegranats; out of Quinces, *Cydonites*, or wine of Quinces: out of Peares, *Apyites* or Perry; and that which is compounded of Barley is called *Zythum*, or Barley wine: in English, Ale or Beere.

And other certain wines have borrowed syrnames of the plants that have bin infused or steeped in them; and yet all wines of the Vine, as Wormwood wine, Myrtle wine, and Hyssop wine, which are all called artificiall wines.

That is properly and simply called wine which is pressed out of the grapes of the wine, and is without any manner of mixture.

The kindes of Wines are not of one nature, nor of one facultie or power, but of many, differing one from another; for there is one difference thereof in taste, another in colour, the third is re-ferred to the consistence or substance of the Wine; the fourth con-sisteth in the vertue and strength thereof. *Galen* addeth that which is found in the smell, which belongs to the vertue and strength of the Wine.

It is good for such as are in a consumption, by reason of some disease, and that have need to have their bodies nourished and re-freshed (alwaies provided they have no fever,) as *Galen* saith in his seventh booke of the Method of curing. It restoreth strength most of all other things, and that speedily: It maketh a man merry and joyfull:

It putteth away feare, care, troubles of minde, and sorrow: and bringeth sleepe gently.

And these things proceed of the moderate use of wine: for immoderate drinking of wine doth altogether bring the contrarie. They that are drunke are distraughted in minde, become foolish, and oppressed with a drowsie sleepinesse, and be afterward taken with the Apoplexy, the gout, or altogether with other most grievous diseases.

And seeing that every excesse is to be shunned, it is expedient most of all to shun this, by which not only the body, but also the minde receiveth hurt.

Wherefore we thinke, that wine is not fit for men that be already of full age, unlesse it be moderately taken, because it carrieth them headlong into fury and lust, and troubleth and dulleth the reasonable part of the minde.

¶ *Of the liquor which is distilled out of Wine, commonly called*, Aqua vitæ.

THere is drawne out of Wine a liquor, which in Latine is commonly called *Aqua vitæ*, or water of life, and also *Aqua ardens*, or burning water, which as distilled waters are drawne out of herbes and other things, is after the same manner distilled out of strong wine, that is to say, by certaine instruments made for this purpose, which are commonly called Limbeckes.

This kinde of liquor is in colour and substance like unto waters distilled out of herbes, and also resembleth cleere simple water in colour, but in faculty it farre differeth.

It beareth the syrname of life, because that it serveth to preserve and prolong the life of man.

It is called *Ardens*, burning, for that it is easily turned into a burning flame: for seeing it is not any other thing than the thinnest and strongest part of the wine, it being put to the flame of fire, is quickly burned.

This water distilled out of wine is good for all those that are made cold either by a long disease, or through age, as for old and impotent men: for it cherisheth and increaseth naturall heate; upholdeth strength, repaireth and augmenteth the same: it prolongeth life, quickeneth all the senses, and doth not only preserve the memory, but also recovereth it when it is lost: it sharpeneth the sight.

It is fit for those that are taken with the Catalepsie (which is a disease in the braine proceeding of drinesse and cold) and are subject to dead sleepes, if there be no fever joyned; it serveth for the weakenesse, trembling, and beating of the heart; it strengtheneth and heateth a feeble stomacke; it consumeth winde both in the stomacke, sides, and bowels; it maketh good concoction of meate, and is a singular remedy against cold poysons.

It hath such force and power, in strengthening of the heart, and stirreth up the instruments of the senses, that it is most effectuall, not onely inwardly taken to the quantity of a little spoonefull, but also outwardly applied: that is to say, set to the nosthrils, or laid upon the temples of the head, and to the wrests of the armes; and also to foment and bath sundry hurts and griefes.

Being held in the mouth it helpeth the toothache: it is also good against cold cramps and convulsions, being chafed and rubbed therewith.

If I should take in hand to write of every mixture, of each infusion, of the sundry colours, and every other circumstance that the vulgar people doe give unto this water, and their divers use, I should spend much time but to small purpose.

¶ *The briefe summe of that hath beene said of the Vine.*

ALmighty God for the comfort of mankinde ordained Wine; but decreed withall, That it should be moderately taken, for so it is wholsome and comfortable: but when measure is turned into excesse, it becommeth unwholesome, and a poyson most venomous. Besides, how little credence is to be given to drunkards it is evident; for though they be mighty men, yet it maketh them monsters, and worse than brute beasts. Finally in a word to conclude; this excessive drinking of Wine dishonoreth Noblemen, beggereth the poore, and more have beene destroied by surfeiting therewith, than by the sword.

CHAP. 139. *Of Hops.*

¶ *The Description.*

1 THe Hop doth live and flourish by embracing and taking hold of poles, pearches, and other things upon which it climeth. It bringeth forth very long stalkes, rough, and hairie; also rugged leaves broad like those of the Vine, or rather of Bryony, but yet blacker, and with fewer dented divisions: the floures hang downe by clusters from the tops of the branches, puffed up, set as it were with scales like little canes, or scaled Pine apples, of a whitish colour tending to yellownesse, strong of smell: the roots are slender, and diversly folded one within another.

Lupus ſaliĉtarius.
Hops.

¶ *The Place.*

The Hop joyeth in a fat and fruitfull ground: also it groweth among briers and thornes about the borders of fields, I meane the wilde kinde.

¶ *The Time.*

The floures of hops are gathered in August and September, and reserved to be used in beere: in the Spring time come forth new shoots or buds: in the Winter onely the roots remaine alive.

¶ *The Vertues.*

The buds or first sprouts which come forth in the Spring are used to be eaten in sallads; yet are they, as *Pliny* saith, more toothsome than nourishing, for they yeeld but very small nourishment.

The floures are used to season Beere or Ale with, and too many do cause bitternesse thereof, and are ill for the head.

The floures make bread light, and the lumpe to be sooner and easilier leavened, if the meale be tempered with liquor wherein they have been boiled.

The manifold vertues of Hops do manifest argue the wholesomenesse of beere above ale; for the hops rather make it a physicall drinke to keepe the body in health, than an ordinary drinke for the quenching of our thirst.

---

(325)   Chap. 140. *Of Travellers-Joy.*

¶ *The Description.*

1   THe plant which *Lobel* setteth forth under the title of *Viorna, Dodonæus* makes *Vitis alba*; but not properly; whose long wooddy and viny branches extend themselves very far, and into infinite numbers, decking with his clasping tendrels and white starre-like floures (being very sweet) all the bushes, hedges, and shrubs that are neere unto it. It sends forth many branched stalkes, thicke, tough, full of shoots and clasping tendrels, wherewith it foldeth it selfe upon the hedges, and taketh hold and climeth upon every thing that standeth neere unto it. The leaves are fastned for the most part by fives upon one rib or stem, two on either side, and one in the midst or point standing alone; which leaves are broad like those of Ivy, but not cornered at all: among which come forth clusters of white floures, and after them great tufts of flat seeds, each seed having a fine white plume like a feather fastned to it, which maketh in the Winter a goodly shew, covering the hedges white all over with his feather-like

Clematis Bætica.
The Spanish Trauellers-Joy.

tops. The root is long, tough, and thicke, with many strings fastned thereto.

¶ *The Place.*

The Travellers-Joy is found in the borders of fields among thornes and briers, almost in every hedge as you go from Gravesend to Canturbury in Kent; in many places of Essex, and in most of these Southerly parts about London, but not in the North of England that I can heare of.

¶ *The Time.*

The floures come forth in July: the beautie thereof appeares in November and December.

¶ *The Names.*

The first is commonly called *Viorna, quasi vias ornans,* of decking and adorning waies and hedges, where people travel; and thereupon I have named it the Travellers-Joy.

¶ *The Temperature and Vertues.*

These plants have no use in physicke as yet found out, but are esteemed onely for pleasure, by reason of the goodly shadow which they make with their thicke bushing and clyming, as also for the beauty of the floures, and the pleasant sent or savour of the same.

---

(328)   Chap. 141. *Of Wood-binde, or Hony-suckle.*

¶ *The Description.*

1   WOod-binde or Hony-suckle climeth up aloft, having long slender wooddy stalkes, parted into divers branches: about which stand by certaine distances smooth leaves, set together by couples one right against another; of a light greene colour above, underneath of a whitish greene. The floures shew themselves in the tops of the branches, many in number, long, white, sweet of smell, hollow within; in one part standing more out, with certaine threddes growing out of the middle. The fruit is like little bunches of grapes, red when they be ripe, wherein is contained small hard seed. The root is wooddy, and not without strings.

¶ *The Place*.

The Woodbinde groweth in woods and hedges, and upon shrubs and bushes, oftentimes winding it selfe so straight and hard about, that it leaveth his print upon those things so wrapped.

Periclymenum.
Woodbinde or Honisuckles.

The double Honisuckle groweth now in my Garden, and many others likewise in great plenty, although not long since, very rare and hard to be found, except in the garden of some diligent Herbarists.

¶ *The Time*.

The leaves come forth betimes in the spring: the floures bud forth in May and June: the fruit is ripe in Autumne.

¶ *The Vertues*.

The floures steeped in oile, and set in the Sun, are good to annoint the body that is benummed, and growne very cold.

---

(334)   CHAP. 142. *Of Indian Swallow-woort.*

¶ *The Description*.

THere groweth in that part of Virginia, or Norembega, where our English men dwelled (intending there to erect a certaine Colonie) a kinde of *Asclepias*, or Swallow-woort, which the Savages call *Wisanck*: there riseth up from a single crooked root, one upright stalk a foot high, slender, and of a greenish colour: whereupon do grow faire broad leaves sharp pointed, with many ribs or nerves running through the same like those of Ribwort or Plaintaine, set together by couples at certaine distances. The floures come forth at the top of the stalks, which as yet are not observed by reason the man that brought the seeds & plants hereof did not regard them: after which, there come in place two cods (seldome more) sharp pointed like those of our Swallow-woort, but greater, stuffed full of a most pure silke of a shining white colour: among which silke appeareth a small long tongue (which is the seed) resembling the tongue of a bird, or that of the herbe called Adders tongue. The cods are not only full of silke, but every nerve or sinew wherewith the leaves be ribbed are likewise most pure silke; and also the pilling of the stems, even as flax is torne from his stalks. This considered, behold the justice of God, that as he hath shut up those people and nations in infidelity and nakednes, so hath he not as yet given them understanding to cover their nakednesse, nor mater wherewith to do the same; notwithstanding the earth is covered over with this silke, which daily they tread under their feet, which were sufficient to apparell many kingdomes, if they were carefully manured and cherished.

¶ The Place.

It groweth, as before is rehearsed, in the countries of Norembega, now called Virginia, by the honourable Knight Sir *Walter Raleigh*, who hath bestowed great sums of money in the discoverie thereof; where are dwelling at this present English men.

---

(337)

CHAP. 143. *Of Solomons Seale.*

¶ The Description.

1   THe first kinde of Solomons Seale hath long round stalks, set for the most part with long leaves somewhat furrowed and ribbed, not much unlike Plantain, but narrower, which for the most part stand all upon one side of the stalke, and hath small white floures resembling the floures of Lilly Conval: on the other side when the floures be vaded, there come forth round berries, which at the first are green and of a blacke colour tending to blewnesse, and being ripe, are of the bignesse of Ivy berries, of a very sweet and pleasant taste. The root is white and thicke, full of knobs or joints, in some places resembling the mark of a seale, whereof I thinke it tooke the name *Sigillum Solomonis*; it is sweet at the first, but afterward of a bitter taste with some sharpnesse.

¶ *The Place*.

The first sort of Solomons seale growes naturally wilde in Somerset-shire, upon the North side of a place called Mendip, in the parish of Shepton Mallet: also in Kent by a village called Crayford, upon Rough or Row hill: also in Odiam parke in Hampshire; in Bradfords wood, neere to a towne in Wiltshire foure miles from Bath; in a wood neere to a village called Horsley, five miles from Gilford in Surrey, and in divers other places.

1 *Polygonatum*.
Solomons Seale.

¶ *The Time*.

They spring up in March, and shew their floures in May: the fruit is ripe in September.

¶ *The Names*.

Solomons seale is called in Latine, *Polygonatum*, of many, Knees, for so the Greeke word doth import: in shops, *Sigillum Salomonis*, and *Scala cæli*: in English likewise, Scala cœly, Solomons seale, and Whitewoort, or White-root.

¶ *The Vertues*.

Dioscorides writeth, That the roots are excellent good for to seale or close up greene wounds, being stamped and laid thereon; whereupon it was called *Sigillum Salomonis*, of the singular vertue that it hath in sealing or healing up wounds, broken bones, and such like. Some have thought it tooke the name *Sigillum* of the markes upon the roots: but the first reason seemes to be more probable.

The root of Solomons seale stamped while it is fresh and greene, and applied, taketh away in one night, or two at the most, any bruise, blacke or blew spots gotten by fals or womens wilfulnesse, in stumbling upon their hasty husbands fists, or such like.

Galen saith, that neither herbe nor root hereof is to be given inwardly: but note what experience hath found out, and of late daies, especially among the vulgar sort of people in Hampshire, which

Galen, Dioscorides, or any other that have written of plants have not so much as dreamed of; which is, That if any of what sex or age soever chance to have any bones broken, in what part of their bodies soever; their refuge is to stampe the roots hereof, and give it unto the patient in ale to drinke: which sodoreth and glues together the bones in very short space, and very strangely, yea although the bones be but slenderly and unhandsomely placed and wrapped up. Moreover, the said people do give it in like manner unto their cattell, if they chance to have any bones broken, with good successe; which they do also stampe and apply outwardly in manner of a pultesse, as well unto themselves as their cattell.

The root stamped and applied in manner of a pultesse, and laid upon members that have beene out of joynt, and newly restored to their places, driveth away the paine, and knitteth the joynt very firmely, and taketh away the inflammation, if there chance to be any.

The same stamped, and the juyce given to drinke with ale or white wine, as aforesaid, or the decoction thereof made in wine, helps any inward bruise, disperseth the congealed and clotted bloud in very short space.

That which might be written of this herbe as touching the knitting of bones, and that truely, would seeme unto some incredible; but common experience teacheth, that in the world there is not to be found another herbe comparable to it for the purposes aforesaid: and therefore in briefe, if it be for bruises inward, the roots must be stamped, some ale or wine put thereto, strained, and given to drinke.

It must be given in the same manner to knit broken bones, against bruises, blacke or blew marks gotten by stripes, falls, or such like; against inflammation, tumors or swellings that happen unto members whose bones are broken, or members out of joynt, after restauration: the roots are to be stamped small, and applied pultesse or plaisterwise, wherewith many great workes have beene performed beyond credit.

Matthiolus teacheth, That a water is drawne out of the roots, wherewith the women of Italy use to scoure their faces from Sunneburning, freckles, morphew, or any such deformities of the skinne.

(340)

CHAP. 144. *Of Cucumbers.*

§ *The Description.*

1 THe Cucumber creepes alongst upon the ground all about, with long rough branches; whereupon doe grow broad rough leaves uneven about the edges: from the bosome whereof come forth crooked clasping tendrels like those of the Vine. The floures shoot forth betweene the stalkes and the leaves, set upon tender foot-stalkes composed of five small yellow leaves: which being past, the fruit succeedeth, long, cornered, rough, and set with certaine bumpes or risings, greene at the first, and yellow when they be ripe, wherein is contained a firme and sollid pulpe or substance transparent or thorow-shining, which together with the seed is eaten a little before they be fully ripe. The seeds be white, long, and flat.

Melo Hispanicus.
Spanifh Melons.

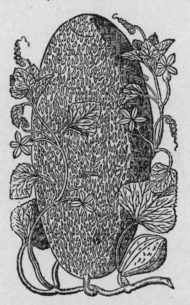

2 There be also certaine long cucumbers, which were first made (as is said) by art and manuring, which Nature afterwards did preserve: for at the first, when as the fruit is very little, it is put into some hollow cane, or other thing made of purpose, in which the cucumber groweth very long, by reason of that narrow hollownesse, which being filled up, the cucumber encreaseth in length. The seeds of this kinde of cucumber being sowne bringeth forth not such as were before, but such as art hath framed; which of their own growth are found long, and oftentimes very crookedly turned: and thereupon they have beene called *Anguini*, or long Cucumbers.

§ *The Names.*

The Cucumber is named generally *Cucumis:* in shops, *Cucumer:* in English, Cowcumbers and Cucumbers.

¶ *The Vertues.*

The fruit cut in pieces or chopped as herbes to the pot, and boiled
in a small pipkin with a piece of mutton, being made into potage
with Ote-meale, even as herb potage are made, whereof a messe eaten
to break-fast, as much to dinner, and the like to supper; taken in this
manner for the space of three weekes together without intermission,
doth perfectly cure all manner of sauce flegme and copper faces, red
and shining fierie noses (as red as red Roses) with pimples, pumples,
rubies, and such like precious faces.

Provided alwaies that during the time of curing you doe use to
wash or bathe the face with this liquor following.

Take a pinte of strong white wine vinegre, pouder of the roots of
Ireos or Orrice three dragmes, searced or bolted into most fine dust,
Brimmestone in fine pouder halfe a ounce, Camphire two dragmes,
stamped with two blanched Almonds, foure Oke apples cut thorow
the middle, and the juyce of foure Limons: put them all together in
a strong double glasse, shake them together very strongly, setting the
same in the Sunne for the space of ten daies: with which let the face
be washed and bathed daily, suffering it to drie of it selfe without
wiping it away. This doth not onely helpe fierie faces, but also taketh
away lentils, spots, morphew, Sun-burne, and all other deformities of
the face.

---

(349)

CHAP. 145. *Of Potato's.*

¶ *The Description.*

THis Plant (which is called of some Skyrrets of Peru) is generally
of us called Potatus or Potato's. It hath long rough flexible
branches trailing upon the ground like unto those of Pompions,
whereupon are set greene three cornered leaves very like those of the
wilde Cucumber. There is not any that have written of this plant,
have said any thing of the floures; therefore I refer their description
unto those that shall hereafter have further knowledge of the same.
Yet have I had in my garden divers roots that have flourished unto
the first approch of Winter, and have growne unto a great length of
branches, but they brought forth no floures at all; whether because

the Winter caused them to perish before their time of flouring, or that they be of nature barren of floures, I am not certain. The roots are many, thicke, and knobby, like unto the roots of Peonies, or rather of the white Asphodill, joined together at the top into one head, in maner of the Skyrret, which being divided into divers parts and planted, do make a great increase, especially if the greatest roots be cut into divers goblets, and planted in good and fertile ground.

¶ The Place.

The Potato's grow in India, Barbarie, Spaine, and other hot regions; of which I planted divers roots (which I bought at the Exchange in London) in my garden, where they flourished until winter, at which time they perished and rotted.

¶ The Names.

Clusius calleth it *Batata, Camotes, Amotes,* and *Ignames:* in English, Potatoes, Potatus, and Potades.

¶ The Vertues.

The Potato roots are among the Spaniards, Italians, Indians, and many other nations, ordinarie and common meat; which no doubt are of mighty and nourishing parts, and doe strengthen and comfort nature; whose nutriment is as it were a mean between flesh and fruit, but somewhat windie; yet being rosted in the embers they lose much of their windinesse, especially being eaten sopped in wine.

Of these roots may be made conserves no lesse toothsome, wholesome, and dainty, than of the flesh of Quinces; and likewise those comfortable and delicate meats called in shops, *Morselli, Placentulæ,* and divers other such like.

These roots may serve as a ground or foundation whereon the cunning Confectioner or Sugar-Baker may worke and frame many comfortable delicat Conserves and restorative sweet-meats.

They are used to be eaten rosted in the ashes. Some when they be so rosted infuse and sop them in wine: and others to give them the greater grace in eating, do boile them with prunes and so eat them: likewise others dresse them (being first rosted) with oile, vineger, and salt, every man according to his owne taste and liking. Notwithstanding howsoever they be dressed, they comfort, nourish, and strengthen the body.

(350)   CHAP. 146. *Of Potato's of Virginia.*

¶ *The Description.*

VIrginian Potato hath many hollow flexible branches trailing upon the ground, three square, uneven, knotted or kneed in sundry places at certaine distances: from the which knots commeth forth one great leafe made of divers leaves, some smaller, and

Battata Virginiana ſive Virginianorum, & Pappus.
Virginian Potatoes.

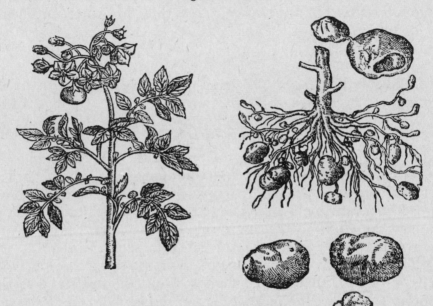

others greater, set together upon a fat middle rib by couples, of a swart greene colour tending to rednesse; the whole leafe resembling those of the Winter-Cresses, but much larger; in taste at the first like grasse, but afterward sharp and nipping the tongue. From the bosome of which leaves come forth long round slender footstalkes, whereon grow very faire and pleasant floures.

¶ *The Place.*

It groweth naturally in America, where it was first discovered, as reporteth *Clusius*, since which time I have received roots hereof from

Virginia, otherwise called Norembega, which grow & prosper in my garden as in their owne native country.

¶ *The Names.*

The Indians call this plant *Pappus*, meaning the roots; by which name also the common Potatoes are called in those Indian countries. Wee have it's proper name mentioned in the title. Because it hath not only the shape and proportion of Potato's, but also the pleasant taste and vertues of the same, we may call it in English, Potatoes of America or Virginia.

¶ *The Temperature and Vertues.*

The temperature and vertues be referred to the common Potato's, being likewise a food, as also a meat for pleasure, equall in goodnesse and wholesomnesse to the same, being either rosted in the embers, or boiled and eaten with oile, vineger and pepper, or dressed some other way by the hand of a skilfull Cooke.

(351)
CHAP. 147. *Of the garden Mallow called Hollyhocke.*

¶ *The Description.*

1   THe tame or garden Mallow bringeth forth broad round leaves of a whitish greene colour, rough, and greater than those of the wilde Mallow: the stalke is streight, of the height of foure or six cubits; whereon do grow upon slender foot-stalks single floures, not much unlike to the wilde Mallow, but greater, consisting only of five leaves, sometimes white or red, now and then of a deep purple colour, varying diversly as Nature list to play with it: in their places groweth up a round knop like a little cake, compact or made up of a multitude of flat seeds like little cheeses. The root is long, white, tough, easily bowed, and groweth deep in the ground.

3   The double Hollihocke with purple floures hath great broad leaves, confusedly indented about the edges, and likewise toothed

like a saw. The stalke groweth to the height of foure or five cubits. The floures are double, and of a bright purple colour.

Malua purpurea multiplex.
Double purple Hollihocke.

¶ *The Place.*

These Hollihockes are sowne in gardens, almost every where, and are in vaine sought elsewhere.

¶ *The Time.*

The second yeere after they are sowne they bring forth their floures in July and August, when the seed is ripe the stalke withereth, the root remaineth and sendeth forth new stalkes, leaves and floures, many yeares after.

¶ *The Names.*

The Hollihocke is called of divers, *Rosa ultra-marina,* or outlandish Rose.

¶ *The Vertues.*

The roots, leaves, and seeds serve for all those things for which the wilde Mallowes doe, which are more commonly and familiarly used.

(356)

Chap. 148. *Of Cranes-bill.*

¶ *The Description.*

DOves-foot hath many hairy stalks, trailing or leaning toward the ground, of a brownish colour, somewhat kneed or joynted; wherupon do grow rough leaves of an overworn green color, round, cut about the edges, and like unto those of the common Mallow: amongst which come forth the floures of a bright purple colour: after which is the seed, set together like the head and bill of a bird; wherupon it was called Cranes-bill, or Storks-bill, as are also all the other of his kind. The root is slender, with some fibres annexed thereto.

¶ *The Place.*

It is found neere to common high waies, desart places, untilled grounds, and specially upon mud walls almost every where.

¶ *The Time.*

It springeth up in March and Aprill: floureth in May, and bringeth his seed to ripenesse in June.

¶ *The Names.*

Geranium Columbinum.
Doues foot, or Cranes-bill.

It is commonly called in Latine, *Pes Columbinus*: in French, *Pied de Pigeon*: hereupon it may be called *Geranium Columbinum*: in English, Doves-foot, and Pigeons foot.

¶ *The Vertues.*

The herbe and roots dried, beaten into most fine pouder, and given halfe a spoonfull fasting, and the like quantitie to bedwards in red wine, or old claret, for the space of one and twenty daies together, cure miraculously ruptures or burstings, as my selfe have often proved, whereby I have gotten crownes and credit: if the ruptures be in aged persons, it shall be needfull to adde thereto the powder of red snailes (those without shels) dried in an oven in number nine, which fortifieth the herbes in such sort, that it never faileth, although the rupture be great and of long continuance: it likewise profiteth much those that are wounded into the body, and the decoction of the herbe made in wine, prevaileth mightily in healing inward wounds, as my selfe have likewise proved.

(367)

CHAP. 149. *Of Crow-feet.*

¶ *The Kindes.*

THere be divers sorts or kinds of these pernitious herbes comprehended under the name of *Ranunculus*, or Crow foot, whereof most are very dangerous to be taken into the body, and therefore they require a very exquisite moderation, with a most exact and due maner of tempering, not any of them are to be taken alone by themselves, because they are of most violent force, and therefore have the greater need of correction.

Ranunculus pratensis, etiamque hortensis.
Common Crow-foot.

The knowledge of this herbe is as necessarie to the Physitian as of other herbes, to the end they may shun the same, as *Scribonius Largus* saith, and not take them ignorantly: or also, if necessitie at any time require, that they use them, and that with some deliberation and speciall choice, and with their proper correctives. For these dangerous simples are likewise many times of themselves beneficial, & oftentimes profitable: for some of them are not so daungerous, but that they may in some sort, and oftentimes in fit and due season profit and doe good.

¶ *The Description.*

1   THe common Crow-foot hath leaves divided into many parts, commonly three, sometimes five, cut here and there in the edges, of a deep green colour, in which stand divers white spots: the stalks be round, somthing hairie, some of them bow downe toward the ground, and put forth many little roots, whereby it taketh hold of the ground as it traileth along: some of them stand upright, a foot high or higher; on the tops whereof grow

small flours with five leaves apiece, of a yellow glittering colour like gold: in the middle part of these floures stand certaine small threads of like colour: which being past, the seeds follow, made up in a rough ball: the roots are white and threddy.

2   The second kind of Crow-foot is like unto the precedent, saving that his leaves are fatter, thicker, and greener, and his small twiggy stalks stand upright, otherwise it is like: of which kinde it chanced, that walking in the field next to the Theatre by London, in the company of a worshipfull Merchant named M^r. *Nicholas Lete*, I found one of this kind there with double floures, which before that time I had not seene.

¶ *The Place.*

They grow of themselves in pastures and medowes almost everie where.

¶ *The Time.*

They floure in May and many moneths after.

¶ *The Names.*

Crow-foot is called of *Lobel, Ranunculus pratensis*: in English, King Kob, Gold cups, Gold knobs, Crow-foot, and Butter-floures.

---

(372)   Chap. 150. *Of Wolfes-bane.*

¶ *The Kindes.*

THere be divers sorts of Wolfs-banes, whereof some bring forth flours of a yellow color, others of a blew or tending to purple: among the yellow ones there are some greater, others lesser; some with broader leaves, and others with narrower.

¶ *The Description.*

THe first kinde of Aconite, of some called *Thora*, others adde thereto the place where it groweth in great aboundance, which is the Alps, and call it *Thora Valdensium*. This plant tooke his name of the Greeke word signifying corruption, poison, or death, which are the certaine effects of this pernitious plant: for this they use very much in poison, and when they mean to infect their arrow heads, the more speedily and deadly to dispatch the wilde beasts which greatly annoy those Mountaines of the Alpes. To which purpose also it is brought into the Mart townes neere those places, to be sold unto the hunters, the juyce thereof being prepared by pressing forth, and so kept in hornes and hoofes of beasts for the most speedy poyson of the Aconites: for an arrow touched therewith leaves the wound uncurable (if it but fetch bloud where it entred in) unlesse that round about the wound the flesh bee speedily cut away in great quantitie: this plant therefore may rightly be accounted as first and chiefe of those called Sagittaries or Aconites, by reason of the malignant qualities aforesaid. This that hath beene sayd, argueth also that *Matthiolus* hath unproperly called it *Pseudoaconitum*, that is, false or bastard Aconite; for without question there is no worse or more speedie venome in the world, nor no Aconite or toxible plant comparable hereunto. And yet let us consider the fatherly care and providence of God, who hath provided a conquerour and triumpher over this plant so venomous, namely his *Antigonist*, *Antithora*, or to speake in shorter and fewer syllables, *Anthora*, which is the very antidote or remedie against this kinde of Aconite.

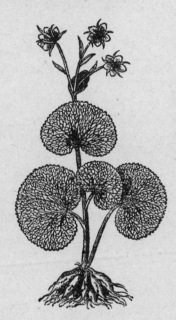

Thora Valdensis.
Broad leafed Wolfs-bane.

¶ *The Place.*

These venomous plants do grow on the Alpes, and the mountaines of Savoy and Switzerland: the first growes plentifully in the countrey of the Valdens, who inhabite part of those mountains towards Italy. The other is found on Baldus, a mountaine of Italy. They are strangers in England.

¶ *The Vertues.*

The force of these Wolfes-banes, is most pernitious and poisonsome, and (as it is reported) exceedeth the malice of *Napellus*, or any of the other Wolfes-banes, as we have said.

They say that it is of such force, that if a man especially, and then next any foure footed beast be wounded with an arrow or other instrument dipped in the juice hereof, they die within halfe an houre after remedilesse.

(375) CHAP. 151. *Of yellow Wolfes-bane.*

¶ *The Description.*

THe yellow kinde of Wolfes-bane hath large shining green leaves fashioned like a vine. His stalks grow up to the height of three cubits, bearing very fine yellow floures, fantastically fashioned, and in such manner shaped, that I can very hardly describe them to you. This plant groweth naturally in the darke hilly forrests, & shadowie woods, that are not travelled nor haunted, but by wilde and savage beasts, and is thought to bee the strongest and next unto *Thora* in his poisoning qualitie, of all the rest of the Aconites, or Woolfes banes; insomuch that if a few of the floures be chewed in the mouth, and spit forth againe presently, yet forthwith it burneth the jaws and tongue, causing them to swell, and making a certain swimming or giddinesse in the head. This calleth to my remembrance an history of a certain Gentleman dwelling in Lincolneshire, called *Mahewe*, the true report whereof my very good friend M^r. *Nicholas Belson*, somtimes Fellow of Kings Colledge in Cambridge, hath delivered unto me: M^r. *Mahewe* dwelling in Boston, a student in physick, having occasion to ride through the fens of Lincolnshire, found a root that the hogs had turned up, which seemed unto him very strange and unknowne, for that it was in the spring before the leaves were out: this he tasted, and it so inflamed his mouth, tongue, and lips, that it caused them to swell very extremely, so that before he could get to the towne of Boston, he could not speake, and no doubt had lost his life if that the Lord God had not blessed those good remedies which presently he procured and used. I have here thought good to expresse this history, for two speciall causes; the first is, that some industrious and diligent observer of nature may be provoked to seeke forth that venomous plant, or some of his kindes: for I am certainly persuaded that it is either the *Thora Valdensium*, or *Aconitum luteum*, whereof this gentleman tasted, which two plants have not at any time bin thought to grow naturally in England: the other cause is, for that I would warne others to beware by that gentlemans harme. ‡ I am of opinion that this root which M^r. *Mahewe* tasted was of the *Ranunculus flammeus major*, for that grows plentifully in such places, and is of a very hot taste and hurtfull qualitie. ‡

¶ *The Place.*

The yellow Wolfes-bane groweth in my garden, but not wilde in England, or in any other of these Northerly regions.

¶ *The Nature and Vertues.*

The facultie of this Aconite, as also of the other Wolfes-banes, is deadly to man, and likewise to all other living creatures.

It is used among the hunters which seeke after wolves, the juice whereof they put into raw flesh which the wolves devoure, and are killed.

(376)

Chap. 152. *Of other Wolfes-banes and Monkes hoods.*

¶ *The Description.*

1   HElmet-floure, or the great Monkes-hood, beareth very faire and goodly blew floures in shape like an Helmet; which are so beautifull, that a man would thinke they were of some excellent vertue, but *non est semper fides habenda fronti*. This plant is universally knowne in our London gardens and else-where; but naturally it groweth in the mountaines of Rhetia, and in sundry places of the Alps, where you shall find the grasse that groweth round it eaten up with cattell, but no part of the herbe it selfe touched, except by certaine flies, who in such abundant measure swarme about the same that they cover the whole plant: and (which is very straunge) although these flies do with great delight feed hereupon, yet of them

there is confected an Antidot or most availeable medicine against the deadly bite of the spider called *Tarantala*, or any other venomous beast whatsoever; yea, an excellent remedy not only against the Aconites, but all other poisons whatsoever. The medicine of the foresaid flies is thus made: Take of the flies which have fed themselves as is above mentioned, in number twentie, of *Aristolochia rotunda*, and bole Armoniack, of each a dram.

Aconitum maximum nutante coma.
Monkes-hood, with the bending or nodding head.

¶ *The Place.*

Divers of these Wolfs-banes grow in some gardens.

¶ *The Nature and Vertues.*

The force and facultie of Wolfs-bane is deadly to man and all kindes of beasts: the same was tried of late in Antwerpe, and is as yet fresh in memorie, by an evident experiment, but most lamentable; for when the leaves hereof were by certaine ignorant persons served up in sallads, all that did eat thereof were presently taken with most cruell symptomes, and so died.

The symptomes that follow those that doe eat of these deadly Herbs are these; their lipps and tongue swell forthwith, their eyes hang out, their thighes are stiffe, and their wits are taken from them, as *Avicen* writes, *lib.* 4. The force of this poison is such, that if the points of darts or arrowes be touched therewith, it brings deadly hurt to those that are wounded with the same.

Against so deadly a poison *Avicen* reckoneth up certain remedies, which help after the poyson is vomited up: and among these he maketh mention of the Mouse (as the copies every where have it) nourished and fed up with *Napellus*, which is altogether an enemie to the poisonsome nature of it, and delivereth him that hath taken it from all perill and danger.

Antonius Guanerius of Pavia, a famous physition in his age, in his treaty of poisons is of opinion, that it is not a mouse which *Avicen* speaketh of, but a fly: for he telleth of a certaine Philosopher who did very carefully and diligently make search after this mouse, and neither could find at any time any mouse, nor the roots of Wolfs-bane gnawn or bitten, as he had read: but in searching he found many flies feeding on the leaves, which the said Philosopher tooke, and made of them an antidote or counterpoison, which hee found to be good and effectuall against other poisons, but especially against the poison of Wolfs-bane.

The composition consisteth of two ounces of *Terra lemnia*, as many of the berries of the Bay tree, and the like weight of Mithridate, 24 of the flies that have taken their repast upon Wolfes-bane, of hony and oile Olive a sufficient quantitie.

The same opinion that *Guanerius* is of, *Pena* and *Lobel* do also hold; who affirme, that there was never seene at any time any mouse feeding thereon, but that there bee flies which resort unto it by swarmes, and feed not only upon the floures, but on the herb also.

¶ *The Danger.*

There hath bin little heretofore set down concerning the Vertues of Aconites, but much might be said of the hurts that have come hereby, as the wofull experience of the lamentable example at Antwerp yet fresh in memorie, doth declare, as we have said.

---

(377)   CHAP. 153. *Of blacke Hellebore.*

¶ *The Description.*

1 THis plant hath thicke and fat leaves of a deep green colour, the upper part whereof is somewhat bluntly nicked or toothed, having sundry divisions or cuts, in some leaves many, in others fewer. It beareth Rose-fashioned floures upon slender stems, growing immediatly out of the ground an hand-full high, somtimes very white, and oftentimes mixed with a little shew of purple: which being vaded, there succeed small husks full of blacke seeds: the roots are many, with long blacke strings comming from one head.

¶ *The Place.*

These Hellebors grow upon rough and craggy mountains: we
have them all in our London gardens.

¶ *The Time.*

The first floureth about Christmasse, if the Winter be milde and
warme.

¶ *The Names.*

It is agreed among the later writers, that these plants are *Veratra
nigra*: in English, blacke Hellebores: of divers, *Melampodium*, because it was first found by *Melampos*, who was first thought to purge
therewith *Prætus* his mad daughters, and to restore them to health.
Dioscorides writeth, that this man was a shepheard: others, a Sooth-
sayer. In high Dutch it is called Christs herbe, and that because it
floureth about the birth of our Lord Jesus Christ.

The kind called of *Fuchsius*, *Pseudohelleborus*, is in English, false
or bastard blacke Hellebor. Most name it *Consiligo*, because the
husbandmen of our time doe herewith cure their cattell, no otherwise
than the old Farriers or horse-leeches were wont to doe, that is, they
cut a slit or hole in the dewlap, as they terme it (which is an emptie
skinne under the throat of the beast) wherein they put a piece of the
root of Setter-wort or Beare-foot, suffering it there to remaine for
certaine daies together: which manner of curing they do call Settering
of their cattell, and is a manner of rowelling, as the said Horse-leeches
doe their horses with horse haire twisted, or such like, and as in
Surgerie we doe use with silke, which in stead of the word *Seton*, a
certaine Physitian called it by the name Rowell; a word very unproperly spoken of a learned man, because there would be some
difference betweene men and beasts. This manner of Settering of
cattell helpeth the disease of the lungs, the cough, and wheesing. And
it is called in English, Beare-foot, Setterwort, and Setter-grasse.

¶ *The Vertues.*

A purgation of Hellebor is good for mad and furious men, for
melancholy, dull and heavie persons, and briefly for all those that are
troubled with blacke choler, and molested with melancholy.

(380)

CHAP. 154. *Of Peionie.*

¶ *The Description.*

1 PEionie (being the male, called *Pæonia mas*: in English, Male Peiony) hath thicke red stalkes a cubit long: the leaves be great and large, consisting of divers leaves growing or joyned together upon one slender stemme or rib, not much unlike the leaves of the Wall-nut tree both in fashion and greatnesse: at the top of the stalkes grow faire large redde floures very like roses, having also in the midst, yellow threds or thrums like them in the rose called *Anthera*; which being vaded and fallen away there come in place three or foure great cods or husks, which do open when they are ripe; the inner part of which cods is of a faire red colour, wherein is contained blacke shining and polished seeds, as big as a Pease, and betweene every blacke seed is couched a red or crimson seed, which is barren and empty.

¶ *The Place.*

All the sorts of Peionies do grow in our London gardens, except that double Peiony with white floures, which we do expect from the Low-countries or Flanders.

The male Peionie groweth wild upon a conny berry in Betsome, being in the parish of South-fleet in Kent, two miles from Gravesend, and in the ground sometimes belonging to a farmer there called *John Bradley.*

‡ I have beene told that our Author himselfe planted that Peionie there, and afterwards seemed to finde it there by accident: and I doe beleeve it was so, because none before or since have ever seene or heard of it growing wilde in any part of this kingdome. ‡

¶ *The Names.*

It is called of divers *Aglaophotis,* or brightly shining, taking his name of the shining and glittering graines, which are of the colour of scarlet.

There be found two *Aglaophotides,* described by *Ælianus* in his 14 booke; one of the sea, in the 24. chapter: the other of the earth, in the 27. chapter. That of the sea is a kinde of *Fucus,* or sea mosse, which groweth upon high rocks, of the bignesse of Tamarisk, with the head of Poppy; which opening in the Summer Solstace doth yeeld in the night time a certaine fierie, and as it were sparkling brightnesse or light.

That of the earth, saith he, which by another name is called *Cynospastus*, lieth hid in the day time among other herbes, and is not knowne at all, and in the night time it is easily seene: for it shineth like a star, and glittereth with a fiery brightnesse.

And this *Aglaophotis* of the earth, or *Cynospastus*, is *Pæonia*; for *Apuleius* saith, that the seeds or graines of Peionie shine in the night time like a candle, and that plenty of it is in the night season found out and gathered by the shepheards. *Theophrastus* and *Pliny* do shew that Peionie is gathered in the night season; which *Ælianus* also affirmeth concerneth *Aglaophotis*.

Ælianus saith, that *Cynospastus* is not plucked up without danger; and that it is reported how he that first touched it, not knowing the nature thereof, perished. Therefore a string must be fastned to it in the night, and a hungry dog tied therto, who being allured by the smell of rosted flesh set towards him, may plucke it up by the roots.

Moreover, it is set downe by the said Author, as also by *Pliny* and *Theophrastus*, that of necessitie it must be gathered in the night; for if any man shall pluck off the fruit in the day time, being seene of the Wood-pecker, he is in danger to lose his eies. The like fabulous tale hath been set forth of Mandrake, the which I have partly touched in the same chapter. But all these things be most vaine and frivolous: for the root of Peionie, as also the Mandrake, may be removed at any time of the yeare, day or houre whatsoever.

But it is no marvell, that such kindes of trifles, and most superstitious and wicked ceremonies are found in the books of the most Antient Writers; for there were many things in their time very vainly feined and cogged in for ostentation sake, as by the Ægyptians and

Pæonia fœmina polyanthos flore albo.
The double white Peionie.

other counterfeit mates, as *Pliny* doth truly testifie. It is reported that these herbes tooke the name of Peionie, or *Pæan*, of that excellent Physition of the same name, who first found out and taught the knowledge of this herbe unto posteritie.

(382) CHAP. 155. *Of Cinkefoile, or five finger Grasse.*

¶ *The Description.*

CInkefoile is so common and so universally knowne, that I thinke it a needlesse travell to stand about the description.

Quinquefolium Tormentilla facie.
Wall Cinkfole.

¶ *The Time.*

These plants do floure from the beginning of May to the end of June.

¶ *The Names.*

Cinke-foile is called in Latine, *Quinquefolium*: the Apothecaries use the Greeke name *Pentaphyllon*: and sometime the Latine name. There be very many bastard names, wherewith I will not trouble your eares: in Italian, *Cinquefoglio*: in French, *Quinte fueille*: in Spanish, *Cinco en rama*: in English Cink-foile, Five finger Grasse, Five leaved grasse, and Sinkfield.

¶ *The Vertues.*

The decoction of the roots held in the mouth doth mitigate the paine of the teeth.

(386)

Chap. 156. *Of Straw-berries.*

¶ *The Kindes.*

THere be divers sorts of Straw-berries; one red, another white, a third sort greene, and likewise a wilde Straw-berry, which is altogether barren of fruit.

Fragaria & Fraga ſubalba.
White Straw-berries.

¶ *The Place.*

Straw-berries do grow upon hills and vallies, likewise in woods and other such places that bee somewhat shadowie: they prosper well in Gardens.

¶ *The Names.*

The fruit or berries are called in Latine by *Virgil* and *Ovid*, *Fraga*: neither have they any other name commonly knowne: in French, *Fraises*: in English, Straw-berries.

¶ *The Vertues.*

The leaves boyled and applied in manner of a pultis taketh away the burning heate in wounds: the decoction thereof strengthneth the gummes, and fastneth the teeth.

The distilled water drunke with white Wine is good against the passion of the heart, reviving the spirits, and making the heart merry.

The ripe Strawberries quench thirst, and take away, if they be often used, the rednesse and heate of the face.

(388)
CHAP. 157. *Of herbe* Gerard.

¶ *The Description.*

HErba Gererda, in English, herbe Gerard, or wilde Masterwort, and in some places after *Lyte*, Ashweed is of a resonable good savour.

Herba Gerardi.
Herbe Gerard, or Aiſh-weed.

¶ *The Place.*

Herbe Gerard groweth of it selfe in gardens without setting or sowing, and is so fruitfull in his increase, that where it hath once taken root, it will hardly be gotten out againe, spoiling and getting every yeere more ground, to the annoying of better herbes.

¶ *The Vertues.*

Herbe Gerard with his roots stamped, and laid upon members that are troubled or vexed with the gout, swageth the paine, and taketh away the swelling and inflammations thereof, which occasioned the Germanes to give it the name *Podagraria* because of his vertues in curing the gout.

(390)
CHAP. 158. *Of Clownes Wound-wort, or All-heale.*

¶ *The Description.*

CLownes All-heale, or the Husbandmans Wound-wort, hath long slender square stalkes of the height of two cubits: at the top of the stalkes grow the floures spike fashion, of a purple colour mixed with some few spots of white, in forme like to little hoods.

¶ *The Place.*

It groweth in moist medowes by the sides of ditches, and likewise in fertile fields that are somewhat moist, almost every where; especially in Kent about South-fleet, neer to Gravesend, and likewise in the medowes by Lambeth neere London.

¶ *The Time.*

It floureth in August, and bringeth his seed to perfection in the end of September.

¶ *The Names.*

That which hath been said in the description shall suffice touching the names, as well in Latine as English.

¶ *The Vertues.*

The leaves hereof stamped with *Axungia* or hogs grease, and applied unto greene wounds in manner of a pultesse, heale them in short time, and in such absolute manner, that it is hard for any that have not had the experience thereof to beleeve: for being in Kent about a Patient, it chanced that a poore man in mowing of Peason did cut his leg with a sithe, wherein hee made a wound to the bones, and withall very large and wide, and also with great effusion of bloud; the poore man crept unto this herbe, which he bruised with his hands, and tied a great quantitie of it unto the wound with a piece of his shirt, which presently stanched the bleeding, and ceased the paine, insomuch that the poore man presently went to his daies worke againe, and so did from day to day, without resting one day untill he was perfectly whole; which was accomplished in a few daies, by this herbe stamped with a little hogs grease, and so laid upon it in manner of a pultesse, which did as it were glew or sodder the lips of the wound together, and heale it according to the first intention, as wee terme it, that is, without drawing or bringing the wound to suppuration or matter; which was fully performed in seven daies, that would have required forty daies with balsam it selfe. I saw the wound and offered to heale the same for charity; which he refused, saying that I could not heale it so well as himselfe: a clownish answer I confesse, without any thankes for my good will: whereupon I have named it Clownes Wound-wort, as aforesaid. Since which time my selfe have cured many grievous wounds, and some mortall, with the same herbe; one for example done upon a Gentleman of Grayes Inne in Holborne, M^r. *Edmund Cartwright*, who was thrust into the lungs, the wound entring in at the lower part of the *Thorax*, or the brest-blade, even through that cartilaginous substance called *Mucronata Cartilago*, insomuch that from day to day the frothing and puffing of the lungs did spew forth of the wound such excrements as it was possessed of, besides the Gentleman was most dangerously vexed with a double quotidian fever; whom by Gods permission I perfectly cured in very short time, and with this Clownes experiment, and some of my foreknowne helpes, which were as followeth.

First I framed a slight unguent hereof thus: I tooke foure handfulls of the herbe stamped, and put them into a pan, whereunto I added foure ounces of Barrowes grease, halfe a pinte of oyle Olive, wax three ounces, which I boyled unto the consumption of the juyce (which is knowne when the stuffe doth not bubble at all) then did I straine it, putting it to the fire againe, adding thereto two ounces of Turpentine, the which I suffered to boile a little, reserving the same for my use.

The which I warmed in a sawcer, dipping therein small soft tents, which I put into the wound, defending the parts adjoyning with a plaister of *Calcitheos*, relented with oyle of roses: which manner of dressing and preserving I used even untill the wound was perfectly whole: notwithstanding once in a day I gave him two spoonfulls of this decoction following.

I tooke a quart of good Claret wine, wherein I boyled an handfull of the leaves of *Solidago Saracenica*, or Saracens consound, and foure ounces of honey, whereof I gave him in the morning two Spoonefulls to drinke in a small draught of wine tempered with a little sugar.

In like manner I cured a Shoo-makers servant in Holborne, who intended to destroy himselfe for causes knowne unto many now living: but I deemed it better to cover the fault, than to put the same in print, which might move such a gracelesse fellow to attempt the like: his attempt was thus; First, he gave himselfe a most mortall wound in the throat, in such sort, that when I gave him drinke it came forth at the wound, which likewise did blow out the candle: another deepe and grievous wound in the brest with the said dagger, and also two others in *Abdomine*: the which mortall wounds, by Gods permission, and the vertues of this herbe, I perfectly cured within twenty daies: for the which the name of God be praised.

(406)

Chap. 159. *Of Skirrets.*

¶ *The Description.*

THe leaves of the Skirret consist of many small leaves fastened to one rib, every particular one whereof is something nicked in the edges, but they are lesser, greener, & smoother than those of the Parsnep. The stalkes be short, and seldome a cubit high; the floures in the spokie tufts are white, the roots bee many in number, growing out of one head an hand breadth long, most commonly not a finger thick, they are sweet, white, good to be eaten, and most pleasant in taste.

¶ *The Place and Time.*

This skirret is planted in Gardens, and especially by the root, for the greater and thicker ones being taken away, the lesser are put into the earth againe: which thing is best to be done in March or Aprill, before the stalkes come up, and at this time the roots which bee gathered are eaten raw, or boyled.

¶ *The Names.*

This herb is called in Latine, *Sisarum*: in English, Skirret and Skirwort. And this is that *Siser* or Skirret which *Tiberius* the Emperour commanded to bee conveied unto him from Gelduba a castle about the river of Rhene, as *Pliny* reporteth in *lib*. 16. *cap*. 5. The Skirret is a medicinable herbe, and is the same that the foresaid Emperour did so much commend, insomuch that he desired the same to be brought unto him every yeare out of Germany.

¶ *The Vertues.*

They be eaten boiled, with vineger, salt, and a little oyle, after the manner of a sallad, and oftentimes they be fried in oile and butter, and also dressed after other fashions, according to the skill of the cooke, and the taste of the eater.

(411)   CHAP. 160. *Of Fennell.*

¶ *The Description.*

1   THe Fennell, called in Latine, *Fœniculum*, is so well knowne amongst us, that it were but lost labour to describe the same.

2   The second kinde of Fennell is likewise well knowne by the name of Sweet Fennell, so called because the seeds therof are in taste sweet like unto Annise seeds, resembling the common Fennell, saving that the leaves are larger and fatter, or more oleous: the seed greater and whiter, and the whole plant in each respect greater.

Fœniculum vulgare.
Common Fennell.

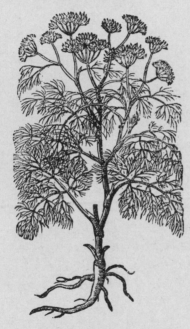

¶ *The Place.*

These herbs are set and sowne in gardens; but the second doth not prosper well in this Countrey: for being sowne of good and perfect seed, yet in the second yeare after his sowing it will degenerate from the right kinde, and become common Fennell.

¶ *The Time.*

They floure in June and July, and the seed is ripe in the end of August.

¶ *The Vertues.*

The pouder of the seed of Fennell drunke for certaine daies together fasting preserveth the eye-sight: whereof was written this Distichon following:

Of Fennell, Roses, Vervain, Rue, and Celandine,
Is made a water good to cleere the sight of eine.

(416)

Chap. 161. *Of Chervill.*

¶ *The Description.*

1 THe leaves of Chervill are slender, and diversly cut, something hairy, of a whitish greene: the stalkes be short, slender, round, and hollow within, which at the first together with the leaves are of a whitish green, but tending to a red when the seeds are ripe: the floures be white, and grow upon scattered tufts.

2 Great Chervill hath large leaves deepely cut or jagged, in shew very like unto Hemlockes, of a very good and pleasant smell and taste like unto Chervill, and something hairy, which hath caused us to call it sweet Chervill.

‡ There is found in some part of the Alps, as about Genua and in other places, another *Myrrhis*, which in the leaves and umbels is like that of the last described, but the whole plant is lesse.

Cerefolium fylveftre.
Hedge Cheruill.

¶ *The Place.*

The common Chervill groweth in gardens with other pot-herbes: it prospers in a ground that is dunged and somewhat moist. The great sweet Chervill groweth in my garden, and in the gardens of other men who have bin diligent in these matters.

¶ *The Time.*

These herbs floure in May, and their seed is ripe in July.

¶ *The Names.*

Columella nameth it *Chærephyllum*, and it is thought to be so called, because it delights to grow with many leaves, or rather in that it causeth joy and gladnesse.

Myrrhis is also called *Myrrha*, taken from his pleasant savor of

Myrrh: in English it is called Chervill, sweete Chervill, or sweete Cicely.

¶ *The Nature and Vertues.*

It is used very much among the Dutch people in a kinde of Loblolly or hotchpot which they do eat, called Warmus.

The leaves of sweet Chervill are exceeding good, wholesome and pleasant among other sallad herbs, giving the taste of Anise seed unto the rest.

The seeds eaten as a sallad whiles they are yet green, with oile, vineger, and pepper, exceed all other sallads by many degrees, both in pleasantnesse of taste, sweetnesse of smell, and wholsomnesse for the cold and feeble stomacke.

The roots are likewise most excellent in a sallad, if they be boiled and afterwards dressed as the cunning Cooke knoweth how better than my selfe: notwithstanding I use to eat them with oile and vineger, being first boiled; which is very good for old people that are dull and without courage: it rejoiceth and comforteth the heart, and increaseth their lust and strength.

---

(419)   CHAP. 162. *Of Mede-sweet, or Queene of the Medowes.*

¶ *The Description.*

1   THis herbe hath leaves like Agrimony, consisting of divers leaves set upon a middle rib like those of the ash tree, every small leaf sleightly snipt about the edges, white on the inner side, and on the upper side crumpled or wrinkled like unto those of the Elme tree; whereof it tooke the name *Ulmaria*, of the similitude or likenesse that the leaves have with the Elme leaves. The stalke is three or foure foot high, rough, and very fragile or easie to bee broken, of a reddish purple colour: on the top whereof are very many little floures clustering and growing together, of a white colour tending to yellownesse, and of a pleasant sweet smell, as are the leaves likewise: after which come the seeds, small, crookedly turning or winding one with another, made into a fine little head: the root hath a sweet smell, spreading far abroad, black without, & of a darkish red color within.

¶ *The Place.*

It groweth in the brinkes of waterie ditches and rivers sides, and also in medowes: it liketh watery and moist places, and groweth almost every where.

Regina prati.
Queene of the Medow.

¶ *The Time.*

It floureth and flouresheth in June, July, and August.

¶ *The Names.*

It is called of the later age *Regina prati*: in English, Meads-sweet, Medowsweet, and Queen of the medowes.

¶ *The Vertues.*

It is reported, that the floures boiled in wine and drunke, do make the heart merrie.

The leaves and floures farre excell all other strowing herbes, for to decke up houses, to straw in chambers, halls, and banqueting houses in the Summer time; for the smell thereof makes the heart merrie, delighteth the senses: neither doth it cause head-ache, or lothsomenesse to meat, as some other sweet smelling herbes do.

The distilled water of the floures dropped into the eies, taketh away the burning and itching thereof, and cleareth the sight.

---

(431) Chap. 163. *Of Earth-Nut, Earth Chestnut, or Kippernut.*

¶ *The Description.*

1   Earth-nut or Kipper-nut hath small even crested stalks a foot or somewhat more high: whereon grow next the ground, leaves like those of Parsley, and those that do grow higher like unto those of Dill; the white floures do stand on the

top of the stalks in spokie rundles, like the tops of Dill, which turne into small seed, growing together by couples, of a very good smell, not unlike to those of Fennell, but much smaller: the root is round, knobbed, with certaine eminences or bunchings out; browne without, white within, of a firme and sollid substance, and of a taste like the Chesse-nut, or Chest-nut, whereof it tooke his name.

¶ The Place.

These herbes do grow in pastures and corne fields almost every where: there is a field adjoining to High-gate, on the right side of the middle of the village, covered over with the same; and likewise in the next field to the conduit heads by Maribone, neer the way that leads to Padington by London, and in divers other places.

¶ The Time.

They floure in June and July: the seed commeth to perfection afterward.

¶ The Vertues.

The Dutch people doe use to eat them boiled and buttered, as we do Parseneps and Carrots.

There is a plaister made of the seeds hereof, whereof to write in this place were impertinent to our historie.

---

(435)   ## Chap. 164. *Of the great Celandine or Swallow-wort.*

¶ The Description.

1   THe great Celandine hath a tender brittle stalke, round, hairy, and full of branches, each whereof hath divers knees or knotty joints set with leaves not unlike to those of Columbine, but tenderer, and deeper cut or jagged, of a grayish green under, and greene on the other side tending to blewnesse: the floures grow at the top of the stalks, of a gold yellow colour, in shape like those of the Wal-floure: after which come long cods full of bleak or pale seeds: the whole plant is of a strong unpleasant smell,

and yeeldeth a thicke juice of a milky substance, of the colour of Saffron: the root is thicke and knobby, with some threds anexed thereto, which beeing broken or bruised, yeeldeth a sap or juice of the colour of gold.

¶ *The Place*.

It groweth in untilled places by common way sides, among briers and brambles, about old wals, and in the shade rather than in the Sun.

¶ *The Time*.

It is greene all the yeare: it floureth from Aprill to a good part of Summer: the cods are perfected in the mean time.

Chelidonium majus folio magis diſſecto.
Great Celandine with more cut leaues.

¶ *The Names*.

It is called in Latine, *Chelidonium majus*, and *Hirundinarium major*: in English, Celandine, Swallow-wort, and Tetter-wort.

It is called Celandine not because it first springeth at the comming in of Swallowes, or dieth when they go away, (for as we have said, it may be found all the yere) but because some hold opinion, that with this herb the dams restore sight to their yong ones when they cannot see. Which things are vain and false; for *Cornelius Celsus, lib. 6.* witnesseth, That when the sight of the eies of divers yong birds is put forth by some outward means, it will after a time be restored of it selfe, and soonest of all the sight of the Swallow: whereupon (as the same Author saith) the tale grew, how thorow an herb the dams restore that thing which healeth of it selfe. The very same doth *Aristotle* alledge, *lib. 6. de Animal.* The eies of Swallowes (saith he) that are not fledge, if a man do pricke them out, do afterwards grow againe and perfectly recover their sight.

¶ *The Vertues*.

The juice of the herbe is good to sharpen the sight, for it clenseth and consumeth away slimie things that cleave about the ball of the eye, and hinder the sight, and especially being boiled with hony in a brasen vessell, as *Dioscorides* teacheth.

The root being chewed is reported to be good against the tooth-ache.

The juice must be drawn forth in the beginning of Summer, and dried in the sunne, saith *Dioscorides*.

The root cut into small pieces is good to be given unto Hauks against sundry diseases, wherunto they are subject.

(440)   CHAP. 165. *Of Valerian, or Setwall.*

¶ *The Description.*

1   THe tame or garden Valerian hath his first leaves long, broad, smooth, greene, and undivided; and the leaves upon the stalkes greater, longer, and deeply gashed on either side, like the leaves of the greater Parsenep, but yet lesser: the stalke is above a cubit high, smooth, and hollow, with certaine joynts farre distant one from another: out of which joynts grow forth a couple of leaves, and in the tops of the stalkes upon spokie rundles stand floures heaped together, which are small, opening themselves out of a long little narrow necke, of colour whitish, and sometimes withall of a light red: the root is an inch thicke, growing aslope, fastned on the upper part of the earth by a multitude of strings, the most part of it standing out of the ground, of a pleasant sweet smell when it is broken.

Valeriana Petræa.
Stone Valerian.

¶ *The Place.*

The first and likewise the Greeke Valerian are planted in gardens; the wilde ones are found in moist places hard to rivers sides, ditches, and watery pits; yet the greater of these is brought into gardens where it flourisheth, but the lesser hardly prospereth.

¶ *The Time.*

These floure in May, June, and July, and most of the Summer moneths.

¶ *The Names.*

Generally the Valerians are called by one name, in Latine, *Valeriana*: in shoppes also *Phu*, which for the most part is meant by the garden Valerian: in English, Valerian, Capons taile, and Setwall; but unproperly, for that name belongeth to *Zedoaria*, which is not Valerian.

¶ *The Vertues.*

The dry root is put into counterpoysons and medicines preservative against the pestilence, as are treacles, mithridates, and such like: whereupon it hath been had (and is to this day among the poore people of our Northerne parts) in such veneration amongst them, that no broths, pottage or physicall meats are worth any thing, if Setwall were not at an end: whereupon some woman Poët or other hath made these verses.

> They that will have their heale,
> Must put Setwall in their keale.

It is used generally in sleight cuts, wounds, and small hurts.

---

(442)   Chap. 166. *Of Larks heele or Larks claw.*

¶ *The Description.*

1 THe garden Larks spur hath a round stem ful of branches, set with tender jagged leaves very like unto the small Sothernwood: the floures grow alongst the stalks toward the tops of the branches, of a blew colour, consisting of five little leaves which grow together and make one hollow floure, having a taile or spur at the end turning in like the spur of Todeflax. After come the seed, very blacke, like those of Leekes: the root perisheth at the first approch of Winter.

2 The second Larks spur is like the precedent, but somewhat smaller in stalkes and leaves: the floures are also like in forme, but of

a white colour, wherein especially is the difference. These floures are sometimes of a purple colour, sometimes white, murrey, carnation, and of sundry other colours, varying infinitely, according to the soile or country wherein they live.

3   The wilde Larks spur hath most fine jagged leaves, cut and backt into divers parts, confusedly set upon a small middle tendrell: among which grow the floures, in shape like the others, but a great deale lesser, sometimes purple, otherwhiles white, and often of a mixt colour. The root is small and threddy.

Confolida fatiua flore albo vel rubro.
White or red Larks fpur.

¶ *The Place.*

These plants are set and sowne in gardens: the last groweth wilde in corne fields, and where corn hath grown.

¶ *The Time.*

They floure for the most part all Summer long, from June to the end of August, and oft-times after.

¶ *The Names.*

Larks heele is called *Flos Regius*: of divers, *Consolida regalis*: who make it one of the Consounds or Comfreyes. It is also thought to be the *Delphinium* which *Dioscorides* describes in his third booke; wherewith it may agree: for the floures, and especially before they be perfected, have a certaine shew and likenesse of those Dolphins, which old pictures and armes of certain antient families have expressed with a crooked and bending figure or shape, by which signe also the heavenly Dolphine is set forth.

¶ *The Vertues.*

We finde little extant of the vertues of Larks heele, either in the antient or later writers, worth the noting, or to be credited; yet it is set downe, that the seed of Larks spur drunken is good against the stingings of Scorpions; whose vertues are so forceable, that the herbe onely throwne before the Scorpion or any other venomous beast, couseth them to be without force or strength to hurt, insomuch that they cannot move or stirre until the herbe be taken away: with many other such trifling toyes not worth the reading.

(443) ### Chap. 167. *Of Gith, or Nigella.*

¶ *The Description.*

Nigella, which is both faire and pleasant, called Damaske Nigella, is very like unto the wilde Nigella in his small cut and jagged leaves, but his stalke is longer: the flours are like the former, but greater, and every floure hath five small greene leaves under him, as it were to support and beare him up: which floures being gone, there succeed and follow knops and seed like the former, but without smell or savour.

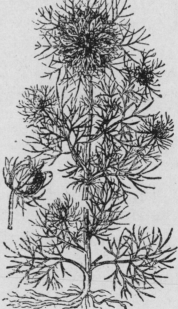

Nigella flore albo multiplici.
Damaske Nigella.

¶ *The Place.*

The tame are sowne in gardens: the wilde ones doe grow of themselves among corne and other graine, in divers countries beyond the seas.

¶ *The Time.*

The seed must be sowne in Aprill: it floureth in July and August.

¶ *The Names.*

Gith is called in Italian, *Nigella*: in English, Gith, and Nigella Romana, in Cambridgeshire, Bishops wort: and also *Divæ Catherinæ flos*, Saint Katharines floure.

¶ *The Vertues.*

The seed parched or dried at the fire, brought into pouder, and wrapped in a piece of fine lawne or sarcenet, cureth all murs, catarrhes, rheumes, and the pose, drieth the braine, and restoreth the sence of smelling unto those which have lost it, being often smelled unto from day to day, and made warme at the fire when it is used.

It takes away freckles, being laid on mixed with vineger. To be briefe, as *Galen* saith, it is a most excellent remedy.

It serveth well among other sweets to put into sweet waters, bagges, and odoriferous pouders.

(444)   ## Chap. 168. *Of Cockle.*

¶ *The Description.*

Cockle is a common and hurtfull weed in our Corne, and very well knowne by the name of Cockle. This plant hath straight, slender, and hairy stems, garnished with long hairy and grayish leaves, which grow together by couples, inclosing the stalke round about: the floures are of a purple colour, declining to rednesse, consisting of five small leaves, in proportion very like to wilde Campions; when the floures be vaded there follow round knobs or heads full of blackish seed, like unto the seed of *Nigella*, but without any smell or savour at all.

¶ *The Place and Time.*

The place of his growing and time of his flouring, are better knowne than desired.

¶ *The Temperature.*

The seed of Cockle is hot and dry in the later end of the second degree.

¶ *The Vertues.*

What hurt it doth among corne, the spoile of bread, as well in colour, taste, and unwholesomnesse, is better knowne than desired.

CHAP. 169. *Of Columbine.*

¶ *The Description.*

THe blew Columbine hath leaves like the great Celandine, but somewhat rounder, indented on the edges, parted into divers sections, of a blewish green colour, which beeing broken, yeeld forth little juice or none at all: the stalke is a cubit and a halfe high, slender, reddish, and sleightly haired: the slender sprigs whereof bring forth everie one one floure with five little hollow hornes, as it were hanging forth, with small leaves standing upright, of the shape of little birds: these floures are of colour somtimes blew, at other times of a red or purple, often white, or of mixt colours, which to distinguish severally were to small purpose, being things so familiarly known to all: after the floures grow up cods, in which is contained little black and glittering seed: the roots are thicke, with some strings thereto belonging, which continue many yeres.

Aquileia rubra.
Red Columbines.

¶ *The Place.*

They are set and sowne in gardens for the beautie and variable colour of the floures.

¶ *The Time.*

They floure in May, June, and July.

¶ *The Names.*

Columbine is called of the later Herbarists, *Aquilegia*: of some, *Herba Leonis*, or the herbe wherein the Lion doth delight.

¶ *The Vertues.*

They are used especially to decke the gardens of the curious, garlands and houses.

(453) Chap. 170. *Of Mugwort*.

¶ *The Description*.

Ugwort hath broad leaves, very much cut or cloven like the leaves of common Wormewood, but larger, of a darke greene colour above, and hoarie underneath: the stalkes are long and straight, and full of branches, whereon do grow small round buttons, which are the floures, smelling like Marjerome when they wax ripe: the root is great, and of a wooddie substance.

¶ *The Place*.

The common Mugwort groweth wilde in sundry places about the borders of fields, about high waies, brooke sides, and such like places.

Sea Mugwort groweth about Rie and Winchelsea castle, and at Portsmouth by the Isle of Wight.

¶ *The Time*.

They floure in July and August.

¶ *The Names*.

Mugwort is called in Latine, *Artemisia*, which name it had of *Artemisia* Queene of Halicarnassus, and wife of noble *Mausolus* King of Caria, who adopted it for her owne herbe.

¶ *The Vertues*.

Pliny saith, That the traveller or wayfaring man that hath the herbe tied about him feeleth no wearisomnesse at all; and that he who hath it about him can be hurt by no poysonsome medicines, nor by any wilde beast, neither yet by the Sun it selfe; and also that it is drunke against *Opium*, or the juyce of blacke Poppy. Many other fantasticall devices invented by Poëts are to be seene in the Works of the Antient Writers, tending to witchcraft and sorcerie, and the great dishonour of God: wherefore I do of purpose omit them, as things unworthy of my recording, to your reviewing.

(457) Chap. 171. *Of Sperage or Asparagus.*

¶ *The Description.*

THe manured or garden Sperage, hath at his first rising out of the ground thicke tender shoots very soft and brittle, of the thicknesse of the greatest swans quill, in taste like the green bean having at the top a certaine scaly soft bud, which in time groweth to a branch of the height of two cubits, divided into divers other smaller branches, wheron are set many little leaves like haires, more fine than the leaves of Dill: amongst which come forth small mossie yellowish floures which yeeld forth the fruit, green at the first, afterward as red as Corall, of the bignesse of a small pease; wherein is contained grosse blackish seed exceeding hard, which is the cause that it lieth so long in the ground after his sowing, before it spring up: the roots are many thicke soft and spongie strings hanging downe from one head, and spred themselves all about, whereby it greatly increaseth.

Asparagus sativus.
Garden Sperage.

¶ *The Place.*

Our garden Asparagus groweth wilde in Essex, in a medow neere to a mill, beyond a village called Thorp; and also at Singleton not far from Carby, and in the medowes neere Moulton in Lincolnshire. Likewise it growes in great plenty neere Harwich, at a place called Bandamar lading, and at North Moulton in Holland a part of Lincolnshire.

¶ *The Time.*

The bare naked tender shoots of Sperage spring up in Aprill, at what time they are eaten in sallads; they floure in June and July, the fruit is ripe in September.

¶ *The Names.*

It is named Asparagus, of the excellency, because *asparagi,* or the springs hereof are preferred before those of other plants whatsoever: for this Latine word *Asparagus* doth properly signifie the first spring or sprout of every plant, especially when it is tender, and before it do grow into an hard stalk, as are the buds, tendrels, or yong springs of wild Vine or hops, and such like.

¶ *The Vertues.*

The first sprouts or naked tender shoots hereof be oftentimes sodden in flesh broth and eaten; or boiled in faire water, and seasoned with oile, vineger, salt, and pepper, then are served up as a sallad: they are pleasant to the taste.

(460)

CHAP. **172.** *Of Madder.*

Rubia ſpicata Cretica,
Small Candy Madder.

¶ *The Kindes.*

THere is but one kinde of Madder only which is manured or set for use, but if all those that are like it in leaves and manner of growing were referred thereto, there should be many sorts, as Goose-grasse, soft Cliver, our Ladies Bedstraw, Woodroofe, and Crossewort; all which are like to Madder in leaves, and therefore thought to be wilde kindes thereof.

¶ *The Description.*

THe garden Madder hath long stalkes or trailing branches dispiersed farre abroad upon the ground, square, rough, and full of joints, at every joint set round with greene rough leaves in manner of a starre, or like those of Woodroofe: the floures grow at the top of the branches, of a feint yellow colour.

¶ *The Vertues.*

The decoction of the root of Madder is every where commended for those that are bursten, brused, wounded, and that are fallen from high places.

It stencheth bleeding, mitigateth inflammations, and helpeth those parts that bee hurt and brused.

For these causes they be mixed with potions, which the later Physitians call wound drinkes.

(475/476)

CHAP. 173. *Of Thistles.*

¶ *The Kindes.*

THe matter of the Thistles is divers, some Thistles serve for nourishment, as the Artichoke without prickles, and the Artichoke with prickles; other for medicine, as the root of Carline which is good for many things; the blessed Thistle also, otherwise called *Carduus benedictus*; Sea Hulver, and divers others: some are poisonsome, as *Chamæleon niger*; one smooth, plaine, and without prickles, as the Thistle called Beares Breech, or *Acanthus sativus*, whereof there is another with prickles, which we make the wilde.

¶ *The Description.*

1   THe common Thistle, whereof the greatest quantity of down is gathered for divers purposes, as well by the poore to stop pillowes, cushions, and beds for want of feathers, as also bought of the rich upholsters to mix with the feathers and down they do sell, which deceit would be looked unto: this Thistle hath great leaves, long and broad, gashed about the edges, and set with sharpe and stiffe prickles all alongst the edges, covered all over with a soft cotton or downe: out from the middest whereof riseth up a long stalke about two cubits high, cornered, and set with filmes, and also full of prickles: the heads are likewise cornered with prickles, and bring forth floures consisting of many whitish threds:

the seed which succeedeth them is wrapped up in downe; it is long, of a light crimson colour, and lesser than the seed of bastard Saffron: the root groweth deep in the ground, being white, hard, wooddy, and not without strings.

Acanthium album.
The white Cotton Thistle.

¶ *The Place.*

These Thistles grow by high waies sides, and in ditches almost every where.

¶ *The Time.*

They floure from June untill August, the second yeare after they be sowne: and in the mean time the seed waxeth ripe, which being thorow ripe the herbe perisheth, as doe likewise most of the other Thistles, which live no longer than till the seed be fully come to maturity.

¶ *The Names.*

This Thistle is called in English, Cotton-Thistle, white Cotton-Thistle, wilde white Thistle, Argentine or the Silver Thistle.

¶ *The Vertues.*

Dioscorides saith, That the leaves and roots hereof are a remedy for those that have their bodies drawne backwards.

---

(480)

CHAP. 174. *Of Golden Thistle.*

¶ *The Description.*

1   THe stalkes of Golden Thistle rise up forthwith from the root, being many, round, and branched. The leaves are long, of a beautifull greene, with deepe gashes on the edges, and set with most sharpe prickles: the floures come from the bosome of the leaves, set in a scaly chaffie knap, very like to Succory

floures, but of colour as yellow as gold: in their places come up broad flat and thin seeds, not great, nor wrapped in downe: the root is long, a finger thicke, sweet, soft, and good to be eaten, wherewith swine are much delighted: there issueth forth of this Thistle in what part soever it is cut or broken, a juyce as white as milke.

2   The golden Thistle of Peru, called in the West Indies, *Fique del Inferno*, a friend of mine brought it unto me from an Island there called Saint Johns Island, among other seeds. What reason the inhabitants there have to call it so, it is unto me unknowne, unlesse it bee because of his fruit, which doth much resemble a fig in shape and bignesse, but so full of sharpe and venomous prickles, that whosoever had one of them in his throat, doubtlesse it would send him packing either to heaven or to hell. The vertues hereof are yet unknowne unto me, wherefore I purpose not to set downe any thing thereof by way of conjecture, but shall, God willing, be ready to declare that which certaine knowledge and experience either of mine owne or others, shall make manifest unto me.

¶ *The Place.*

The golden Thistle is sowne in gardens of the Low-Countries. *Petrus Bellonius* writes, That it groweth plentifully in Candy, and also in most places of Italy: *Clusius* reporteth that he found it in the fields of Spaine, and of the kingdome of Castile, and about Montpelier, with fewer branches, and of a higher growth.

The Indian Thistle groweth in Saint Johns Island in the West Indies, and prospereth very well in my garden.

¶ *The Vertues.*

Pliny saith that the root hereof was commended by *Eratosthenes*, in the poore mans supper.

(484)

CHAP. 175. *Of Sea Holly.*

¶ *The Description.*

1   SEa Holly hath broad leaves almost like to Mallow leaves, but cornered in the edges, and set round about with hard prickles, fat, of a blewish white, and of an aromatical or spicy taste: the stalke is thick, about a cubit high, now and then som-

what red below: it breaketh forth in the tops into prickly round heads or knops, of the bignesse of a Wall-nut, held in for the most part with six prickly leaves compassing the top of the stalke round about; which leaves as well as the heads are of a glistering blew: the floures forth of the heads are likewise blew, with white threds in the midst: the root is of the bignesse of a mans finger, so very long, as that it cannot be all plucked up but very seldome; set here and there with knots, and of taste sweet and pleasant.

¶ The Place.

Eryngium marinum growes by the sea side upon the baich and stony ground. I found it growing plentifully at Whitstable in Kent, at Rie and Winchelsea in Sussex, and in Essex at Landamer lading, at Harwich, and upon Langtree point on the other side of the water, from whence I brought plants for my garden.

¶ The Vertues.

The roots condited or preserved with sugar as hereafter followeth, are exceeding good to be given to old and aged people that are consumed and withered with age, and which want natural moisture: they are also good for other sorts of people, nourishing and restoring the aged, and amending the defects of nature in the yonger.

¶ The manner to condite Eringos.

Refine sugar fit for the purpose, and take a pound of it, the white of an egge, and a pinte of cleer water, boile them together and scum it, then let it boile until it be come to good strong syrrup, and when it is boiled, as it cooleth adde thereto a saucer full of rose water, a spoone full of Cinnamon water, and a grain of muske, which have been infused together the night before, and now strained: into which syrrup being more than halfe cold, put in your roots to soke and infuse untill the next day; your roots being ordered in manner hereafter following:

These your roots being washed and picked, must be boiled in faire water by the space of foure houres, til they be soft: then must they be pilled clean as ye pil parsneps, & the pith must be drawn out at the end of the root: but if there be any whose pith cannot be drawn out at the end, then you must slit them and so take it out: these you must also keep from much handling, that they may be clean: let them remain in the syrrup till the next day, and then set them on the fire in a faire broad pan untill they be very hot, but let them not boile at all: let them remain over the fire an houre or more, remooving them easily in the pan from one place to another with a wooden slice. This done, have in a readinesse great cap or royall papers, whereupon strow some sugar, upon which lay your roots, having taken them out of the pan. These papers you must put into a stouve or hot-house to harden; but if you have not such a place, lay them before a good fire: in this maner if you condite your roots, there is not any that can prescribe you a better way. And thus you may condite any other root whatsoever, which will not only be exceeding delicat, but very wholsome, and effectual against the diseases above named.

They report of the herb sea Holly, if one goat take it into her mouth, it causeth her first to stand still, and afterwards the whole flocke, untill such time as the sheepheard take it from her mouth. *Plutarch.*

---

(487)

Chᴀᴘ. 176. *Of Teasels.*

¶ *The Description.*

I Garden Teasell is also of the number of the Thistles; it bringeth forth a stalke that is straight, very long, jointed, and ful of prickles: the leaves grow forth of the joynts by couples, not onely opposite or set one right against another, but also compassing the stalke about, and fastened together; and so fastened, that they hold dew and raine water in manner of a little bason: these be long, of a light greene colour, and like to those of Lettice, but full of prickles in the edges, and have on the outside all alongst the ridge stiffer prickles: on the tops of the stalkes stand heads with sharpe prickles like those of the Hedge-hog, and crooking backward at the point like hookes: out of which heads grow little floures: The seed is like Fennell-seed, and in taste bitter: the heads wax white when they grow old, and there are found in the midst of them when they are cut, certaine little magots: the root is white, and of a meane length.

¶ *The Place.*

The first called the tame Teasell is sowne in this country in gardens, to serve the use of Fullers and Clothworkers.

¶ *The Time.*

These floure for the most part in June and July.

Dipſacus ſylueſtris.
Wilde Teaſell.

¶ *The Names.*

Teasell is called in Latine, *Dipsacus*, and *Laver Lavacrum*, of the forme of the leaves made up in fashion of a bason, which is never without water: in English, Teasell, Carde Teasell, and Venus bason.

¶ *The Vertues.*

There is small use of Teasell in medicines: the heads (as we have said) are used to dresse woollen cloth with.

It is needlesse here to alledge those things that are added touching the little wormes or magots found in the heads of the Teasell, and which are to be hanged about the necke, or to mention the like thing that *Pliny* reporteth of Galedragon: for they are nothing else but most vaine and trifling toies, as my selfe have proved a little before the impression hereof, having a most grievous ague, and of long continuance: notwithstanding Physicke charmes, these worms hanged about my neck, spiders put into a walnut shell, and divers such foolish toies that I was constrained to take by fantasticke peoples procurement; notwithstanding, I say, my helpe came from God himselfe, for these medicines and all other such things did me no good at all.

(494) CHAP. 177. *Of three leafed Grasse or Medow Trefoile.*

¶ *The Description.*

1   MEdow Trefoile bringeth forth stalkes a cubit long, round and something hairy, the greater part of which creepeth upon the ground: whereon grow leaves consisting of three joined together, one standing a little from another, of

which those that are next the ground and roots are rounder, and they that grow on the upper part longer, having for the most part in the midst a white spot like a halfe moone. The floures grow at the tops of the stalks in a tuft or small Fox-taile eare, of a purple colour, and sweet of taste. The seed growes in little husks, round and blackish: the root is long, wooddy, and groweth deep.

2   Likewise we have in our fields a smaller Trefoile that brings forth yellow flours, a greater and a lesser, & divers others also, differing from these in divers notable points, the which to distinguish apart would greatly inlarge our volume, and yet to small purpose: therefore we leave them to be distinguished by the Curious, who may at the first view easily perceive the difference, and also that they be of one stocke or kindred.

Trifolium pratenſe.
Medow Trefoile.

¶ *The Place.*

Common medow Trefoile grows in medowes, fertile pastures, and waterish grounds: the others love the like soile.

¶ *The Time.*

They floure from May to the end of Summer.

¶ *The Names.*

Medow Trefoile is called in Latine *Trifolium pratense*: in English, Common Trefoile, Three leafed grasse: of some, Suckles, Hony-suckles, and Cocks-heads: in Irish, *Shamrocks*.

¶ *The Vertues.*

Oxen and other cattell do feed on the herb, as also calves and yong lambs. The flours are acceptable to Bees.

Pliny writeth and setteth it downe for certaine, that the leaves hereof do tremble and stand right up against the comming of a storme or tempest.

CHAP. 178. *Of Wood Sorrell, or Stubwort.*

¶ *The Description.*

1 OXys Pliniana, or *Trifolium acetosum*, being a kinde of three leafed grasse, is a low and base herbe without stalke; the leaves immediately rising from the root upon short stemmes at their first comming forth folded together, but afterward they do spred abroad, and are of a faire light greene

Oxys alba.
White Wood Sorrell.

colour, in number three, like the rest of the Trefoiles, but that each leafe, hath a deep cleft or rift in the middle: among these leaves come up small and weake tender stems, such as the leaves do grow upon, which beare small starre-like floures of a white colour, with some brightnes of carnation dasht over the same: the floure consisteth of five small leaves; after which come little round knaps or huskes full of yellowish seed: the root is very threddy, and of a reddish colour: the whole herbe is in taste like Sorrell, but much sharper and quicker, and maketh better greene sauce than any other herbe or Sorrell whatsoever.

¶ *The Place.*

These plants grow in woods and under bushes, in sandie and shadowie places in every countrey.

¶ *The Time.*

They floure from the beginning of Aprill unto the end of May and midst of June.

¶ *The Names.*

Wood Sorrell or Cuckow Sorrell is called in Latine *Trifolium acetosum*: the Apothecaries and Herbarists call it *Alleluya*, and *Panis*

Cuculi, or Cuckowes meate, because either the Cuckow feedeth thereon or by reason when it springeth forth and floureth the Cuckow singeth most, at which time also *Alleluya* was wont to be sung in Churches. In French, *Pain de Cocu*: in English, wood Sorrell, wood Sower, Sower Trefoile, Stubwort, Alleluia, and Sorrell du Bois.

¶ *The Vertues*.

Sorrell du Bois or Wood Sorrell stamped and used for greene sauce, is good for them that have sicke and feeble stomackes; for it strengthneth the stomacke, procureth appetite, and of all Sorrell sauces is the best, not onely in vertue, but also in the pleasantnesse of his taste.

(527)

CHAP. 179. *Of some Pulses*.

¶ *The Description*.

‡ THis though it be not frequently found, is no stranger with us; for I have found it in the corne fields about Dart-

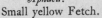

Aphaca.
Small yellow Fetch.

ford in Kent and some other places. It hath long slender joynted creeping stalkes, divided into sundry branches, whereon stand pretty greene three cornered leaves two at a joynt, in shape and bignesse like those of the lesser Binde-weed. Out of the bosomes of these leaves at each joynt comes a clasping tendrel, and commonly together with it a foot-stalke some inch or more long, bearing a pretty little pease-fash-ioned yellow flour, which is succeeded by a short flattish cod containing six or seven little seeds. This floures in June, July, and August, and so ripens the seed.

I finde mention in *Stowes* Chronicle, in *Anno* 1555, of a certaine Pulse or Pease, as they term it, wherewith the poore people at that time there being a great dearth, were miraculously helped: he thus mentions it; In the moneth of August (saith he) in Suffolk at a place by the sea side all of hard stone and pibble, called in those parts a shelfe, lying betweene the townes of Orford and Aldborough, where nether grew grasse, nor any earth was ever seene; it chanced in this barren place suddenly to spring up without any tillage or sowing, great abundance of Peason, whereof the poore gathered (as men judged) above an hundred quarters, yet remained some ripe and some blossoming, as many as ever there were before: to the which place rode the Bishop of Norwich and the Lord *Willoughby*, with others in great number, who found nothing but hard rockie stone the space of three yards under the roots of these Peason: which roots were great and long, and very sweet.

Gesner also, *de Aquatilibus, lib.* 4. *pag.* 256 making mention, out of Dr *Caius* his letters, of the spotted English Whale, taken about that time at Lin in Northfolke, also thus mentions those Pease: [*Anno* 1555]. These Pease, which by their great encrease did such good to the poore that yeare, without doubt grew there for many yeares before, but were not observed till hunger made them take notice of them, and quickned their invention, which commonly in our people is very dull, especially in finding out food of this nature. ‡

⁽⁵³¹⁾ **Chap. 180.** *Of Rue, or herbe Grace.*

¶ *The Description.*

GArden Rue is a shrub full of branches, now and then a yard high, or higher: the stalkes whereof are covered with a whitish barke, the branches are more green: the leaves hereof consist of divers parts, and be divided into wings, about which are certaine little ones, of an odde number, something broad, more long than round, smooth and somewhat fat, of a gray colour or greenish blew: the floures in the top of the branches are of a pale yellow consisting of foure little leaves, something hollow: in the middle of which standeth up a little head or button foure square, seldome five square, containing as many little coffers as it hath corners, being compassed about with divers little yellow threds: out of which hang pretty fine tips of one colour; the seed groweth in the little coffers: the root is wooddy, and fastned with many strings: this Rue hath a very strong and ranke smell, and a biting taste.

¶ *The Place*.

Garden Rue joyeth in sunny and open places: it prospereth in rough and bricky ground and among ashes.

The wild are found on mountains in hot countries, as in Cappadocia, Galatia, and in divers provinces of Italy and Spain, and on the hills of Lancashire and Yorke.

Pliny saith that there is such friendship between it and the fig-tree, that it prospers no where so well as under the fig tree. The best for physicks use is that which groweth under the fig tree, as *Dioscorides* saith: the cause is alledged by *Plutarch*, *lib*. 1. of his *Symposiacks* or Feasts, for he saith it becomes more sweet and milde in taste, by reason it taketh as it were some part of the sweetnesse of the fig tree, whereby the over-ranke qualitie of the Rue is allayed; unlesse it be that the figge tree whilest it drawes nourishment to it selfe, draweth also the ranknesse away from the Rue.

¶ *The Time*.

They floure in these cold countries in July and August: in other countries sooner.

¶ *The Vertues*.

The herb a little boiled or skalded, and kept in pickle as Sampier, and eaten, quickens the sight.

The same applied with hony and the juice of Fennell, is a remedie against dim eies.

The juice of Rue made hot in the rinde of a pomegranat and dropped into the eares, takes away the pain of thereof.

Dioscorides saith, That Rue put up in the nosthrils stayeth bleeding.

So saith *Pliny* also: when notwithstanding it is of power rather to procure bleeding, through its sharpe and biting quality.

The leaves of Rue beaten and drunke with wine are an antidote against poisons, as *Pliny* saith.

Dioscorides writeth, That a twelve penny weight of the seed drunke in wine is a counterpoison against deadly medicines or the poison of Wolfes-bane, Mushroms or Toad-stooles, the biting of Serpents, the stinging of Scorpions, Bees, hornets, and wasps; and is reported, That if a man bee anointed with the juice of Rue, these will not hurt him; and that the serpent is driven away at the smell thereof when it is burned: insomuch that when the Weesell is to fight with the serpent, shee armeth her selfe by eating Rue, against the might of the Serpent.

The leaves of Rue eaten with the kernels of Walnuts or figs stamped together and made into a masse or paste, is good against all evill aires, the pestilence or plague, resists poison and all venome.

Ruta sylvestris or wild Rue is more vehement both in smel and operation, and therefore the more virulent or pernitious; for sometimes it fumeth out a vapor or aire so hurtfull that it scorches the face of him that looketh upon it, raising up blisters, wheals, and other accidents: it venometh their hands that touch it, and will infect the face also if it be touched before they be clean washed: wherfore it is not to be admitted to meat or medicine.

THE THIRD BOOKE OF THE HISTORY OF PLANTS.

Containing the Description, Place, Time, Names, Nature, and Vertues, of Trees, Shrubs, Bushes, Fruit-bearing Plants, Rosins, Gums, Roses, Heath, Mosses, some Indian Plants, and other rare Plants not remembred in the Proeme to the first Booke. Also Mushroms, Corall, and their severall Kindes, &c.

The Proeme.

HAving finished the treatise of Herbs and Plants in general, used for meat, medicine, or sweet smelling use, only some few omitted for want of perfect instruction; and also being hindered by the slacknesse of the Cutters or gravers of the Figures: these wants we intend to supply in this third and last part. The Tables as well general as particular shall be set forth in the end of this present Volume.

(1)

CHAP. 181. *Of Roses.*

¶ *The Kindes.*

THe Plant of Roses, though it be a shrub full of prickles, yet it had bin more fit and convenient to have placed it with the most glorious floures of the world, than to insert the same here among base and thorny shrubs: for the Rose doth deserve the chief and prime place among all floures whatsoever; beeing not onely esteemed for his beauty, vertues, and his fragrant and odoriferous smell; but also because it is the honor and ornament of our English Scepter, as by the conjunction appeareth, in the uniting of those two most Royall Houses of Lancaster and Yorke. Which pleasant floures deserve the chiefest place in crownes and garlands, as *Anacreon Thius* a most antient Greeke Poet affirmes in those Verses of a Rose, beginning thus;

> The Rose is the honour and beauty of floures,
> The Rose in the care and love of the Spring:
> The Rose is the pleasure of th' heavenly Pow'rs.
> The Boy of faire *Venus*, *Cythera's* Darling,
> Doth wrap his head round with garlands of Rose,
> When to the dances of the Graces he goes.

Augerius Busbequius speaking of the estimation and honor of the Rose, reporteth, That the Turks can by no means endure to see the leaves of Roses fall to the ground, because some of them have dreamed, that the first or most antient Rose did spring out of the bloud of *Venus:* and others of the Mahumetans say that it sprang of the sweat of *Mahumet.*

But there are many kindes of Roses, differing either in the bignesse of the floures, or the plant it selfe, roughnesse or smoothnesse, or in the multitude or fewnesse of the flours, or else in colour and smell; for divers of them are high and tall, others short and low, some have five leaves, others very many.

Moreover, some be red, others white, and most of them or all sweetly smelling, especially those of the garden.

¶ *The Description.*

1   IF the Curious could so be content, one generall description might serve to distinguish the whole stock or kindred of the Roses, being things so wel knowne: notwithstanding I thinke it not amisse to say somthing of them severally, in hope to satisfie all. The white Rose hath very long stalkes of a wooddy substance, set or armed with divers sharpe prickles: the branches wherof are likewise full of prickles, whereon grow leaves consisting of five leaves for the most part, set upon a middle rib by couples, the old leaf standing at the point of the same, and every one of those small

leaves somwhat snipt about the edges, somewhat rough, and of an overworne greene colour: from the bosome whereof shoot forth long foot-stalks, whereon grow very faire double flours of a white colour, and very sweet smell, having in the middle a few yellow threds or chives; which being past, there succeedeth a long fruit, greene at the first, but red when it is ripe, and stuffed with a downy choking matter, wherein is contained seed as hard as stones. The root is long, tough, and of a wooddy substance.

Rofa Provincialis, five Damafcena.
The Province or Damaske Rofe.

2 The red Rose groweth very low in respect of the former: the stalks are shorter, smoother, and browner of colour: The leaves are like, yet of a worse dusty colour: The floures grow on the tops of the branches, consisting of many leaves of a perfect red colour: the fruit is like-wise red when it is ripe: the root is wooddy.

3 The common Damaske Rose in stature, prickely branches, and in other respects is like the white Rose; the es-peciall difference consists in the colour and smell of the flours: for these are of a pale red colour, of a more pleasant smel, and fitter for meat and medicine.

4 The *Rosa Provincialis minor* or lesser Province Rose differeth not from the former, but is altogether lesser: the floures and fruit are like: the use in physicke also agreeth with the precedent.

5 The Rose without prickles hath many young shoots comming from the root, dividing themselves into divers branches, tough, and of a wooddy substance as are all the rest of the Roses, of the height of two or three cubits, smooth and plain without any roughnesse or prickles at all: whereon grow leaves like those of the Holland Rose, of a shining deep green colour on the upper side, underneath some-what hoary and hairy. The flours grow at the tops of the branches, consisting of an infinite number of leaves, greater than those of the Damaske Rose, more double, and of a colour between the red and damask Roses, of a most sweet smell. The fruit is round, red when it

is ripe, and stuffed with the like flocks and seeds of those of the damaske Rose. The root is great, wooddy, and far spreading.

6 The Holland or Province Rose hath divers shoots proceeding from a wooddy root ful of sharpe prickles, dividing it selfe into divers branches, wheron grow leaves consisting of five leaves set on a rough middle rib, & those snipt about the edges: the flours grow on the tops of the branches, in shape and colour like the damaske Rose, but greater and more double, insomuch that the yellow chives in the middle are hard to be seene; of a reasonable good smell, but not fully so sweet as the common damaske Rose: the fruit is like the other of his kinde.

¶ *The Place*.

All these sorts of Roses we have in our London gardens, except that Rose without pricks, which as yet is a stranger in England. The double white Rose groweth wilde in many hedges of Lancashire in great aboundance, even as Briers do with us in these Southerly parts, especially in a place of the country called Leyland, and at Roughford not far from Latham. Moreover, in the said Leyland fields doth grow our garden Rose wilde, in the plowed fields among the corne, in such aboundance, that there may be gathered daily during the time, many bushels of roses, equal with the best garden Rose in each respect: the thing that giveth great cause of wonder, is, That in a field in the place aforesaid, called Glovers field, every yeare that the field is plowed for corne, that yeare it wil be spred over with Roses, and when it lieth ley, or not plowed, then is there but few Roses to be gathered; by the relation of a curious gentleman there dwelling, so often remembred in our history.

‡ I have heard that the Roses which grow in such plenty in Glovers field every yere the field is plowed, are no other than Corn Rose, that is, red Poppies, however our Author was informed. ‡

¶ *The Time*.

These floure from the end of May to the end of August, and divers times after, by reason the tops and superfluous branches are cut away in the end of their flouring: and then doe they somtimes floure even untill October and after.

¶ *The Vertues.*

The distilled water of Roses is good for the strengthning of the heart, and refreshing of the spirits, and likewise for all things that require a gentle cooling.

The same being put in junketting dishes, cakes, sauces, and many other pleasant things, giveth a fine and delectable taste.

It mitigateth the paine of the eies proceeding of a hot cause, bringeth sleep, which also the fresh roses themselves provoke through their sweet and pleasant smell.

Of like vertue also are the leaves of these preserved in Sugar, especially if they be onely bruised with the hands, and diligently rempered with Sugar, and so heat at the fire rather than boyled.

¶ *The Temperature and Vertues of the parts.*

The conserve of Roses, as well that which is crude and raw, as that which is made by ebullition or boiling, taken in the morning fasting, and last at night, strengthneth the heart, and taketh away the shaking and trembling thereof, and in a word is the most familiar thing to be used for the purposes aforesaid, and is thus made:

Take Roses at your pleasure, put them to boyle in faire water, having regard to the quantity; for if you have many Roses you may take more water; if fewer, the lesse water will serve: the which you shall boyle at the least three or foure houres, even as you would boile a piece of meate, untill in the eating they be very tender, at which time the Roses will lose their colour, that you would thinke your labour lost, and the thing spoiled. But proceed, for though the Roses have lost their colour, the water hath gotten the tincture thereof; then shall you adde unto one pound of Roses, foure pound of fine sugar in pure pouder, and so according to the rest of the Roses. Thus shall you let them boyle gently after the sugar is put therto, continually stirring it with a woodden Spatula untill it be cold, whereof one pound weight is worth six pound of the crude or raw conserve, as well for the vertues and goodnesse in taste, as also for the beautifull colour.

The making of the crude or raw conserve is very well knowne, as also Sugar roset, and divers other pretty things made of Roses and

Sugar, which are impertent unto our history, because I intend nether to make thereof an Apothecaries shop, nor a Sugar-Bakers store-house, leaving the rest for our cunning confectioners.

CHAP. 182. *Of the wilde Roses.*

¶ *The Description.*

1   THe sweet Brier doth oftentimes grow higher than all the kindes of Roses; the shoots of it are hard, thicke, and wooddy; the leaves are glittering, and of a beautifull greene colour, of smell most pleasant: the Roses are little, five leaved, most commonly whitish, seldom tending to purple, of little or no smell at all: the fruit is long, of colour somewhat red, like a little olive stone, & like the little heads or berries of the others, but lesser than those of the garden: in which is contained rough cotton, or hairy downe and seed, folded and wrapped up in the same, which is small and hard: there be likewise found about the slender shoots hereof, round, soft, and hairy spunges, which we call Brier Balls, such as grow about the prickles of the Dog-Rose.

2   We have in our London gardens another sweet Brier, having greater leaves, and much sweeter: the floures likewise are greater, and somewhat doubled, exceeding sweet of smell, wherein it differeth from the former.

3   The Brier Bush or Hep tree, is also called *Rosa canina*, which is a plant so common and well knowne, that it were to small purpose to use many words in the description thereof: for even children with great delight eat the berries thereof when they be ripe, make chaines and other prettie gewgawes of the fruit: cookes and gentlewomen make Tarts and such like dishes for pleasure thereof, and therefore this shall suffice for the description.

¶ *The Place.*

These wilde Roses do grow in the borders of fields and woods, in most parts of England. The last growes very plentifully in a field as you go from a village in Essex, called Graies (upon the brinke of the river Thames) unto Horndon on the hill, insomuch that the field is full fraught therewith all over.

It groweth likewise in a pasture as you goe from a village hard by London called Knights brige unto Fulham, a Village thereby, and in many other places.

We have them all except the Brier Bush in our London gardens, which we think unworthy the place.

¶ *The Vertues.*

The fruit when it is ripe maketh most pleasant meats and banqueting dishes, as tarts and such like; the making whereof I commit to the cunning cooke, and teeth to eate them in the rich mans mouth.

---

(4) ## Chap. 183. *Of the Bramble or blacke-berry bush.*

¶ *The Description.*

1   THe common Bramble bringeth forth slender branches, long, tough, easily bowed, ramping among hedges and whatsoever stands neere unto it; armed with hard and sharpe prickles, whereon doe grow leaves consisting of many set upon a rough middle ribbe, greene on the upper side, and underneath somewhat white: on the tops of the stalkes stand certaine floures, in shape like those of the Brier Rose, but lesser, of colour white, and sometimes washt over with a little purple: the fruit or berry is like that of the Mulberry, first red, blacke when it is ripe, in taste betweene sweet and soure, very soft, and full of grains: the root creepeth, and sendeth forth here and there young springs.

2   The Raspis or Framboise bush hath leaves and branches not much unlike the common Bramble, but not so rough nor prickly, and sometimes without any prickles at all, having onely a rough hairinesse about the stalkes: the fruit in shape and proportion is like those of the Bramble, red when they be ripe, and covered over with a little downinesse; in taste not very pleasant. The root creepeth far abroad, whereby it greatly encreaseth. ‡ This growes either with prickles upon the stalks, or else without them: the fruit is usually red, but sometimes white of colour. ‡

¶ *The Place.*

The Bramble groweth for the most part in every hedge and bush. The Raspis is planted in gardens: it groweth not wilde that I know of, except in the field by a village in Lancashire called Harwood, not far from Blackeburne.

Rubus.
The Bramble Bush.

I found it among the bushes of a causey, neere unto a village called Wisterson, where I went to schoole, two miles from the Nantwich in Cheshire.

¶ *The Time.*

These floure in May and June with the Roses: their fruit is ripe in the end of August and September.

¶ *The Names.*

The Bramble is called in Latine, *Rubus*, and *Sentis*, and *Vepres*, as *Ovid* writeth in the first booke of Metamorphosis:

> Or to the Hare, that under Bramble
> closely lying, spies
> The hostile mouth of Dogs.——

Of divers it is called in English, Bramble bush, and Blacke-berry bush.

The Raspis is called in Latine, *Rubus Idæa*, of the mountaine Ida on which it groweth: in English, Raspis, Framboise, and Hindeberry.

¶ *The Vertues.*

They heale the eies that hang out.

The ripe fruit is sweet, and containeth in it much juyce of a temperate heate, therefore it is not unpleasant to be eaten.

The leaves of the Bramble boyled in water, with honey, allum, and a little white wine added thereto, make a most excellent lotion or washing water, and the same decoction fastneth the teeth.

(6)

CHAP. 184. *Of dwarfe kindes of Cistus.*

¶ *The Description.*

1 THe English dwarfe Cistus, called of *Lobel*, *Panax Chironium* (but there is another *Panax* of *Chirons* description which I hold to be the true and right *Panax*, notwithstanding hee hath inserted it amongst the kindes of Cistus, as being indifferent to joyne with us and others for the insertion) is a

Helianthemum album Germanicum. The white dwarfe Ciftus of Germanie.

low and base plant creeping upon the ground, having many small tough branches of a browne colour; wherupon grow little leaves set together by couples, thicke, fat, and ful of substance, and covered over with a soft downe; from the bosome whereof come forth other lesser leaves: the floures before they be open are small knops or buttons, of a browne colour mixed with yellow, and beeing open and spred abroad are like those of the wilde Tansie, & of a yellow colour, with some yellower chives in the middle: the root is thicke, and of a wooddy substance.

¶ *The Place.*

Those of our English growing I have found in very many places, especially in Kent upon the chalky banks about Gravesend, South-fleet, and for the most part all the way from thence to Canturbury and Dover.

¶ The Time.

They floure from July to the end of August.

¶ The Names.

Valerius Cordus nameth it *Helianthemum*, and *Solis flos* or Sun-floure.

Pliny writeth, that *Helianthemum* growes in the champian country Temiscyra in Pontus, and in the mountains of Cilicia neere the sea: saying further, that the wise men of those countries & the Kings of Persia do anoint their bodies herewith, boiled with Lions fat, a little Saffron, and Wine of Dates, that they may seem faire and beautifull; and therefore have they called it *Heliocaliden*, or the beauty of the Sun.

(8)

Chap. 185. *Of Rosemary.*

¶ The Description.

ROsemarie is a wooddy shrub, growing oftentimes to the height of three or foure cubits, especially when it is set by a wall: it consisteth of slender brittle branches, whereon do grow very many long leaves, narrow, somewhat hard, of a quicke spicy taste, whitish underneath, and of a full greene colour above, or in the upper side, with a pleasant sweet strong smell; among which come forth little floures of a whitish blew colour: the seed is blackish: the roots are tough and wooddy.

¶ The Place.

Rosemary groweth in France, Spaine, and in other hot countries; in woods, and in untilled places: there is such plenty thereof in Languedocke, that the inhabitants burne scarce any other fuell: they make hedges of it in the gardens of Italy and England, being a great ornament unto the same: it groweth neither in the fields nor gardens of the Easterne cold countries; but is carefully and curiously kept in pots, set into the stoves and cellers, against the injuries of their cold Winters.

Wild Rosemary groweth in Lancashire in divers places, especially in a field called Little Reed, amongst the Hurtle berries, neere unto a small village called Maudsley; there found by a learned Gentleman often remembred in our History (and that worthily) M^r. *Thomas Hesketh.*

¶ *The Time.*

Rosemary floureth twice a yeare, in the Spring, and after in August.

The wilde Rosemary floureth in June and July.

¶ *The Names.*

Rosemary is called in Latine, *Rosemarinus Coronaria*: it is sur-named *Coronaria*, because women have beene accustomed to make crownes and garlands thereof.

¶ *The Vertues.*

The distilled water of the floures of Rosemary being drunke at morning and evening first and last, taketh away the stench of the mouth and breath, and maketh it very sweet, if there be added thereto, to steep or infuse for certaine daies, a few Cloves, Mace, Cinnamon, and a little Annise seed.

The Arabians and other Physitions succeeding, do write, that Rosemary comforteth the braine, the memorie, the inward senses, and restoreth speech unto them that are possessed with the dumbe palsie, especially the conserve made of the floures and sugar, or any other way confected with sugar, being taken every day fasting.

The floures made up into plates with Sugar after the manner of Sugar Roset and eaten, comfort the heart, and make it merry, quicken the spirits, and make them more lively.

---

(73)   CHAP. 186. *Of Worts or Wortle berries.*

¶ *The Kindes.*

VAccinia, or Worts, of which we treat in this place, differ from Violets, neither are they esteemed for their floures but berries: of these Worts there be divers sorts found out by the later Writers.

¶ *The Description.*

1 Vaccinia nigra, the blacke Wortle or Hurtle, is a base and low shrub or wooddy plant, bringing forth many branches of a cubit high, set full of small leaves of a darke greene colour, not much unlike the leaves of Box or the Myrtle tree: amongst which come forth little hollow floures turning into small berries, greene at the first, afterward red, and at the last of a blacke colour, and full of a pleasant and sweet juyce: in which doe lie divers little thinne whitish seeds: these berries do colour the mouth and lips of those that eat them, with a blacke colour: the root is wooddy, slender, and now and then creeping.

2 *Vaccinia rubra*, or red Wortle, is like the former in the manner of growing, but that the leaves are greater and harder, almost like the leaves of the Box tree, abiding greene all the Winter long: among which come forth small carnation floures, long and round, growing in clusters at the top of the branches: after which succeed small berries, in shew and bignesse like the former, but that they are of an excellent red colour and full of juyce, of so orient and beautifull a purple to limme withall, that Indian *Lacca* is not to be compared thereunto, especially when this juyce is prepared and dressed with Allom according to art, as my selfe have proved by experience: the taste is rough and astringent: the root is of a wooddy substance.

¶ *The Place.*

These plants prosper best in a leane barren soile, and in untoiled wooddy places: they are now and then found on high hills subject to the winde, and upon mountaines: they grow plentifully in both the Germanies, Bohemia, and in divers places of France and England; namely in Middlesex on Hampsted heath, and in the woods thereto adjoyning, and also upon the hills in Cheshire called Broxen hills, neere Beeston castle, seven miles from the Nantwich; and in the wood by Highgate called Finchley wood, and in divers other places.

¶ *The Time.*

The Wortle berries do floure in May, and their fruit is ripe in June.

¶ *The Vertues.*

The people of Cheshire do eat the blacke Wortles in creame and milke, as in these South parts we eate Strawberries.

The Red Wortle is not of such a pleasant taste as the blacke, and therfore not so much used to be eaten; but (as I said before) they make the fairest carnation colour in the World.

Chap. 187. *Of the Mosse of Trees.*

¶ *The Description.*

TRee Mosse hath certaine things like haires, made up as it were of a multitude of slender leaves, now and then all to be jagged, hackt, and finely carved, twisted and interlaced one in another, which cleave fast to the barkes of trees, hanging downe from the bodies: one of this kinde is more slender and thinne, another more thicke, another shorter, another longer; all of them for the most being of a whitish colour, yet oftentimes there is a certaine one also which is blacke, but lesser and thinner: the most commendable of them all, as *Pliny* saith, be those that are whitish, then the reddish, and lastly such as be blacke.

Muſcus quernus.
The Moſſe of the Oke and other trees.

¶ *The Place.*

This Mosse is found on the Oke tree, the white and blacke Poplar tree, the Olive tree, the Birch tree, the Apple tree, the Peare tree, the Pine tree, the wilde Pine tree, the Pitch tree, the Firre tree, the Cedar tree, the Larch tree, and on a great sort of other trees. The best, as *Dioscorides* saith, is that of the Cedar tree, the next of the Poplar, in which kinde the White and the sweet smelling Mosse is the chiefest; the blackish sort is of no account. *Matthiolus* writeth, that in Italy that Mosse is sweet which groweth on the Pine tree, the Pitch tree, the Fir tree, and the Larch tree, and the sweetest, that of the Larch tree.

¶ *The Time*.

Mosse upon the trees continueth all the yeare long.

¶ *The Vertues*.

Serapio saith, that the wine in which Mosse hath been steeped certain daies, bringeth sound sleep.

It is fit to be used in compositions which serve for sweet perfumes, and that take away wearisomnesse; for which things that is best of all which is most sweet of smell.

---

(171) CHAP. 188. *Of the Goose tree, Barnacle tree, or the tree bearing Geese*.

¶ *The Description*.

HAving travelled from the Grasses growing in the bottome of the fenny waters, the Woods, and mountaines, even unto Libanus it selfe; and also the sea, and bowels of the same, wee are arrived at the end of our History; thinking it not impertinent to the conclusion of the same, to end with one of the marvels of this land (we may say of the World.) The history whereof to set forth according to the worthinesse and raritie thereof, would not only require a large and peculiar volume, but also a deeper search into the bowels of Nature, than my intended purpose will suffer me to wade into, my sufficiencie also considered; leaving the History thereof rough hewen, unto some excellent man, learned in the secrets of nature, to be both fined and refined: in the meane space take it as it falleth out, the naked and bare truth, though unpolished. There are found in the North parts of Scotland and the Islands adjacent, called Orchades, certaine trees whereon do grow certaine shells of a white colour tending to russet, wherein are contained little living creatures: which shells in time of maturity doe open, and out of them grow those little living things, which falling into the water do become fowles, which we call Barnacles; in the North of England, brant Geese; and in Lancashire, tree Geese: but the other that do fall upon the land perish and come to nothing. Thus much by the writings of others, and also from the mouthes of people of those parts, which may very well accord with truth.

But what our eies have seene, and hands have touched we shall declare. There is a small Island in Lancashire called the Pile of Foulders, wherein are found the broken pieces of old and bruised ships, some whereof have beene cast thither by shipwracke, and also the trunks and bodies with the branches of old and rotten trees, cast up there likewise; whereon is found a certaine spume or froth that in time breedeth unto certaine shells, in shape like those of the Muskle,

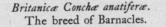

Britanicæ Conchæ anatiferæ.
The breed of Barnacles.

but sharper pointed, and of a whitish colour; wherein is contained a thing in forme like a lace of silke finely woven as it were together, of a whitish colour, one end whereof is fastned unto the inside of the shell, even as the fish of Oisters and Muskles are: the other end is made fast unto the belly of a rude masse or lumpe, which in time commeth to the shape and forme of a Bird: when it is perfectly formed the shell gapeth open, and the first thing that appeareth is the foresaid lace or string; next come the legs of the bird hanging out, and as it groweth greater it openeth the shell by degrees, til at length it is all come forth, and hangeth onely by the bill: in short space after it commeth to full maturitie, and falleth into the sea, where it gathereth feathers, and groweth to a fowle bigger than a Mallard, and lesser than a Goose, having blacke legs and bill or beake, and feathers blacke and white, spotted in such manner as is our Magpie, called in some places a Pie-Annet, which the people of Lancashire call by no other name than a tree Goose: which place aforesaid, and all those parts adjoyning do so much abound therewith, that one of the best is bought for three pence. For the truth hereof, if any doubt, may it please them to repaire unto me, and I shall satisfie them by the testimonie of good witnesses.

Moreover, it should seeme that there is another sort hereof; the History of which is true, and of mine owne knowledge: for travelling upon the shore of our English coast betweene Dover and Rumney, I found the trunke of an old rotten tree, which (with some helpe that I procured by Fishermens wives that were there attending their husbands returne from the sea) we drew out of the water upon dry land: upon this rotten tree I found growing many thousands of long crimson bladders, in shape like unto puddings newly filled, before they be sodden, which were very cleere and shining; at the nether end whereof did grow a shell fish, fashioned somewhat like a small Muskle, but much whiter, resembling a shell fish that groweth upon the rockes about Garnsey and Garsey, called a Lympit: many of these shells I brought with me to London, which after I had opened I found in them living things without forme or shape; in others which were neerer come to ripenesse I found living things that were very naked, in shape like a Bird: in others, the Birds covered with soft downe, the shell halfe open, and the Bird ready to fall out, which no doubt were the Fowles called Barnacles. I dare not absolutely avouch every circumstance of the first part of this history, concerning the tree that beareth those buds aforesaid, but will leave it to a further consideration; howbeit, that which I have seene with mine eies, and handled with mine hands, I dare confidently avouch, and boldly put downe for verity. Now if any will object that this tree which I saw might be one of those before mentioned, which either by the waves of the sea or some violent wind had beene overturned as many other trees are; or that any trees falling into those seas about the Orchades, will of themselves beare the like Fowles, by reason of those seas and waters, these being so probable conjectures, and likely to be true, I may not without prejudice gainesay, or indeavour to confute.

¶ *The Place.*

The bordes and rotten plankes whereon are found these shels breeding the Barnakle, are taken up in a small Island adjoyning to

Lancashire, halfe a mile from the main land, called the Pile of Foulders.

¶ *The Time.*

They spawn as it were in March and Aprill; the Geese are formed in May and June, and come to fulnesse of feathers in the moneth after.

And thus having through Gods assistance discoursed somewhat
at large of Grasses, Herbes, Shrubs, Trees, and Mosses, and
certaine Excrescences of the earth, with other things
moe, incident to the historie thereof, we conclude and end our present Volume, with
this wonder of England. For the
which Gods Name be ever honored
and praised.

FINIS.

THE NOTES.

Lib. I.

1. "Our Author" (as his Editor, Johnson, would always say) first leads us to his grass plot, where we find as strange an assortment of grasses as ever mortal eyes beheld at once. Some he shows us, little or nothing known or touched before; and some he describes were never known, "feigned plants" still lacking place in the *Hortus Kewensis.*

The old names ring pleasantly. Windle-strawes—"The Grasse," says Johnson, popping in his inevitable word, "with which we in London do usually adorn our chimneys in Sommer time." The Elizabethan names are forgotten, "Amourettes," that is, Lonely-grasse, Shadowe-grasse, Lady's-laces. Flote-grasses swim in water. Kneed-grasse has joints like as it were to knees; Hedgehog-grasse has prickles. As to Feather-grasse, this is worn in lieu of a feather by "sundry Ladies and Gentlewomen." Some grasses have "Vertues," like those which, as Coles finely wrote in his "Art of Simpling," are enveloped within the compass of the Green Mantles wherewith Plants are adorned; thus, if a plaister be made of Dew-grasse, with hog's-grease and leaven of bread, it cureth the biting of mad dogs. Our Author makes up the names as he goes: "This I have thought good to call Silver-grasse."

Attention is soon riveted on a grass or rush growing from a pool, bearing at the top a bush of most pleasant cotton, like fine and soft white silk, while alongside it (in a relationship arbitrarily thrust upon them) grows the rush which of all others is the fairest and most pleasant to behold.

Those who inquire into the history of plants as given in such records as Loudon's "Encyclopædia of Plants" or the "Botanical Magazine" will observe that a remarkable number are stated to have been introduced to Britain about the year of the publication of the "Herball." As if in compliment to Gerard, credit for a plant's introduction seems to have been given to the year 1596, or 1597, whenever exact dates were uncertain.

The figures refer to the chapters as numbered for this edition.

.   .   .   .

3. Several pieces of Cotton-grass (*Eriophorum*) grow on British moors and bogs and Scottish mountains. "Water Gladiole" is the Flowering Rush (*Butomus umbellatus*).

4. The Common Reed mentioned (*Arundo Phragmites*) is that "growing almost everywhere," and used for thatching in the Eastern counties. Gerard's "Cypress Canes" (*A. Donax*) commonly serve as screens in Italian gardens.

5. Common Sugar-Cane (*Saccharum officinarum*) is supposed to have been brought to England in 1597.

7. "Branched Burre-Reed" retains the names given in the Herbal, botanic and popular. "Great Water-Burre" is Unbranched Bur-reed (*Sparganium simplex*).

8. "Cats-taile" is that Reedmace more usually associated in rustic plant lore with the cradle of Moses than Papyrus.

9. Our Author did not know Stitchwort by its pretty name *Stellaria*, though describing its floral leaves as star-like.

10. He cultivated in his garden a dozen sorts of Iris, and described about as many more, including Yellow Water Flag (*Iris Pseudacorus*) and the Chalcedonian (*I. susiana*) introduced from the Levant, 1596. This chapter brings to mind Shakespeare's line, "Lilies of all kinds, the flower-de-luce being one."

11. *Zingiber* is the original Indian name of Ginger, a plant little known in Elizabethan times, but at home in the herbalist's garden.

12. Several varieties of red and white Wheat (*Triticum*) are described in the Herbal, including one named "Flat Wheat," on which Johnson remarks, "I know not what our Author means."

13. Like other botanists, Gerard could assign no place of origin to the Common Oat (*Avena sativa*). He gives a pleasant note on the Naked Oat (*A. nuda*) in his time commonly cultivated on account of the clean way in which the ripe grains are shed from the husks, and associated with the old cottage "quern mills" of Scotland.

14. Indian Corn (*Zea Mays*) was introduced to Britain from N. America, 1562.

15. "Blew Hare-Bell," says Dodoens, was so named by Parkinson because no other before him had written thereof; the name distinguishes it from the Poets' Hyacinth, with leaves marked AI, emblem of woe.

16. *Tigridis flos*, Gerard's "feigned plant," at once suggests the splendid *Tigridia Pavonia*. We owe to the Director of Kew Gardens the suggestion that the plant first described may be a species of *Hypoxis*.

17. Of Daffodils "or Narcisses" Gerard and Johnson describe some forty sorts, with such pleasant names as Nonpareille, King's-chalice, Camel's-neck, and Longshanks. Johnson gave a figure of one "vulgarly called Gerrard's Narcisse," since he was the first observer thereof. We reproduce a figure of *Narcissus Jonquilla*. Others described are *N. poeticus*.

18. Of "Dalmatian Caps" the Author and his Editor give illustrations of thirty varieties, but grew weary of describing the infinite numbers. Johnson commended those in love with flowers to find somewhat more about Tulips in the Florilegies of Robin and Parkinson.

19. *Fritillaria Meleagris* does not seem to have been recognized as an English wild flower until the middle of the nineteenth century. The description of the flowers as surpassing the "curiosest painting" is often remembered, and how they beautify the bosoms of the beautiful.

20. The Saffron Crocus (*Crocus sativus*) was cultivated in our Author's garden (his *C. Anglicus*) also *C. nudiflorus* (his *C. montanus*) *C. vernus*, and *C. luteus* referred to in this chapter, which he received from the curious searcher of Simples, Robin of Paris.

21. The three sorts of Meadow Saffron here described are all *Colchicum autumnale*. To his cultivated specimens of this Gerard gave various names, as "White Meadow Saffron," "Hungarie Meade Saffron," and "Deadly Meade Saffron." Johnson remarked that in naming the plant "Our Author was of many mindes." "*Hermodactylus*" was a name he gave to an Iris.

22. The Common Star of Bethlehem (*Ornithogalum umbellatum*) is a doubtful native of England. "The yellow kinde" is the rare *Gagea lutea*, formerly included in the genus *Ornithogalum*.

24. Gerard's "White Lilly" is *Lilium candidum*, a mediaeval inhabitant of British gardens. His "Lilly of Constantinople" is *L. candidum* var. *cernuum* (*L. peregrinum*) with narrower petals, introduced from Constantinople by way of Vienna late in the 16th century.

25. Johnson was dissatisfied with the original description of "*Lilium rubrum*" and its figure, and substituted a figure of *L. bulbiferum*.

26. "Mountaine Lillies" are *Lilium Martagon*, of the cottage garden.

27. "Persian Lilly" is *Fritillaria persica*.

28. "Crowne Imperiall" is *F. Imperialis*: these Fritillaries are stated to have been introduced 1596.

29, 30. Sixteen Orchids are described in this chapter. "Waspe Satyrion" may be *Ophrys arachnites*. Gerard himself found a plant of *Neottia Nidus-avis*, but the figure he gave originally was at fault.

Lib. 2.

31. The Turnip was certainly cultivated in England during the sixteenth century. The author of the "Haven of Health," published in the same year as this Herbal, remarks that although men do love to eat Turnips, yet do swine abhor them.

32. Tarragon and *Draco herba* are the old names for *Artemisia Dracunculus*.

33. With respect to our Author's opinion it must be remarked that the Nasturtium (*Tropæolum*) is wrongly named with the name of the Cresses, and wrongly described as a kind of Cress; and it is a native of South America, not India. (Gerard sometimes referred to America as the West Indies.)

34. "Lady-smockes" are old favourites, witness Shakespeare's lines about them, and the perfect description "all silver white," also references by Chatterton ("a Ladie-smock soe white") and by Izaak Walton. *Cardamine impatiens*, referred to by Johnson, is so named from the sudden bursting of the ripe seed-pods when touched.

36. Groundsel appears under the name *Erigerum* now belonging to another genus, but the name *Senecio* is mentioned, that of the genus to which Groundsel (*S. vulgaris*) belongs. The Asarabacca referred to (*Asarum europæum*) has leaves which act as an emetic.

37. "St. James his wort" (*Senecio Jacobæa*) may have been named from blooming about the day of the patron saint of horses. The plant was reputed to cure the disease "staggers."

38. Dandelion has lost the suggestive Latin name Gerard gave it in *Taraxacum officinale*. His figure happily shows the flowers in various stages.

39. Garden Lettuce seems to have been introduced in Gerard's time.

40. "Wilde Colewort" (*Brassica oleracea*) is the mother of all Cabbages; in few instances has one plant produced such marked varieties. The "Fennugreeke" (*Trigonella Fænum-græcum*) was a crop cultivated by the Romans, but never in general use in England.

41. *Beta* has more uses than those with which it is credited in the Herbal, as forming a varnish, a pickle, a comfiture, and a substitute for coffee, also as yielding sugar.

42. "Floure-gentle" excited delight when introduced from the East Indies, as "very brave to look upon." The Amaranth described as Floramor is *Amaranthus tricolor*. The "Purple Floure-gentle" first described is identified with *Celosia cristata*.

43. Few English plants smell more disgustingly than *Chenopodium Vulvaria*.

44. The "Scorpion grasse" first described and illustrated is *Scorpiurus sulcatus*. The British Water Forget-me-not now bears the name *Myosotis scorpioides*; its three possible varieties include the true Forget-me-not, the sentimental plant which this generation would hardly recognise under its old name of Water Mouse-ear Scorpion-grass.

45. *Atropa Belladonna* grows wild in places in England. It may have sprung from plants cultivated for the sake of that kind of potion which quietened the unneighbourly neighbour. Old-time poets often mention the plant:

Arise, quod she; what, have ye dronken Dwale?

46. "Marvel of Peru" deserves its name, *Mirabilis*, for its diversity of colours. A species is the "Four o'Clock Flower" of the West Indies. The Hemerocallis referred to is the Day Lily.

47. The baneful Nightshade represents the Solanum Family to which belongs the Mad-Apple (*Solanum insanum*).

48. The Love Apple we know as the Tomato, *Lysopersicon esculentum*. The old specific name, with its reference to a wolf and a peach, alludes to the beauty of the fruit and its deceptive worth. It may be observed that the plant figured has been judiciously pruned.

49. This chapter has the special interest that Thorn-Apple (*Datura Stramonium*) is an instance of a Central American plant which has by now made itself more or less at home in southern England (though it can scarcely be considered as naturalized), the seeds having been introduced from Constantinople and dispersed through the land by Gerard. (Some botanists say the seeds came more probably from Italy or Spain.) In Virginia it is named Fire-weed, from springing up after fires. A name given in the Herbal is "Thorny apples of Peru." The plant first described in this chapter is *Datura Metel*; the names are from the Arabic, the specific one expressing the narcotic effect of the plant. Large shrubby *Daturas* from South America are distinguished as *Brugmansias* on account of their smooth capsules. Johnson's promised note on *Ficus infernalis* is referred to in the note on Chapter 174.

50. The popular name Bittersweet conveys the idea that the stems or roots when bitten give a sharp taste which changes to a sweet one, as in the old name *Amaradulcis*, but the reverse sensations are indicated by *Solanum Dulcamara*.

51. The roots of *Mandragora officinalis* were supposed by the old herbalists to resemble the human figure, and they pictured the male Mandrake with a long beard, the female with long hair.

52-53. Common Henbane (*Hyoscyamus niger*) is the well-known fœtid weed; others described were introduced to Britain.

54. Tobacco plants, said to have been first brought from America in 1570, were named *Nicotiana* in honour of John Nicot, French Ambassador in Portugal, who procured the seeds.

55. Gerard cultivated several Poppies in his garden, including *Papaver Rhœas* and *P. somniferum*, and the Horned Poppy (*Glaucium flavum*).

56. The first kind of Anemone described, which Gerard named Purple Windflower, is *Anemone coronaria*; the second, "Double Skarlet Windflower," is a variety of this. The third, "Great double Windflower of Bithynia" is *A. pavonina* var. *pavonina*. He gave four different styles and titles to this Anemone. Parkinson in his "Paradisus" wrote of Windflowers as being so delightsome that the sight of them enforces an earnest longing desire to be a possessor, but it passed his abilities to describe their infinite varieties: "I think it would gravell the best experienced in Europe." Gerard cultivated twelve sorts, and described about thirty according to his ideas of distinction.

57. In writing "Of Dockes" our author enters on a large subject, considering the many species of *Rumex*, and Johnson complained of his descriptions, and that these did not tally with his figures. We recognise the Great Water Dock (*R. Hydrolapathum*), the largest of the numerous British species. A Dock which grows everywhere and is one of the most common and troublesome weeds is *R. obtusifolius*, the leaves of which being used for wrapping butter earned in some parts the name Butter-dock. The famous Dock of Monastery gardens, *R. Patientia*, came from Italy in Gerard's day, and may have been named derisively from the patience needed by those who would be cured of the stinging of serpents with this medicine. "Bloudwort" suggests *R. sanguineus*, having leaves veined with bright red, a plant formerly cultivated for food. An old writer remarked of Blood-wort that if boiled with meat it makes it boil the sooner, and lamented that such was the nicety of his time that women would not put it in the pot as it made the pottage black, and thus they preferred nicety before health.

58. Two plants make strange bed-fellows in this plot, *Paris quadrifolia* and *Botrychium Lunaria*. Two other ferns referred to are Hart's-tongue and Ceterach.

59. Lily of the Valley still grows wild in Ken Wood, Hampstead.

60. *Limonium vulgare* (*Statice Limonium*) inhabits English salt-marshes. *L. binervosum* was long regarded as a variety but is now accepted as a distinct species.

61. *Aster Tripolium*, known as Sea Starwort or Michaelmas Daisy, is allied to that Michaelmas Daisy brought to England from North America by the elder John Tradescant, gardener to Charles I.

62. There are five British species of *Plantago*, of which Gerard describes the greater (*P. major*) and Hoary Plaintain (*P. media*).

63. There is but one British species of Golden Rod (*Solidago Virgaurea*), but numbers from North America are cultivated.

64. "White Hellebor" is *Veratrum album*, a sixteenth-century introduction to England, cultivated by Gerard, who named "Wilde white Hellebor" after the plant.

65. Lady's Slipper (*Cypripedium Calceolus*) is the most beautiful of European Orchids. Johnson notes: "It is also reported to grow in the North parts of this kingdome. I saw it in floure with Mr. Tradescant," but it seems now to be almost extinct in the northern counties, and is found if anywhere only in Durham and Yorkshire.

66. Gerard cultivated "divers sorts of Marian Violets, or Coventrie bels" identified with *Campanula Medium*.

67. Honesty's old name, White Satin, is an allusion, like that of the generic name *Lunaria*, to the silvery silicles.

68. The "Yellow-herb" first described is *Lysimachia vulgaris*. The "bastard kinde" is Rose-bay (*Epilobium angustifolium*), and "Codlins-and-cream" (*E. hirsutum*) is also

described. Johnson gives a note of the Evening Primrose (*Œnothera biennis*), an importation of his time from America.

69. Alpine Barrenwort (*Epimedium alpinum*) is not native but is occasionally naturalised.

70. The various "Starworts" described are not easily identified, and Johnson by changing Gerard's figures and by his notes added confusion. In B. Daydon Jackson's edition of Gerard's Catalogue "*Aster Atticus flore luteo*—Yellow Starwoort" is identified with "*Pallenis spinosa, Cass.*" and Gerard's "Blew Starwoort" with "*Aster Amellus, L.*" The plant given in the Catalogue as *A. inguinalis* is probably one of those Michaelmas Daisies mentioned by Johnson as cultivated by Mr. Tradescant.

71. Woad (*Isatis tinctoria*) is considered not to be truly wild in Britain, but grows in various places; this is the one British species.

72. Sea Spurge (*Euphorbia Paralias*) is found on some sandy English shores. Sun Spurge, an annual herb of waste places, retains Gerard's name (*E. Helioscopia*). The figure illustrates the Wood Spurge (*E. amygdaloides*).

73. Various plants are grouped in the Herbal as Pennywort, of which there is one recognised British native, *Cotyledon Umbilicus*. Marsh Penny-wort is *Hydrocotyle vulgaris*, named also Sheep's-bane. No. 2 described is *Sedum rosea*.

74. There is but one British species of Samphire (*Crithmum maritimum*); another species belongs to the Canaries. The Sea Parsnep referred to (*Echinophora spinosa*) is a singular prickly plant, with the popular name Prickly Samphire, which formerly grew on some English sandy shores. The roots were said to taste like those of Parsnep.

75. Glassworts (*Salicornia*) were formerly used in the manufacture of glass.

78. Gerard cultivated *Linum angustifolium* and the *L. maritimum* of Southern Europe. He dwelt much on the virtues of the oil expressed from the seed—linseed—but no more than hinted at the use of Flax for making fine linen.

79. Five British species of *Polygala* (or three with two varieties of one of them) are now generally recognised. The small plants and flowers would hardly seem to lend themselves for garlands. The three plants described, white, blue and red, are all *P. vulgaris*. The illustration shows *Illecebrum verticillatum*.

80. *Thymus* is a genus of several variable species, chiefly from the Mediterranean region. The pot-herb, Garden Thyme, is *T. vulgaris* from southern Europe. Besides the British Wild Thyme proper (*T. Serpyllum*), having flowering branches ascending from trailing shoots, a distinct form (*T. ovatus*) has branches all ascending from the rootstock. White Thyme was among the rarities of Gerard's garden, with its thousand and one different herbs.

81. The Herbal describes many kinds of Hyssop, all probably garden varieties of the exotic potherb *Hyssopus officinalis*.

82. Lavender was considered of old as of "especial good use," as Parkinson said, for grief of the head and a comfort to the brain.

83. The plants described are identified with *Plantago Psyllium* and *P. Cynops*, introductions to English gardens from southern Europe.

84, 85. Some thirty Carnations, Gillofloures, Pinkes, Sweet-Johns, Sweet-Williams, and Crow floures or Wilde Williams are described in the Herbal. The "Gillofloure with yellow flours," procured from Poland, was a variety of *Dianthus caryophyllus* (ancestor of the garden Carnation), as were many others described. References are made in this Herbal as in Parkinson's to Master Ralph Tuggie, a famed grower of Gillyflowers, of Westminster. Parkinson named one variety "Master Tuggies Princesse," a flower "exceedingly delightsome." Others he named "Daintie Ladie," "The Red Hulo," and "Lustie Gallant."

86. Some of the Sweet Johns and Sweet Williams of the Herbal have been identified with *Dianthus Carthusianorum*, others with *D. barbatus* or *D. superbus*. The last is the plant referred to by Gerard as the Pride of Austria.

87. *Armeria maritima*, now commonly called Thrift, is still found bordering cottage gardens, "for the which it serveth very fitly." Another Thrift known to Gerard was *A. arenaria* (*A. plantaginea*), native to Jersey.

88. The small Sneezewort described is *Achillea Ptarmica*, of which the double-flowered is a variety. The third described is given a figure entitled "Sneesewort of Austrich."

89. Old-time herbalists termed the Scarlet Pimpernel (*Anagallis arvensis*) the Male, and the more precious blue variety (*A. cœrulea*) the Female. Yellow Pimpernel still bears that popular name, and that of Wood Loosestrife; botanically, *Lysimachia nemorum*. The plant illustrated is *Anagallis monelli*.

90. Herb Two-pence (*Lysimachia Nummularia*) still has the popular name Money-wort, and those of Creeping Loosestrife and Creeping Jenny.

91. Gerard cultivated as a garden flower a white variety of *Ajuga reptans*.

92. Besides Self-heal (*Prunella vulgaris*) Gerard described a favourite cottage-garden plant, a native of the continent of Europe, *P. grandiflora*, which he also cultivated.

93. *Bellis perennis* is the one British species of a small genus happily deriving its name from *bellus*.

94. Mouse-ear Hawkweed (*Hieracium Pilosella*) is no doubt one of the Hawkweeds Gerard described, but it is small wonder that he was in difficulties with his descriptions and figures (giving some trouble to Johnson) considering that some modern botanists have split the various forms into 260 species for Britain. ("The difficulty of distinguishing them appears only to increase with their subdivision." Bentham and Hooker.)

95. "English Cudweed" is *Gnaphalium sylvaticum*, one of the four species of this British genus of Everlasting Flowers. The Cotton-weed which English women have called Live-for-ever is *Antennaria margaritacea*. The small Cudweed and the Wicked Cudweed described are given in the Herbal the name *Filago*, now a genus of a few species formerly included in *Gnaphalium*. William Turner relates in his Herbal (1551) that in Northumberland Cudweed is named "Chafwede," as being good for "chafying any man's fleshe."

96. A species of Golden Moth-wort (*Gnaphalium orientale*), from Africa, has the gardener's name, Everlasting Love, in French, *La fleur immortelle*. From Parkinson's Herbal it appears to have been well known in England some twenty years after Gerard's work was issued.

97. The Feverfew and its double variety described (and cultivated by Gerard) are identified with *Chrysanthemum Parthenium*, a plant also named Featherfew from the feathery leaves.

98. Eyebright (*Euphrasia officinalis*) has an age-old reputation for taking away "darknesse and dimnesse of the eyes." Culpeper remarked in his Herbal, "If the herb was but as much used as it is neglected, it would half spoil the spectacle-maker's trade." Milton caused the Archangel to clear the vision of Adam with Euphrasy: "For he had much to see."

99. The year 1597 was about the time when "Marjoram of Candy" (*Origanum creticum*) was introduced to Britain from southern Europe. "Origanum" signifies "brightness of the hill," or "joy of the mountain," and Gerard's note that it easeth such as are given to overmuch sighing is supported by Parkinson, who dwells on the way the herb pleases the outward senses, in nosegays, powders and washing waters, and comforts

the outward parts of the body, the inward also. Wild Marjoram (*O. vulgare*) is spread over England and Ireland but rare in Scotland.

100. A remarkable secret about Pennyroyal (*Mentha Pulegium*) is given in "The Boke of Secretes of Albertus Magnus," that drowning bees and flies may be revived if placed in warm ashes thereof: "they shall recover their lyfe after a little tyme." Gerard has the old name Pudding-grass; speaking of which Parkinson remarked that the former age had these hot herbs in familiar use, for meats and medicines, but his own delicate age wholly refused them (almost) and therefore could not be partakers of the benefit thereof.

101. In Gerard's day many species of Mint were cultivated, by such names as Crosse, Browne, Mackerel, Holy, Heart, Cat, Horse or Brook Mints. Spearmint (*M. spicata*) is occasionally found in Britain where it has been cultivated. Parkinson tells how it would be boiled in his time with mackerel and put into puddings, and how bruised Mint was a good help against stings by bees and such like. Gerard, in saying that the savour of mint rejoices the heart of man, echoed Pliny's remark that it stirred up the mind and taste to a greedy desire of meat.

102. Water Mint (*Mentha aquatica*) is a streamside plant throughout Europe and Russian Asia, and is now naturalized in many other countries.

104. Gerard cultivated "White Archangell" (*Lamium album*) and "Yellow Archangell" (*L. Galeobdolon*) describing them in the Herbal, also describing the Red Deadnettle (*L. purpureum*).

105. The Roman Nettle (*Urtica pilulifera*) is first described, then the Common Nettle. It is an old story that the former was cultivated by Cæsar's soldiers with the idea that by rubbing their limbs with the stinging leaves they might obtain some warmth in an unendurable climate. It is a rare plant of eastern English counties. Parkinson said that it grew in his time at Lidde by Romney.

106. Except for Vervain, no plant was more esteemed by old-time herbalists than Betony (*Stachys officinalis*), whence the Italian proverb, "Sell your coat and buy Betony." Gerard refers to Betony with white flowers which he found in a village called Hampstead, and we find him carrying home all manner of wildings. Finding "Venus Looking-glasse" in cornfields in Kent, he sowed the seeds in his garden where they sowed themselves from year to year. In the "Grete Herball" (1526) a powder of Betony was recommended "for them that be fearful."

107. *Verbena officinalis* is the solitary British representative of the important genus, so that Johnson had cause to doubt if Creeping or Holy Vervain grew wild. The Vervain held sacred to the Druids has not been identified. In the "Grete Herball" it is written that wine in which Vervain has been steeped, if sprinkled about the house, will "make folke mery at ye table" as Gerard noted.

108. Gerard and Johnson described and illustrated eighteen plants as Scabious. Among the kinds cultivated by Gerard was "Scabious of the Sea," *Scabiosa maritima*, a south European species naturalized on the cliffs at Folkestone. The British species are *S. Succisa*, described in the next chapter, *S. Columbaria*, and *S. arvensis*. Parkinson related that Scabious was powerful to draw splinters from the flesh.

109. This plant was among those found by Gerard at the village called Hampstead, along with Lilies of the Valley, Sawwort, Whortleberries, Dwarf Willows and many others.

110. Gerard cultivated in his garden the "Great Blew-Bottle" (*Centaurea montana*, from central and southern Europe) and the Bluebottle of the cornfields (*C. Cyanus*) apparently of south European or west Asiatic origin; and divers sorts which by cunning he made to bloom in divers colours.

111. "Purple Goats-beard" is Salsify, *Tragopogon porrifolius*, established in some localities of southern England, and cultivated before the introduction of the vegetable *Scorzonera hispanica*. "Yellow Goats-beard" is *T. pratensis*.

112. "Divers sorts of Marigoldes" flourished in our Author's garden, representatives of *Calendula officinalis*. Turner in his Herbal referred scathingly to those who use Marigold to make their hair yellow, not being content with the natural colour God hath given them.

113. Gerard cultivated and described several sorts of *Tagetes*, some of which are still popular.

114. *Helianthus annuus* was introduced to England at about Gerard's time. His observation that he could never observe it to turn with the sun agrees with the opinion of others, and four flowers on one stem have been seen to point to the four cardinal points.

115. Gerard was puzzled by the popular name of Jerusalem Artichoke (*Helianthus tuberosus*)—Jerusalem is often traced, but incorrectly, to the Italian *Girasole*.

116. Leopard's-bane (*Doronicum Pardalianches*) is an outcast from gardens in Britain. Gerard cultivated it, and recorded that it had been found in the cold mountains of Northumberland. Despite Gerard's story of Conrad Gesner it is recorded in "Historia Plantarum" that the botanist poisoned and killed himself in the end by the use of the plant. History records that he died of the plague.

117. Several varieties of Mullein (*Verbascum*) were ornaments of Gerard's garden. Parkinson in his *Theatrum Botanicum* recommended the yellow ("male") flower for dyeing the hairs of the head and making them fair and smooth. The rare Moth Mullein (*V. Blattaria*) occasionally bears white flowers, while those of *V. Lychnitis* are pale yellow or nearly white.

118. Among the plants grouped in Gerard's Cowslip-bed we recognise in "Bird-eyne" *Primula farinosa*, in the twin-like Cowslip a variety of *P. veris*, in the "Double Paigle" a variety of *P. vulgaris*, and in the "Primrose with greenish floures" still another variety. Turner in his Herbal expressed indignation with "some weomen" in that they sprinkled the flowers of Cowslip with white wine wherewith to wash their faces, to make them fair in the eyes of the world rather than in the eyes of God.

120. Among the Foxgloves we recognise *Digitalis purpurea* and its white variety, and *D. lutea*. It is remarkable that Gerard should accord the plants no place in medicine, considering that *Digitalis* ranks to-day as one of the most valuable of British "official herbs," of which about two dozen find a place in the British Pharmacopœia.

121. *Baccharis* is *Inula Conyza*.

122. "Dittanie of Candie" is *Origanum Dictamnus*.

123. Johnson interjects a note on "Never dying Borage, *Semper virens*," but this is an evergreen *Anchusa*.

124. Dyer's Bugloss (*Anchusa tinctoria*) is a native of Italy. The *Echium* mentioned is Viper's Bugloss.

125. Colt's-foot's high reputation of old as a cure for coughs is remembered in its generic name, *Tussilago*, but it is no longer "official" in the Materia Medica. The dried leaves keep their reputation for making a sort of tobacco.

127. All species of *Tribulus* are attractive, but are rarely cultivated. Gerard has a later chapter on *T. terrestris*, an introduction from southern Europe, and relates that he carried specimens from a meadow near Croydon.

128. Of "Ducks meat"—*Lemna*—five British species comprise the genus, of which *L. minor* is the commonest.

129. *Ranunculus aquatilis* has puzzled many botanists besides Gerard; eleven forms have been described as distinct species.

130. *Arum maculatum* yielded a starch for the great lawn ruffs such as our Author wore. *Dranunculus vulgaris* of S. Europe was known by such names as Great Dragon and Nedder's Tongue. An old English manuscript asserts that if hands be washed in its juice you shall Nedderis (Adders) withoutyn peryle gaderyn and handelyn hem at thi wylle. John Ray (1686) mentioned that Arum roots served as soap.

132. Various "Birthwoorts"—*Aristolochia*—were cultivated in Gerard's garden. The Birthwort described is *A. longa*, of southern Europe. The North American *A. serpentaria* carries the fable that snakes flee from the traveller who bears the plant.

134. *Colechoma hederacea* (*Nepeta hederacea*) was once used in clearing thick beer, and Tune or Tun Hoof is thus explained by an old writer: "It is good to tun up with new drink, for it will clarify it any night." The expression, "Pinne and web" is an old phrase for any "grief" in the eyes of cattle.

136, 137. *Smilax Sarsaparilla* was brought to Europe in the middle of the sixteenth century as a medicine of virtue. The Smilax of southern Europe still bears Gerard's name, Rough Bindweed, *S. aspera*. He mentioned several kinds of Bindweed, named indifferently *Smilax* and *Convolvulus*, all of which he said grew plentifully in most parts of England, a remark to which Johnson took exception; and he cultivated *Convolvulus arvensis* and *C. scammonia*, this last an importation from the Levant yielding the gummy resin, Scammony.

139. *Humulus Lupulus* is the sole British species.

140. "And therefore have I called it Travellers-Joy"—for that "right pleasant name" generations of travellers by ways and hedges have been in debt to our worthy Master in Chirurgerie. He objected to the title *Vitis alba*, though referring to vine-like branches and white flowers, and it remains the botanical name of the one British species. *Viorna* is a North American species.

141. Besides the Common Honeysuckle, Gerard described also the Perfoliate, which he grew in his garden, with its "fair, beautifull, and well smelling floures, shining with a whitish purple colour, and somewhat dasht with yellow, by little and little stretched out like the nose of an elephant."

142. The "kinde of Asclepias" of Virginia still bears the name of Æsculapius. *A. syriaca* is very fragrant, its scent in the evening charming the traveller in Canadian woods. It was introduced to Britain in the seventeenth century. Parkinson named it Virginian Silk.

144. Gerard cultivated divers sorts of Cucumbers, Gourds and Melons. Of a variety of Melon he remarked that he had seen many nourished at the Queen's house at St. James's, and at the house of the Lord of Sussex at Bermondsey. His credulous nature is again revealed by his story of the "long Cucumbers." Writing "Of Gourds" he quotes a statement that "A long Gourd or Cucumber being laid in the cradle or bed by the yong infant whilest it is asleep and sicke of an ague, it shall be very quickly made whole," a popular tradition, though not recorded in other herbals.

145, 146. Gerard gave the world the first published picture of the so-called Virginian Potato (not a native of that country) supposed to have been brought from Virginia by colonists sent out by Sir Walter Raleigh. The name long remained to distinguish this from "Battatas," or Sweet Potatoes, used in England as a delicacy before the introduction of the other. Shakespeare has references to the Sweet Potato, which Gerard confusingly calls the common Potato. He and Parkinson mention the Potato as a delicacy of the confectioner rather than as common food. Gerard having been among the first to grow Potatoes, it is fitting that in his portrait in the Herbal he is seen holding a branch of the plant.

147. He described and cultivated the Common Mallow (*Malva sylvestris*) and its relative, the Hollyhock (*Althæa rosea*).

148. Besides *Geranium molle* Gerard cultivated and described many other members of a charming family, including one sent from Jean Robin which our Author listed as *G. nondum descriptum*; this was *G. lucidum*.

149. Thirty-five illustrations appear in the Herbal of a variety of plants classed as *Ranunculus*. The name Butter-flowers is given, but not Buttercup.

150-152. Divers sorts of Wolfes-banes (*Delphinium* and *Aconitum*) were cultivated by Gerard and described in the Herbal: his "Yellow Wolfes-bane" is *Aconitum Lycoctonum*. The plant illustrated as *Thora Valdensis* is *Ranunculus Thora*.

153. "Of Hellebores" he described *H. niger* and *H. fœtidus*.

154. Of Pæonies he cultivated and described the "Male," *Pæonia mascula*, and the "Female"—"Single," "Double," "Misbegotten," and "Whitish"—*P. officinalis*. The terms male and female referred to stronger or weaker varieties.

155. He cultivated, described and illustrated a variety of plants named "Cinkefoile, Tormentill, and Silver-weed." "Wall Cinkfole" is *Potentilla argentea*.

156. He cultivated under the names red, white and green strawberries *Fragaria virginiana*, introduced from North America, and the "Barren Strawberrie" *Potentilla sterilis*.

157. *Herba Gerardi* is unfortunately now named *Ægopodium Podagraria*. Culpeper in "The English Physician" names the plant Herb Gerard, declaring that the very bearing of it about one's person eases the pains of gout.

158. Johnson gave the plant which Gerard christened "Clownes Wound-wort" its present name *Stachys palustris*.

159. Skirrets, the Water Parsnip (*Sium Sisarum*) came to England from China, and was cultivated by Gerard; now rare, it may linger in cottage gardens.

160. Slight differences exist between the Common Fennel (*Fœniculum vulgare*) and the Garden Fennel (*F. dulce*) associated with boiled mackerel. Parkinson says that the leaves serve to trim up many fish meats, that Cowcumbers are pickled with it, and the seeds are put for a relish in Pippin-pies.

161. "Sweet Chervill" was not missing from Gerard's herb-garden, or the Garden Chervil (*Anthriscus Cerefolium*), a once-famous pot-herb.

162. "Mede-Sweet" has lost its old name *Regina prati* in *Filipendula Ulmaria*.

163. Earth-nut (*Conopodium majus*) is still known to country children by the popular names Gerard gives; it is the one British species. The tuberous rootstock when roasted much resembles a Chestnut.

164. With respect to our Author we may remark that *Chelidonium majus* might well have been named from its habit of blossoming when the swallows come and continuing to blossom until they go.

165. In addition to Garden Valerian (*Valeriana Phu*) and the Wild (*V. officinalis*) Gerard grouped various distinct plants as Valerians. The old name, Setwall, was known to Chaucer: "He himself was swete as any Setewall."

166. As "Divers sort of Larks heele" our Author grouped and cultivated *Delphinium Consolida*.

167. The Herbal does not mention the name "Love-in-a-mist."

168. Corn Cockle (*Agrostemma Githago*) has the name Gith applied by Gerard to *Nigella*, which name with the adjective "bastard" he gave the Corn Cockle.

170. *Artemisia mater Herbarum* is Gerard's happy name for *Artemisia vulgaris*.

172. He cultivated and described *Rubia tinctoria*, and *R. peregrina* which yields the one reliable red dye among British plants, and is very scarce in England.

173. The Cotton or Scotch Thistle (*Onopordon Acanthium*) is that thistle usually chosen to represent the Scotsman's badge, with its motto, "Ye maunna meddle wi' me," but the plant is not wild in Scotland.

174. Gerard's Golden Thistle is *Scolymus hispanicus*. As to his "Thistle of Peru" Johnson relates that he himself had already described and figured this among the Poppies, as Prickly Poppy. He confesses that it should have been omitted from the former chapter, being here set forth, "whereof indeed I had a little remembrance, and therefore at that time sought his Index by all the names I could remember, but not making it a *Carduus*, I at that time missed thereof."

175. Gerard cultivated *Eryngium maritimum*, from which was made the confection, Kissing Comfits.

176. Three Teasels grow in Britain as the Herbal teaches, *Diplacus fullonum* ssp. *fullonum* and ssp. *sativus*, the famed Fuller's Teasel, and *D. pilosus*.

178. Gerard's notes on the names and virtues of Wood Sorrel (*Oxalis Acetosella*) are often quoted. The plant is believed to be the original Shamrock, though *Trifolium repens* now stands for that emblem.

179. This chapter was added by Johnson, who relates the story mentioned by Stowe and others of a miraculous appearance of the Sea Pea, *Lathyrus maritimus*, on the Suffolk coast, supposed to have sprung from seeds from a wrecked ship, but doubtless it is a native.

180. Gerard cultivated and described several Rues not represented in Britain, as "Garden Rue"—*Ruta graveolens*—and "Wild Rue"—*R. montana*, and he described the Common Meadow Rue, *Thalictrum flavum*.

With these Herbs of Grace our Author concludes his treatise of plants serving for meat, medicine, or sweet smelling use, "Onely some few omitted for want of perfect instruction"; some amends are made in the third Book, which is concerned mainly with Trees.

The Trees are omitted from the present edition, but a few extracts are taken from Book III. to give its savour.

Lib. 3.

181. It is remarkable that Gerard should have described no more than a dozen Roses. Some of those mentioned in his Garden Catalogue, which mostly appear in the Herbal with names amended by Johnson, are identified by the Editor, Daydon Jackson, as follows: "English White Rose," *Rosa arvensis*, "The Red Rose," *R. gallica*, the "Damaske Rose," *R. provincialis*, the "Great Holland Rose," *R. centifolia*, with the "Province Rose" as a probable variety.

182. Gerard cultivated the Sweetbriar (*R. eglanteria*) and its double variety. In this chapter he also described the British wild "*Rosa Pimpinella*, the Burnet Rose," or the "Rose bearing apples," *R. spinosissima*.

184. In contrast to the few Roses he seems to have known above forty plants as "Holly Roses or Cistus" and "Other Plants reckoned for dwarfe kindes of Cistus," and "Divers sorts of Cistus whereof that gummy matter is gathered in shops, Ladanum." The old Linnaean genus *Cistus* is now limited to certain large-flowered species none of which is British, but include the familiar Gum-Cistuses of gardens. The note on the English Cistus "called of Lobel *Panax Chironium*" recalls the wonderful tales told of Ginseng, *Panax quinquefolium*, native of North America, and of China where from time out of mind it has been gathered as the plant of the universal elixir. Travellers say that Ginseng enters into every medicine used by Tartars and Chinese, and that physicians have written volumes on its healing powers.

185. Rosemary is supposed to have been imported to England from southern Europe in Gerard's day.

186. The "Blacke Worts" described is *Vaccinium Myrtillus* (Bilberry, Blaeberry, or Whortleberry); the "Red Worts" is *V. Vitis-idæa* (Cowberry).

187. The "Mosse" is *Lichen plicatus.*

188. The myth of the Barnacle Tree goes back to remote ages, associated with the question whether the Barnacle Goose is flesh, fish or neither. In the twelfth century Giraldus Cambrensis entered his protest against the eating of the geese in Lent, and argued that if a person were to eat the leg of Adam, who was not born of flesh, he could not be judged innocent of eating flesh. Pope Pius II. was anxious to see the Goose-tree when on his travels, but was told that it was to be found in the Orkney Isles alone. Hector Boëce in his history and chronicles of Scotland (1536) favoured the theory that the geese grew on boughs which had fallen into the sea, and would have nothing to do with the story told by rude and ignorant people who had seen the fruit falling and changing into geese. Sebastian Munster in his "Cosmographie," 1572, describes the tree with faith. A great cloud of witnesses was marshalled by Gasper Schott in his "Physica Curiosa" of 1662, and in 1677 a paper was read on the subject before the Royal Society, and afterwards published. Illustrations of the tree are found in several works; Aldrovandus in his "Aldrovandi Ornithologia" gave a woodcut of the tree and fruit; l'Obel's "Stirpium Historia" (1571) shows the tree without the geese. Gerard's credence in the myth was shared by William Turner.   Gerard's opinions were unsettled to some extent; while he introduced the Goose-tree as a tree, he spoke of the geese springing from decayed wood. Johnson gravely related that some Hollanders had found "another originall" for the geese than barnacles, for in voyaging to find the North-East passage to China they came to some islands on one of which were abundance of the geese sitting on their eggs.

Perhaps it is characteristic of our Author that his last words may be taken in two senses, but we shall echo the valediction as a thank-offering for that he lived to see "Finis" crowning his work.

ALPHABETICAL TABLE OF PLANTS